CHEMISTRY 2540

ORGANIC CHEMISTRY LAB
2022–2023 ACADEMIC YEAR

DR. CHRISTOPHER CALLAM
DR. NOEL M. PAUL

McGraw Hill Education

Copyright © 2023 by McGraw-Hill Education LLC. All rights reserved. Printed in the United States of America. Except as permitted under the United States Copyright Act of 1976, no part of this publication may be reproduced or distributed in any form or by any means, or stored in a data base retrieval system, without prior written permission of the publisher.

ISBN-13: 978-1-266-58111-3
ISBN-10: 1-266-58111-1

Solutions Program Manager: Donna Debenedict
Project Manager: Carrie Braun

Contents

1. **Organic Chemistry & Laboratory Overview** 1
   1.1 Important Things to Remember—How to be Successful
       in the Organic Laboratory 1
   1.2 Prelab, Postlab and Digital Lab Report Requirements 2
   1.3 Student Lab Notebook Expectations 6
   1.4 The Art of the Lab Report 8
   1.5 Laboratory Awareness 16

2. **Safety in Organic Chemistry** 17
   2.1 Safety Rules of the Organic Laboratory 17
   2.2 Summary—Safety 19
   2.3 Spills 20
   2.4 Organic Fumes and Vapors 20
   2.5 Fires 20
   2.6 Disposal of Chemical Waste Materials 21

3. **Laboratory Hood Contents** 23
   3.1 Organic Hood Overview 23
   3.2 Organic Lab Equipment 24
   3.3 Cleaning and Drying Glassware 30
   3.4 Hood Operation Controls 30
   3.5 Hardware Use and Operation 33

4. **Organic Reactions: Setting Up and Chemical Handling** 35
   4.1 Safe Handling of Chemicals 35
   4.2 Measuring and Transferring Chemicals 36
   4.3 Filtration 37
   4.4 Reaction Workup with a Conical Vial 38
   4.5 Microscale Distillation Apparatus (Simple) 38
   4.6 Microscale Distillation Apparatus (Fractional) 39
   4.7 Microscale Vacuum Distillation Apparatus 40
   4.8 Reaction Workup with a Separatory Funnel 40
   4.9 Macroscale Distillation Apparatus 41
   4.10 Macroscale Reflux Apparatus 42

iii

5. Analysis of Organic Compounds 43
  5.1   Melting Point 43
  5.2   Boiling Point 46
  5.3   Study Guide—Melting Points 46

6. IR Spectroscopy 47
  6.1   Uses of the Infrared Spectrum 47
  6.2   What to Look for in Examining Infrared Spectra 48
  6.3   Summary: Analyzing an IR Spectrum 56
  6.4   Prelab 58
  6.5   How to Take an IR—Operation Instructions 58
  6.6   IR Unknown Narrative 58
  6.7   Data Submission 58
  6.8   Digital Lab Report 59
  6.9   IR Unknown Structures Part 1 59
  6.10 IR Unknown Structures Part 2 59
  6.11 IR Unknown Structures Part 3 60

7. Recrystallization 63
  7.1   A Review of Intermolecular Forces 63
  7.2   Principles of Recrystallization 64
  7.3   Dissolving the Sample 65
  7.4   Tricks of Recrystallization 66
  7.5   Prelab 67
  7.6   Microscale Recrystallization of Sulfanilamide—Procedure 68
  7.7   Semi-microscale Recrystallization of Benzoic Acid—Procedure 70
  7.8   Postlab Data Submission 72
  7.9   Digital Lab Report Guidelines 73
  7.10 Practice Problems 73
  7.11 Study Guide—Recrystallization 75

8. Extraction 77
  8.1   Solubility 78
  8.2   Partition Coefficients and Extraction 78
  8.3   Techniques of Extraction 79
  8.4   Acid-Base Chemistry 80
  8.5   Acid/Base Example 93
  8.6   Alkaloids 97
  8.7   Extraction Scheme for Caffeine from Tea Leaves 99
  8.8   Prelab 100
  8.9   Extraction of Caffeine from Tea—Procedure 101
  8.10 Postlab Data Submission 103
  8.11 Digital Lab Report Guidelines 103
  8.12 Practice Problems 104
  8.13 Study Guide—Extraction 107

9. Thin Layer Chromatography 109
9.1 Introduction 109
9.2 Technique of Thin Layer Chromatography 109
9.3 Solvents for Thin Layer Chromatography 111
9.4 Prelab 114
9.5 Thin Layer Chromatography—Procedure 115
9.6 Post Lab Data Submission 118
9.7 Digital Lab Report Guidelines 119
9.8 Practice Problems 119
9.9 Study Guide—Thin Layer Chromatography 122

10. Column Chromatography 123
10.1 Introduction 123
10.2 Prelab 125
10.3 Column Chromatography—Procedure 126
10.4 Postlab Data Submission 128
10.5 Digital Lab Report Guidelines 128
10.6 Practice Problems: Column Chromatography 128
10.7 Study Guide—Column Chromatography 129

11. Simple and Fractional Distillation 131
11.1 Distillation of a Liquid 131
11.2 Distillation of Mixtures 132
11.3 Simple Distillation vs. Fractional Distillation 135
11.4 Gas Chromatography 136
11.5 Prelab 144
11.6 Distillation and Gas Chromatography—Procedure 145
11.7 Postlab Data Submission 148
11.8 Digital Lab Report Guidelines 148
11.9 Practice Problems 149
11.10 Study Guide 152

12. Synthesis of Aspirin 153
12.1 Introduction 153
12.2 Prelab 155
12.3 Synthesis of Aspirin—Procedure 156
12.4 Postlab Data 158
12.5 Digital Lab Report Guidelines 158
12.6 Practice Problems 159
12.7 Study Guide—Preparation of Aspirin 161

13. Reduction of Vanillin **163**
    13.1   Introduction 163
    13.2   Prelab 170
    13.3   Reduction of Vanillin Procedure 171
    13.4   Postlab Data Submission 173
    13.5   Digital Lab Report Guidelines 173
    13.6   Practice Problems 174
    13.7   Study Guide—Synthesis of Vanillyl Alcohol 176

14. Grignard Reaction—Synthesis of Triphenylmethanol **177**
    14.1   Introduction 177
    14.2   Sensitivity and Limitations of the Grignard Reaction 179
    14.3   Prelab 182
    14.4   Synthesis of Triphenylmethanol—Grignard Reaction—Procedure 183
    14.5   Postlab Data Submission 188
    14.6   Digital Lab Report Guidelines 188
    14.7   Practice Problems 189
    14.8   Study Guide—Synthesis of Triphenylmethanol 192

15. Diels-Alder Reactions **193**
    15.1   Introduction 193
    15.2   Prelab 196
    15.3   Procedure—Synthesis of 4,7-diphenyltetrahydroisobenzofuran-1,3-dione 197
    15.4   Postlab Data Submission 198
    15.5   Digital Lab Report Guidelines 198
    15.6   Diels-Alder Practice Problems 199
    15.7   Study Guide—Diels Alder Reactions 200

Appendix **201**

Organic Chemistry & Laboratory Overview

CHAPTER 1

1.1 Important Things to Remember—How to be Successful in the Organic Laboratory

Organic chemistry is the science of carbon compounds. Organic chemists often identify many compounds from nature and then synthesize these compounds in the lab. Organic chemists identify structures of organic molecules, work on purification and separation procedures, and study mechanisms of organic reactions.

An important part of this laboratory course is learning to perform the experiment in an efficient and safe manner. It is imperative that you take the time to understand the procedures that we are going to perform each week in advance of coming to lab and pay special attention to the safety precautions associated with organic chemistry laboratories.

Presented below are some keys to success in a laboratory course:

1. Be Prepared to Perform the Experiment (The 5 P's). Prior preparation prevents poor performance. Take the time to complete the prelab, read through the course notes and background material, and familiarize yourself with the techniques and procedures before coming to lab. This prior preparation will make you more efficient in the laboratory and will keep everyone safe.

2. You should come to the lab with a plan for the use of your time and some understanding of what you are about to do. You will learn more if you prepare. Following the instructions line by line, blindly, is a waste of time. Strive to understand the instructions and execute them to your best performance.

3. Plan Ahead While in the Lab: Efficiency Is Key. There are many experiments where you will have to spend some time waiting for your reaction to be completed. Use this time wisely. For example, you could prepare the glassware that you will need for the next steps, clean up your area and wash any dirty glassware, or write down important information in your lab notebook.

4. Lab Is Not a Race. Do not rush around the lab trying to get things done so you can leave. Hurrying jeopardizes both your safety and the safety of those students around you. If you rush, you might increase the chance that you will make a mistake, add the wrong reagent, spill your product, break some glassware, or accidentally dispose of your product.

5. Ask Questions. If you have any questions or doubts, feel free to ask your teaching assistant or instructor. We are here to help you learn. Our goal is to create a lab environment where everyone feels confident and safe and can learn well. By the end of the course, we hope that you have mastered the basic techniques used in an organic laboratory.

6. Do Your Best. Lab can be a frustrating experience. You just have to try to do your best. Organic chemists are concerned with many different factors depending on the specific experiment. In some weeks, we will be focused on the ideas of synthesis: For example, did we make the correct molecule, is the molecule pure, and what was the yield?

At other times your yield and purity will vary, as there are many factors that might affect them (for example, cleanliness of the glassware, rate of addition, temperature, light, efficiency of mixing, purity of reagents, and so on). Just do your best work and everything will usually turn out okay.

Course Objectives and Goals

1. Promote a safe work environment
2. Record data carefully
3. Record important observations
4. Manage your time well
5. Plan for the isolation and purification of an organic substance
6. Solve problems and THINK
7. Improve scientific writing and communication skills
8. Learn and re-enforce the fundamental principles of organic chemistry

1.2 Prelab, Postlab and Digital Lab Report Requirements

Prelab Online

The online portion of your prelab assignments can be found on Carmen in the module for each experiment.

The online portion of these assignments will consist of a series of questions, chemical drawings, problem solving, and calculations. The prelab assignments are due prior to the start of your lab period.

Prelab Written Portion

The written portion of your prelab assignment should be completed on a fresh page in your laboratory notebook. The written portion consists of a title, date, reagent table, reaction equation and plan of procedure. The plan of procedure should highlight the important procedures, techniques and steps of the experiment that are critical for a successful experiment. An appropriate pre-laboratory write-up will include the following: the experiment title, the date, the reaction scheme (when indicated), a property/stoichiometry table (when indicated), a reference, and all the items listed on the lab manual Prelab instruction sheet, such as a brief plan of procedure (complete sentences not needed) or the answers to one or more experiment-specific questions. The prelab entry for each experiment should not be a direct copy of the experimental procedure but should include sufficient detail to perform the experiment without use of the laboratory manual. At any time this semester, you may be required by your instructor to perform the experiment using only the content recorded in your laboratory notebook.

Postlab Online

The online portion of your post-lab assignment can be found on Carmen in the module for each experiment.

The online portion of these assignments will consist largely of calculations. Sample calculation and data tables for these assignments can be found within each chapter of this manual. The online portion of your postlab is due according to the course schedule in your syllabus and the schedule posted to Carmen.

Digital Lab Report

For some experiments, you will be expected to login to Carmen to download the appropriate Digital Lab Report Template.

The template will contain instructions regarding the preparation of ChemDraw drawings, a formal procedure section, and the answering of concept questions. Your completed document should be submitted as a Microsoft Word Document (.doc or .docx file only) or Adobe PDF to the Carmen assignment appropriate for this experiment. Digital Lab Reports are due as listed on the Course Schedule, and late submissions will be penalized per the details in the syllabus.

Sample Pre-lab (Written Portion)

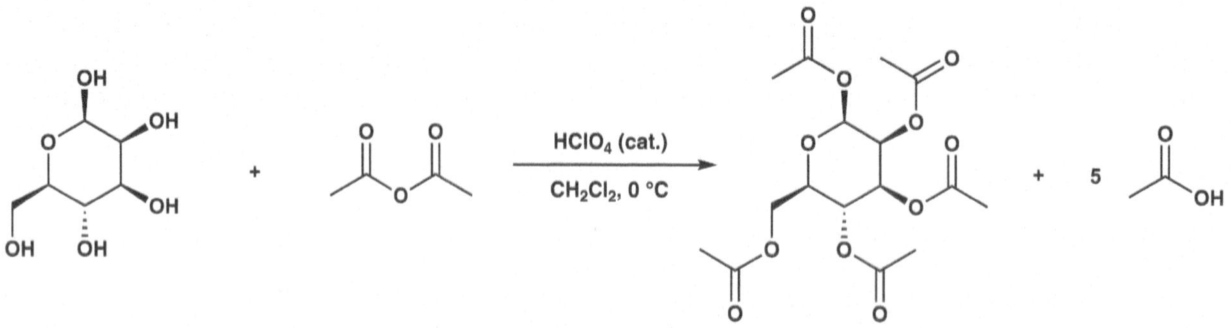

D-mannose
C₆H₁₂O₆
180.16 g/mol

acetic anhydride
C₄H₆O₃
102.09 g/mol

HClO₄ (cat.)
CH₂Cl₂, 0 °C

1,2,3,4,6-penta-O-β-D-mannopyranose
C₁₆H₂₂O₁₁
390.34 g/mol

+ 5 **acetic acid**
C₂H₄O₂
60.05 g/mol

Reagent Table

Reagent	MW	g	mmol	equivalents	d	mL
D-mannose	180.16	12.0	66.6	1.0		
acetic anhydride	102.09	64.8	638	9.6	1.08	60
perchloric acid	100.46	0.08	0.83	0.01	1.664	0.05
Theoretical Products						
1,2,3,4,6-penta-O-β-D-mannopyranose	390.34	26.0	66.6			
acetic acid	60.05	20.0	333		1.049	19.1

Melting point of 1,2,3,4,6-penta-O-β-D-mannopyranose = 148 – 149.5 °C

Plan of Procedure:

1. Reaction – Cool solution of acetic anhydride and catalytic perchloric acid to 0 °C in an ice bath.
2. Reaction – Slowly add solid D-mannose over 1 h period. (Check that the temperature is below 50 °C).
3. Reaction – Allow to stir for 1 h after complete addition.
4. Work-Up – Pour solution into a beaker of crushed ice and saturated NaHCO₃ soln.
5. Work-Up – Extract the aqueous phase with CH₂Cl₂. Dry the organic layer with MgSO₄.
6. Purification – Recrystallize from diethyl ether.

Experimental Narrative

The narrative of the experimental procedure is written while you perform the experiment. Begin each entry on a new page, writing the title of the experiment and date at the top. Always record what you do as you do it and include critical observations such as color changes, temperatures, etc. Quantities, time periods, and the order in which steps are performed are of particular importance. Be sure to include all weights, percent yields, melting points, and any other measurements taken in the lab. Narratives should be kept in your notebook and will be randomly checked by your TA for completeness and quality. A well-written narrative can serve as the rough draft of your formal report (for experiments that require it) and should always be written in paragraph form, using past tense, passive voice and complete sentences. When you complete an experiment, initial and date the bottom of the last notebook page pertaining to that experiment.

Sample Lab Notebook Narrative

Acetic anhydride (60.0 mL, 638 mmol) with a catalytic amount of 70% $HClO_4$ (1 mL, 1.66 g, 11.59 mmol) was added to a 250-mL round bottom flask equipped with a magnetic stir bar. The solution was cooled to 0 °C, and D-mannose (12.0 g, 66.6 mmol) was added over the course of 1 h while maintaining the temperature of the reaction below 50 °C. During the course of the addition, the temperature of the solution never exceeded 30 °C. The solid mannose was added in ~1 g portions, and the next addition was not done until all the solid had dissolved. After completing the addition, the ice bath was removed, and the solution was allowed to stir at room temperature for 1 h. The solution was light yellow in color. After 1 h, the reaction was poured into a 1-L beaker containing crushed ice and a saturated aqueous $NaHCO_3$ solution. The resulting mixture was diluted with CH_2Cl_2 (200 mL) and stirred for 2 h. This stirring was performed to hydrolyze all of the excess acetic anhydride to acetic acid. The organic layer was washed with saturated aqueous $NaHCO_3$ (3 × 50 mL) and water (2 × 50 mL). The solution was dried with $MgSO_4$, filtered and concentrated under reduced pressure to yield product (24.3 g, 93%) as a light clear oil. The resulting oil was recrystallized from diethyl ether to obtain the product as a white crystalline solid (20.4 g, 78%). mp 148–149 °C, R_f (6:1 hexanes:ethyl acetate) = 0.63.

1.3 Student Lab Notebook Expectations

The Laboratory Notebook is an account of your planned activities in the laboratory, a real-time narrative account of their execution and all the resulting data and calculations. A quality Lab Notebook will provide a scientist insight into their own thought processes and experimental decision-making well after the fact, and a poor Lab Notebook might transform a Nobel Prize-winning experimental discovery into an irreproducible joke.

In a professional setting, a Lab Notebook is considered a legal document, and patents and lawsuits have been won (or lost) based on the astute record-keeping skills of experimental scientists. We will practice maintaining the "legal integrity" of your documented work by refraining from removing or destroying Lab Notebook pages, by affixing printouts (templates, spectra, etc.) on clean notebook pages using small pieces of scotch tape (never gluing or permanently affixing these printouts), and making corrections to mistakes in the document by drawing a single line through the mistake and signing your initials and date nearby (do not black-out or redact your mistakes). It is also good practice to date your Lab Notebook whenever you begin writing, and sign and date your narrative and results at the end of the experiment or laboratory period (whichever comes first).

An excellent Lab Notebook entry will include:

- A title of the experiment and a description of the work being performed (naturally, a chemical reaction should be included here whenever possible)
- The date at which the work was conducted, and a date on every page
- A collection of pertinent literature data (tables of reagents with structures, names, and pertinent physical properties, stoichiometry calculations). Leaving room to update mass values and calculations results with "real life" values is also encouraged, as long as you follow the "line out and initial" protocol described above
- For the Chem 2540 Laboratory Course: a plan of procedure that demonstrates prior consideration of the experimental details with a goal of improved efficiency in the laboratory (what is the bare minimum information that you personally need to execute this work? Creative and effective methods of constructing your plan are highly encouraged!)

    Note: The four (4) items listed above constitute the "Written Prelab" component required of each experiment in this course.

- A narrative account (third-person, past tense, complete sentences, paragraph format) of the experiment conducted, written in real-time (as you perform each step), that contains a copious amount of detail (temperatures, times, drawings, color changes, choice of equipment/tools/containers/measuring devices, the mass of any container/vessel in which chemicals or reactants are provided to you, as well as the mass of any container/vessel in which your crude or purified chemical/product will stored), and all of the data that results from your work (product masses and percent yield/recovery calculations, mp/bp values, TLC plate drawings and analyses, physical measurements and retention time calculations, distillation data tables and plots, etc.)
- Drawings/printouts of pertinent experimental results with analysis, clear labeling, and calculations (TLC plates, chromatograms, spectra, etc.)
- For the Chem 2540 Laboratory Course: a completed Postlab data table at the end of experiment in the structure of those included in the Lab Manual Chapters for each experiment
- Pertinent literature references for the items above whenever possible
- A signature and date at the end of the experiment or lab period (whichever comes first)
- All the above constructed in a well-organized, neat, and legible manner

Barriers to an excellent Lab Notebook might include:

- Failing to have your notebook with you in the laboratory while you are working (it is reasonable to expect that you have all the Lab Notebook data you have generated for this course with you in the laboratory at all times, even if you have more than one Lab Notebook)
- Failing to prepare the required "Written Prelab" entry for each experiment before you actually conduct it
- Failing to check each Prelab calculation backwards and forward twice prior to beginning an experiment
- Writing your narrative after you have completed all your work (write what you do as you do it!)
- Writing your narrative using first-person pronouns (I, me, my, we, etc.), and/or in present tense
- Writing your narrative using incomplete sentences, or using a bulleted or numbered list format
- Failing to write the narrative account of your work while you perform it
- Failing to write the narrative account of your work at all
- Failing to use the helpful Notebook Narrative Templates when they are available
- Recording your data (measurements, calculations, masses, temperatures, etc.) ANY PLACE other than your Lab Notebook (like the Lab Manual, on Post-It's, napkins, scrap paper, your hand or other body parts, your dog, etc.)
- Failing to properly label results when they are available (TLC plate drawings, chromatograms, spectra, etc.)
- Failing to acquire the mass of absolutely everything that your compounds will touch (vials, flasks, test tubes, etc.)
- Failing to obtain masses of the final products prior to leaving laboratory for the day
- Failing to check each Postlab calculation backwards and forward twice prior to leaving the laboratory at the conclusion of an experiment
- Failing to construct a Postlab data table at the end of your narrative
- Failing to cite appropriate references for any literature values or references utilized
- Failing to write legibly

1.4 The Art of the Lab Report

A formal lab report is a means to communicate the most important aspects of a chemical experiment and contains both sufficient detail to reproduce the work and a critical analysis of the effectiveness of the procedure. The elements and anatomy of the formal report are explained here in great detail to aid in your understanding. All text within the digital lab report should be typed. This guide is by no means comprehensive or universal, but it does contain suggestions and explanations that will aid your scientific writing skills. Through efforts spent perfecting the formal lab report, students will be given the valuable opportunity to be evaluated on both their ability to clearly communicate and their attention to detail as presented on the written page.

Heading

Each lab report should begin with a heading, which includes the title of the experiment performed, your name, the name of your teaching assistant, your laboratory classroom, and the date that the report was submitted.

Purpose

The purpose statement should include the names of reactants, reagents, and products and explain the type of reaction that is being performed (for example: alkylation, acylation, condensation, amidation, esterification, nitration, substitution). When appropriate, use the phrases "acid-catalyzed" or "base-catalyzed" to speak more generally about conditions, but detailed descriptions of solvents or other reaction conditions should be avoided. Overall, the purpose should contain enough information to draw the reactants and product(s) but not give specific details of how the experiment was conducted.

Reaction Scheme

This graphical representation is the most clear and straightforward means to describe a chemical reaction. The reactants (starting materials AKA substrates) are shown to the left of the reaction arrow while the products and byproducts are shown to the right of the arrow. Reagents in excess, catalysts, and solvents as well as temperature and reaction time are written above and below the arrow. Be sure to include compound names under the structures. Use a chemical structure drawing program (ChemDraw) or website (ChemDraw - https://chemdrawdirect.perkinelmer.cloud/js/sample/index.html#) to create your own graphic. Do not cut and paste the reaction scheme from the lecture notes or internet sources. There is educational value in creating the scheme yourself, and no points will be awarded for inclusion of someone else's work.

Procedure

A formal "Procedure" is a technical summary of the contents of your lab notebook that includes the most critical details of the experiment. Huge differences exist between these report procedures and the step-by-step procedures in the laboratory manual. Unlike the "recipe"-type procedure, the audience of the lab report is someone like you (or your TA or instructor) who has experience in the organic chemistry laboratory and who understands that many details of a procedure are considered common practice or routine (preparing heating or cooling baths, clamping, choosing container sizes, and using measuring instruments). Determining when certain small details are necessary or extraneous is difficult, but when in doubt, always consider the intended audience of this work is an experienced member of the synthetic chemistry community. The procedure is divided into several sentences, and each has a specific function discussed below.

First Sentence: "The reactants (compound data) were combined and reacted."

The reactants and reagents are listed in the order they are added to the reaction mixture. After each chemical name, the number of grams, mmols and volume (if a liquid) are listed in parentheses. A verb like "combined" or "reacted" is used, and a solvent is listed with its volume given in parentheses immediately following. The temperature at which and the amount of time the chemicals were allowed to react is also given.

1. The general structure of the first sentence is as such: A suspension/solution/mixture of [reactant one], [reactant two], and [reactant three/catalyst] were reacted/refluxed in [solvent] at [temperature] °C for [time] min/h. More complicated reaction setups could require more than one sentence. It is important that the correct order and method of combining chemicals is clearly described.
2. Avoid use of "room temperature" or "rt" in favor of an actual temperature reading taken on the day the experiment was performed.
3. Start the sentence with "A solution" (if the solvent has dissolved all the reactants), "A suspension" (if there are one or more undissolved solids) or "A mixture" (if two or more solids are combined without solvent) to avoid having to start the sentence with the name of a chemical, which is helpful when the chemical name starts with a number.
4. Chemical names are never capitalized except in titles or at the beginning of a sentence.
5. Write the grams, millimoles, and milliliters of each reactant directly after each reactant name inside of parentheses.
6. Maintain three decimal places of accuracy in grams and at least three significant figures in mmol calculations.
7. The accuracy of volume measurements depends on what measuring device was used: beakers are not accurate at all, graduated cylinders are good to the whole mL, but volumetric and precision pipettes are very accurate to the microliter.
8. Remember: an ice-water bath = 0 °C and reflux = bp of the solvent.
9. Avoid describing heating devices and cooling baths unless they are unusual or critical to the success of the reaction.
10. Avoid discussing the sizes of glassware used unless unusual, etc.
11. Avoid discussion of clamps and stir bars.
12. If more than one chemical reaction is performed for an experiment, each reaction should have its own sentence.

Middle Sentence(s): "The reaction was stopped, and the crude product was isolated."

The middle sentences describe the reaction "work-up," including the most important details of how the reaction was stopped, how the reaction mixture was treated, and how the product of the reaction was separated from insoluble materials, inorganic byproducts, and the reaction solvent. Not all of the following techniques are needed for every procedure.

Quenching—Water, aqueous acid, or base are often added to the reaction mixture to consume or decompose unreacted reagents that could interfere with product isolation.

Precipitation/Crystallization—If the crude product exists as a solid in the reaction mixture, the solid can be isolated from the liquid using vacuum filtration. The solid may or may not be rinsed with an appropriate solvent to remove residual impurities. The number of rinses and their volume should be included when appropriate. For example, "the crude product was isolated via vacuum filtration, rinsing with cold methanol (3 × 1 mL).

Extraction—If the crude product is dissolved in the reaction solvent, and water and/or water-soluble impurities are present, the organic solvent containing the solvent can usually be isolated from water or impurities using phase separation. Extraction procedures are always presented as a summary, where the extraction solvent is noted, and the number and volume of extractions written after the solvent in parentheses. For example, "the reaction was extracted with CH_2Cl_2 (4 × 5 mL)" means that the reaction was extracted with 5 mL of dichloromethane, this dichloromethane was separated from the aqueous phase and placed in a separate container, and this exact process was repeated three additional times to provide a solution of 20 mL of dichloromethane in a new clean vessel that contains the target product (as well as organic soluble impurities if present).

Washing—An organic solution containing the product can be extracted with additional amounts of aqueous solution to remove persistent water-soluble impurities. Washing steps are summarized in the same manner as extractions (discussed above).

Drying—The combined organic solutions are typically treated with a drying agent such as magnesium sulfate or sodium sulfate to remove residual water dissolved in solution. This solution can then be filtered or decanted to separate it from the solid.

Evaporation—The removal of solvent using heat, time, or rotary evaporation (Rotovap) will provide the target product in its crude form as a solid or oil, depending on the exact product and reaction conditions.

Final Sentence: "The product was purified and isolated (data)."

The details of how the crude product was purified to give the pure product in the appropriate physical form are summarized here. Purification methods discussed include recrystallization methods (solvent, volume and temperature), distillation, or chromatographic separation. The sentence ends with the full compound name and product data listed in parentheses, including isolated weight, millimoles, and percent yield. Significant figures should again be considered for the product mass (typically three decimal places, for example: 0.359 g or 13.000 g) and millimoles (three significant figures, for example: 3.34 mmol or 0.234 mmol), and percent yields should only be reported as integers (no decimal point).

The product data is immediately followed by a colon, the characterization methods that were performed are listed afterwards. For solids, a melting point value is listed with an appropriate reference's literature value in parentheses. Melting points (mp) should always be reported as a range and given the scope of this course, should never include values more accurate than one degree Celsius. For example, if a compound begins melting at 162.6 °C and finishes melting by 165.4 °C, the melting point should be reported as 163–165 °C. Additional decimal places contain no useful information because the equipment and methods used to acquire these data are not capable of higher resolution. For liquids, a boiling point value is listed, and a literature value reference is also included. If thin-layer chromatographic analysis was performed, the R_f value of the pure product in an appropriate solvent should be included. If infrared spectroscopy was performed, the method of sample preparation should be included (liquid, thin film, KBr pellet, etc.) and the pertinent frequencies should be listed.

Discussion

First Sentence: "The starting materials were reacted using conditions specific to the reaction being performed and the target product was obtained in a percent yield."

The first sentence of the discussion is a more detailed version of the purpose statement but is distinct since it refers to the physical state and percent yield of the product.

Second/Middle Sentence(s): "The identity and purity of the product was assessed."

Product identity is most often supported by the relative closeness of your observed mp or bp value to the literature value for the target compound. The most straightforward situation is when your observed range overlaps the range of the literature value, which confirms the identity of your product with little uncertainty.

For mp determination: when the observed range is below that of the literature value, it is best to suggest that slight contamination may be depressing the melting point value. For bp determination: deviation from the literature value usually indicates systematic error in thermometer placement. The purity of your isolated product can also be established by noting a relatively narrow melting/boiling range observed. A narrow range is ideally between 1–2 °C, widening slightly with an increase in the magnitude of the value. An observed range of 5 °C or more warrants a qualification of the product's purity. For TLC analysis, the product should contain only one product band (ideally in a divergent pair of solvent conditions) to be considered pure. For IR data, consider the presence of peaks that confirm the identity of the product, and note the absence of peaks that would correspond to starting materials or other identifiable impurities. List specific values in wavenumbers (cm^{-1}) and when needed, compare those values to the general functional group reference value.

Middle/Final Sentence(s): "The purity and/or percent yield of the reaction could be improved."

This is your chance to showcase your understanding of how a reaction could be improved based on theoretical changes to conditions such as stoichiometry, concentration, and in some cases reaction time and temperature. Regardless of your percent yield, you should discuss ways to increase yield or improve purity. Consider the following when contemplating how to improve the percent yield of any given reaction:

1. DISCUSSION does not mean CONFESSION: avoid discussion of mistakes, accidents, spills, and human error.
2. Avoid discussion of mass loss through transfers, recrystallization, or weighing.
3. DO identify and address assumptions made about the procedure.
   - Are we confident the reaction went to completion? What evidence do we have?
   - Is there an alternate method to produce the desired synthetic target?
   - Are there considerable side-reactions taking place?
4. DO consider a modification that you would actually try if you were to repeat the experiment in our lab.
5. DO discuss specifics about the reaction equation and/or the stoichiometry table
6. DO justify changes in catalyst, solvent, reagent, temperature, time, and/or molar ratio using your chemical/ mechanistic understanding of the reaction.
7. DO be clear and logical about what the change would accomplish.
8. Express your understanding of what a catalyst does and how it cannot improve the percent yield—it only allows a reaction to reach completion, or alternatively reach the equilibrium mixture at a faster rate (which could produce more molecules of final product in a limited reaction time).
9. Express your understanding of what reactions are in equilibrium and when Le Chatelier's principle can be considered.
10. Consider a problem in the current reaction methods and identify a solution with a literature reference.
    - How will the referenced literature improve your yield?
11. Express your understanding of how unstable reagents may result in lower than expected yield.
12. CLASSIC MISTAKE: DO NOT suggest an increase in the mmols of the limiting reagent to improve the percent yield. This modification produces more GRAMS of the product, but the THEORETICAL YIELD also increases, likely leading to the same or lower PERCENT YIELD than you obtained in your initial experiment.

Refer to this list of topics and considerations while composing your discussion of each experiment. Consider it a challenge to use as many of the concepts and vocabulary terms above that could apply to the experiment in an effort to present a complete picture of your understanding of the reaction that was performed.

Literature Resources

All discussions must provide literature evidence that supports the ideas being presented. Though it is sometimes a challenge to find and summarize appropriate sources (peer-reviewed journal articles, review articles, or collections), learning to search the Chemical Literature is a powerful skill to enhance a student's problem-solving abilities. A list of very helpful search tools are listed here:

>Scifinder Scholar – https://scifinder.cas.org
>Reaxys – https://www.reaxys.com/reaxys/secured/start.do
>American Chemical Society Publications – http://pubs.acs.org/

References

Sources of chemical data or procedural information from the lab manual should be referenced using superscript numbers that refer to endnote references. Endnote numbers should always be presented in numerical order.

The information contained in the endnote itself should be adequate to find the source again. There is a standard format for books and journal articles. Internet sources are more flexible, but make sure the font type and size is consistent throughout the reference section. Please use American Chemical Society (ACS) standards for construction of endnote references:

Books

Author 1; Author 2; Author 3; etc. Chapter Title. *Book Title*, Edition Number; Series Information (if any); Publisher:Place of Publication, **Year**; Volume Number, Pagination.

Vollhardt, K. P. C.; Schore, N. E. *Organic Chemistry: Structure and Function*; 5th ed.; W. H. Freeman: New York, **2005**; p 291.

Callam, C. *Organic Chemistry Lab—Chemistry 2540 – 2019-2020 Academic Year*; McGraw-Hill: New York, **2019**; pp 124–130.

Scientific Journal Articles

Author 1; Author 2; Author 3; etc. "Article Title." *Journal Title/Abbreviation* **Year,** *Volume Number* (Edition Number), Pagination.

Callam, C. S.; Gadikota, R. R.; Krein, D. M.; Lowary, T. L. "2,3-Anhydrosugars in Glycoside Bond Synthesis. NMR and Computational Investigations into the Mechanism of Glycosylations with 2,3-Anhydrofuranosyl Glycosyl
Sulfoxides." *J. Am. Chem. Soc.* **2003**, *125* (43), 13112–13119.

Paul, N. M.; Taylor, M.; Kumar, R.; Deschamps, J. R.; Luedtke, R. R.; Newman, A. H. "Structure-Activity
Relationships for a Novel Series of Dopamine D2-like Receptor Ligands Based on N-Substituted 3-Aryl-8-azabicy-clo[3.2.1]octan-3-ol." *J. Med. Chem.* **2008**, *51* (19), 6095–6109.

Internet Sources

Author (if any). Title of Website. URL (accessed date), other identifying information.

CRC Handbook of Chemistry and Physics; 89th Ed. (Online); 2008–2009. http://hbcpnetbase.com (accessed Sept 2009); search term: nicotine.

Sigma-Aldrich Chemical Catalog Online. http://www.sigmaaldrich.com/united-states.html (accessed Aug 2009);search term: benzoic acid.

Take some time to become familiar with your word processor's "Insert Endnote" features (you'll be glad you did). Also, be certain to use consistent formatting in the endnote reference section (font size and style).

The Most Common Mistakes

- Spaces follow every unit of measure except the percent symbol and in the event of describing the size of a piece of equipment (125-mL Erlenmeyer flask).
- Chemical names are only capitalized when they appear at the beginning of a sentence or when they appear in a title (title case).
- Leading zeros are required before all decimal places. For example, 1.6×10^{-1} should be written 0.16.
- Maintain a consistent number of decimal places in all your stoichiometrically-relevant values. More than three decimal places and four significant figures is too much for most applications.
- Melting points values can contain a great deal of useful data, but be careful not to overstate their importance when discussing purity and identity.
- References in the text should always be presented as superscript endnote numbers and should occur in numerical order.
- Be sure to use the correct abbreviations for units (see below page).

Useful Abbreviations			
base quantity	unit of measure	symbol	example
temperature	degrees Celsius	°C	153 °C
time	days	d	7 d
	hours	h	1.5 h
	minutes	min	20 min
	seconds	s	60 s
mass	grams	g	0.45 g
	milligrams (10^{-3} g)	mg	130 mg
number of atoms	moles	mol	0.2 mol
	millimoles	mmol	1.25 mmol
volume	liters	L	0.5 L
	milliliters (10^{-3} L)	mL	32 mL
	percent	%	92%
melting point characterization	melting point	mp	mp 118–120 °C
boiling point characterization	boiling point	bp	bp 78–84 °C
thin-layer chromatography characterization	TLC retention factor	R_f	R_f (CH$_3$Cl) = 0.25
gas chromatography characterization	GC retention time	t_R	t_R = 0.6 min
infrared absorption spectroscopy	IR absorption frequency	IR	IR (liquid) 1682 cm^{-1}

Sample Lab Report

Synthesis of 1,2,3,4,6-penta-O-acetyl-β-D-mannopyranose

Name: Anthony Kucharski
Lab: R 8:00 a.m. – 450 CE

Teaching Assistant: Christopher Callam
Submitted: June 18, 2022

Purpose: To synthesize 1,2,3,4,6-penta-O-β-D-mannopyranose via an acid-catalyzed acylation reaction between acetic anhydride and D-mannose.

Reaction Scheme:

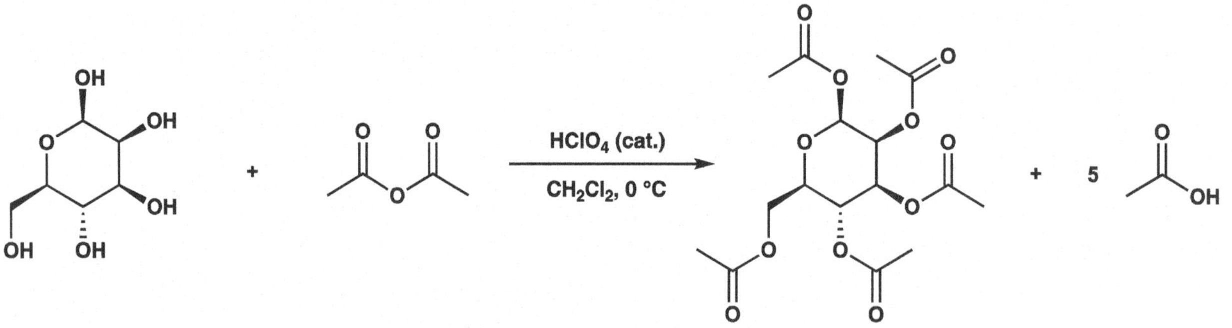

D-mannose	acetic anhydride	1,2,3,4,6-penta-O-β-D-mannopyranose	acetic acid
$C_6H_{12}O_6$	$C_4H_6O_3$	$C_{16}H_{22}O_{11}$	$C_2H_4O_2$
180.16 g/mol	102.09 g/mol	390.34 g/mol	60.05 g/mol

Procedure:[1]

    A solution of acetic anhydride (64.8 g, 60.0 mL, 638 mmol) and perchloric acid (0.05 mL, 70%) was cooled to 0 °C, and D-mannose (12.00 g, 66.6 mmol) was added over the course of 1 h while maintaining the temperature below 30 °C. The solution was subsequently stirred at 23 °C for 1 h. The mixture was poured over crushed ice (500 g) and saturated $NaHCO_3$ (300 mL), and CH_2Cl_2 (200 mL) was added. The organic layer was separated and washed with saturated $NaHCO_3$ (3 × 50 mL) and water (2 × 50 mL). The organic layer was dried with $MgSO_4$, filtered, and concentrated under reduced pressure to yield crude product (24.3 g, 93%) as a light, clear oil. The resulting oil was recrystalized from diethyl ether to obtain 1,2,3,4,6-penta-O-β-D-mannopyranose (20.4 g, 51.9 mmol, 78%) as a white crystalline solid: mp 148–149 °C, (lit mp_2 148 –149.5 °C); R_f (6:1 hexanes:ethyl acetate) = 0.63; IR (thin film, NaCl) 2995, 2986, 1740, 1380, 1260 cm^{-1}.

Discussion:

    D-mannose and acetic anhydride were reacted with catalytic perchloric acid to yield 1,2,3,4,6-penta-O-β-D-mannopyranose as a white crystalline solid in 78% yield. The melting point of the product was determined to be 148–149 °C, which is within the reported literature range and supports the identity of the product. The narrow range of the melting indicates the product is free from significant solvent contamination, residual side-products, and unreacted starting materials. Thin-layer chromatography analysis of the product produced one band (R_f = 0.63, 6:1 hexanes:ethyl acetate) that was different from the starting material. The infrared spectrum of the product features strong absorptions at 1740 cm^{-1} which is characteristic of the ester functional groups in the product. The presence of water may be cause for partial hydrolysis of the product; therefore it would be beneficial to perform the reaction under an anhydrous environment. The yield could also be improved with alternate experimental conditions. The literature reports high yields for the preparation of similar per-acylated sugars with various Lewis acid catalysts.[3] The preparation of per-acylated carbohydrates has been known in the literature for the past 60 years. Historically, the first report of this reaction was by M. L. Wolfrom in which D-glucose was peracylated in 82% yield from a mixture of acetic anhydride and pyridine.[4]

References:

(1) Callam, C.S.; Lowary, T.L. "Synthesis and Conformational Investigation of Methyl 4a-carba-D-arabinofu ranosides." *Journal of Organic Chemistry*, **2001**, *66*, 8961–8972.

(2) Sigma-Aldrich Chemical Catalog Online. http://www.sigmaaldrich.com/united-states.html (accessed Aug 2022); Search: Product No. M6633.

(3) Lu, K.-C.; Hsieh, S.-Y.; Patkar, L.; Chen, C.-T.; Lin, C.-C. "Simple and Efficient per-O-acetylation of carbohydrates by Lewis acid catalyst." *Tetrahedron*, **2004**, *60*, 8967–8973.

(4) Wolfrom, M.L.; Thompson, A.; *Acetylation. Methods in Carbohydrate Chemistry II—Reactions of Carbohydrates*; Academic Press., Inc.: New York, **1963**.

1.5 Laboratory Awareness

	Effective Behaviors	Points deducted for
Safety	compliance to lab dress and eye safety standards	disregard for lab dress and eye safety requirements wearing gloves outside of the laboratory
	respecting the dangers of food and drink in the laboratory	eating or drinking in the lab storage of food/drink items in lab workspace
	adherence to chemical storage, handling, and waste protocols	leaving chemical bottles/solvent cabinets open after use improper chemical handling or disposal
	proper utilization of fume hood safety features	working with fume hood wide open or with your face inside storage/use of portable electronics inside of the hood
	contributing to an organized and clean workspace	chemical contamination of workspace/common equipment poor management of equipment drawers
Awareness	arriving to lab on time and prepared	tardiness and lack of preparedness
	proper implementation of experimental procedures	use of incorrect/faulty experimental setups and reagents miscalculations that effect experimental outcomes
	attentiveness to your work	playing audio/video during lab time, talking on the phone, wearing headphones
	respecting the cost/integrity of chemical reagents	waste of reagents, unlabeled solids left near balance contamination of chemical/reagent bottles
	effective time management and experiment planning	failure to complete work within the allotted lab time failure to comply to TA time points/instructions
Laboratory Technique	proper operation of lab equipment (analytical balance, mp apparatus, chromatograph, spectrometer, etc.)	improper operation of lab equipment incorrectly reported/recorded or missing mass/data values
	effective handling of lab chemicals and products	loss of product due to spills, faulty clamping restarting the experiment
	respect of lab equipment and glassware	breaking or losing equipment and glassware
	submission of pure products	submission of highly-contaminated products
	contributing to a professional atmosphere	any disrespectful or unsafe practices (as determined by your TA or instructor)
	embracing the learning experience that this course affords	ignoring learning opportunities and areas to improve

To create and foster a positive learning environment, we encourage everyone to be prepared and proficient in the laboratory. Your Laboratory Awareness will be assessed for most experiments, and the following points will be considered:

Of course, if you are unsure about something, we encourage you to seek the assistance of your TA or your instructor. At the same time, you need to make an effort to become as independent as possible, as this will make it easier to complete the experiments. It is important that you arrive to class on time as important announcements are usually given at the beginning of the lab period.

Safety in Organic Chemistry

CHAPTER 2

2.1 Safety Rules of the Organic Laboratory

Safety is your number one priority in an organic laboratory. By working safely and being in control of the situation, you will be able to protect yourself and your classmates. Each laboratory room is equipped with safety showers, eyewashes, fire blankets and fire extinguishers. There are multiple exit locations for quick evacuation. If anything goes wrong, your instructor must be notified immediately. Most emergencies can be handled with available personnel. If there is any doubt that help is needed, call 911 from 431 CE. In any laboratory course or environment, familiarity with safety fundamentals is of highest importance. An organic chemical laboratory can be a dangerous place to someone who is unprepared. Understanding the hazards involved in experiments will help to minimize the number of problems. You will be required to complete a safety quiz for this course.

You are required to read, understand, and implement the safety precautions reviewed below.

1. Work in the laboratory only while your instructor is present. Do not perform unauthorized experiments.
2. You are required to wear splash goggles which meet ANSI Z87.1-1989 code in chemistry laboratories; these are provided. It is strongly recommended that contact lenses NOT be worn.
3. Learn emergency procedures and know the locations of the nearest eye wash, safety shower, fire blanket, and fire extinguisher.
4. All chemicals, especially concentrated acids, spilled on the body should be IMMEDIATELY washed with cold, running water ONLY for at least 15 minutes. Know where the hand-held spray attachments are located and how to use them. Contaminated clothing should be removed.
5. If you are injured or if any type of accident or fire occurs, IMMEDIATELY call your instructor or teaching assistant for assistance.
6. Carefully read all instructions, and thoroughly plan your work prior to coming to the laboratory.
7. Appropriate clothing and shoes must be worn in the laboratory. Attire such as shorts, short skirts and sandals are not permitted. Confine long hair. Lab coats are required and can be purchased at the chemical lab store (180 CE).
8. Carefully read all labels on chemical bottles. Never return excess chemicals to the stock bottles.
9. Do not eat, drink, or smoke in the lab. Never taste chemicals. Smell chemicals cautiously by wafting the vapors toward you.
10. When mixing or heating chemicals in a test tube, point the test tube away from yourself and others.

11. Do not use Bunsen burners or other sources of spark or flame near flammable liquids. Note that most organic solvents are flammable.
12. Don't force glass tubing into a rubber stopper. Lubricate the hole and protect your hands with a towel while you insert the tubing into the stopper. Better yet, use a "Handsaver," which you may obtain from your instructor or stockroom personnel. When cutting glass, also protect your hands with a towel. Fire-polish sharp edges of glass. Do not touch hot glass.
13. While mixing acid and water, always add the acid to the water, not vice versa.
14. Fill a pipette by using a pipette bulb only; never pipette by mouth.
15. Clean up all spills immediately by covering the spill with the appropriate cleanup material listed below:
    a. For organic spills, use SOLUSORB.
    b. For acid spills, use sodium bicarbonate.
    c. For base spills, use citric acid.
16. Dispose of chemicals as directed by your instructor and teaching assistant and in a manner consistent with federal, state, and local hazardous waste disposal regulations.
17. Inform your instructor of any broken or malfunctioning equipment or utilities.

Recommendation: enrollment in courses, including laboratory courses, at the Ohio State University does not automatically entitle you to medical coverage. Due to the potentially dangerous nature of laboratory work, you are strongly encouraged to obtain medical insurance coverage through OSU Student Health Services or a private agency when enrolling in chemistry laboratory courses.

- I have read carefully and understand all of the safety rules contained on this sheet and in the laboratory manual or laboratory handouts required for this course. I recognize that it is my responsibility to obey them faithfully.
- I realize that all chemicals are potentially dangerous; therefore, I will exercise care in handling them. If I am unsure of the potential hazards of any chemical, I will discuss this with my instructor prior to using the chemical in question.
- I have read the statements on EYE SAFETY and HAZARDOUS WASTE. I also understand that I am required by Ohio law to wear ANSI (Z87.1-1989) approved chemical splash goggles at all times while I am in the laboratory. I also understand the dangers involved in wearing all types of contact lenses in the chemical lab. If I elect to wear contact lenses in the laboratory, I will inform my instructor, and I will assume all responsibility for damages caused by wearing them in the lab.
- If I have a medical condition such as, but not limited to, hyper- or hypoglycemia, diabetes, epilepsy, pregnancy, heart ailments, or any other medical condition which may cause sudden loss of consciousness, I certify that I am under a doctor's care and that my doctor has given me explicit permission to participate in this laboratory course. I will inform my instructor of my condition at the beginning of the quarter, or as soon as I am aware of the existence of the medical condition.
- In the event of an accident, I understand that I am responsible for the cost of medical treatment, and that I have the right to refuse such treatment. If I refuse treatment, I agree to absolve the Department of Chemistry and The Ohio State University of responsibility for injuries.

2.2 Summary—Safety

- No food and drink should be brought into the laboratory. Do not place anything in your mouth during lab. There are many toxic substances that you can come in contact with when in the organic laboratory. Lab students should be very cautious to avoid contacting their hands or other lab objects with their face and mouth.
- No smoking, eating or drinking are allowed in the laboratory. Food and drink cannot be stored in or around our hood area.
- Never leave an experiment in progress unattended.
- Should you need to leave the lab while an experiment is running, inform your teaching assistant and a classmate so they can watch over your reaction while you are gone.
- Aisles must be kept free of obstructions, such as backpacks, coats and other large items. These items can be stored in the cubbies at the front of the room.
- Wear gloves when needed to protect your skin against any toxic chemicals or concentrated acids.
- Remove your gloves and wash your hands before leaving the laboratory. To prevent the spread of chemicals outside of the lab, always wash your hands after working in the lab and never leave the lab with your gloves on.
- Always wear your safety goggles and lab coat in the laboratory.
- To minimize the risk of accidental injuries to the eye, the Chemistry Department requires the use of safety goggles in all laboratories at all times. This policy is supported by Ohio law and will be strictly enforced by our laboratory instructors. Department-issued ANSI Z87.1-1989-approved chemical splash goggles must be worn immediately after entering the laboratory. If fogging occurs on humid days, students should apply anti-fog solution available from the storeroom.
- Closed-toe shoes are essential. Sandals or flip-flops are not allowed. You also must have clothing that completely covers your legs. Shorts, skirts, and dresses are not allowed.
- If you spill something on yourself, do not be afraid to use the sinks, hoses, eye-washing fountain, or safety shower.
- First aid for chemicals in the eye or on the skin: Rinse the affected area with large amounts of water for at least 15–20 min.
- Contact lenses should not be worn in the laboratory, as they might result in eye irritation or injury even if adequate eye protection is worn. Especially avoid soft contact lenses, as they might discolor or absorb chemicals and chemical vapors that can cause damage to the cornea before the wearer is aware of the problem. Furthermore, lenses are difficult to remove when chemicals get into the eyes, and they have a tendency to prevent natural eye fluids from removing contaminants that may get under the lenses.
- Be careful when handling glassware. If a piece of glassware is chipped or broken, replace it; it is not safe to use in the laboratory.
- Be careful when placing a thermometer into an adapter.
- If you cut yourself:
  1. Notify the TA or instructor.
  2. Remove the glass from the cut.
  3. Rinse the cut with water.
  4. Apply pressure to stop the bleeding.
  5. Band-Aids and Neosporin are available in room 431 CE.

2.3 Spills

Spills on Lab Surfaces

- Leave small amounts of volatile solvents to evaporate or wipe them up with a paper towel. Then place the towel in your hood for the solvent to evaporate.
- Weak acids and weak bases: If you spill a weak acid (acetic acid) or a weak base (ammonia), wipe the spill up with a towel and rinse it into the sink.
- Strong acids: Add solid sodium bicarbonate to the spill, then clean up the area with water and paper towels.
- Strong bases: Add solid citric acid to the spill, then clean up the area with water and paper towels.

Spills on Your Skin or Clothing

- Avoiding spills requires you to be prepared, neat, and organized for lab. If your work area is kept clean, you have decreased the chance that you will be surprised by the spill.
- Spills on your skin: Rinse with copious amounts of cold water for at least 15 min.
- Spills on clothes: Remove the contaminated clothing and rinse the skin with copious amounts of water. Incase of a large spill, remove the clothing and use the safety shower.

2.4 Organic Fumes and Vapors

- Exposure to large amounts of organic vapors can result in headaches, nausea, dizziness, and fatigue. If you notice these symptoms, inform your teaching assistant or instructor, and go out into the hallway or outside to get some fresh air.
- In the organic lab, we will minimize the exposure to chemical vapors by using the appropriate safety fumehoods for dispensing all chemicals and organic reaction apparatuses. Reflux condensers will be used in certain experiments to cool down the heated vapors in the reactions and thereby allow the condensed vapor to flow back down into the flask.

2.5 Fires

- Use care with open flames in the organic laboratory. Many organic liquids are highly flammable, so the danger of a fire is frequently present. Use extreme caution when lighting a Bunsen burner. Ensure that there is no flammable solvent on the bench top near your hood. If there is flammable solvent around, you must delay using your flame until the solvent is removed from the area. Organic substances often have dense vapors that can travel for some distance down the bench top. These vapors present a serious potential for hazard.
- Learn the locations of the fire extinguisher, safety shower, and fire blanket.

2.6 Disposal of Chemical Waste Materials

♦ The proper disposal of waste solvents is an important part of good laboratory practice. Specific waste disposal instructions will be provided for each experiment. Some general procedures for waste disposal are summarized below.

Waste Solvents

1. At the beginning of each laboratory period, the teaching assistant (TA) will provide a chemical waste disposal form. Waste solvent containers will be provided as a temporary place for storing the different waste solvents during the laboratory period.
2. Only organic solvents are to go into the waste solvent container. No acids, bases, solids, or aqueous solutions, unless they contain substantial quantities of organic material, are to go into the waste solvent container.
3. At the end of each laboratory period, the TA will add up the amounts of each solvent and record that information. The TA will transfer the waste solvent from the waste solvent containers to the red solvent can. The TA will then record the amount of solvent added to the can on the attached card. The teaching assistant will submit all chemical waste disposal forms via an online form.

Mineral Acids

♦ Mineral acids such as H_2SO_4, HCl, HNO_3, and H_3PO_4 should never be added to the waste solvent container. Mineral acids should be diluted with water and ice and then carefully and slowly neutralized with sodium hydroxide. Once neutral, the solution can be flushed down the drain with copious amounts of water.

Aqueous Solutions Used in the Experiments

♦ Water solutions that do not contain significant amounts of organic compounds or heavy metals such as lead, silver, or chromium can be flushed down the drain with plenty of water. The filtrate from a reaction where the compound has been precipitated from water solution is an example.

Aqueous Solutions Containing Heavy Metals

♦ We will avoid the use of such solutions whenever possible. However, solutions containing heavy metals (barium, cadmium, chromium, lead, mercury, silver) are never to be flushed down the drain. If they are used, such solutions must be neutralized and put into the container for heavy metal waste. When you mark down amounts, you must estimate the amount of the metal compound, for example "0.5 g of $K_2Cr_2O_7$ in 50 mL of water" Aluminum, copper, iron, tin, and zinc salts are not toxic at low concentration and may be flushed down the drain.

Waste Solids

♦ Organic solids must be placed in the container for waste organic solids.

Laboratory Hood Contents

CHAPTER 3

3.1 Organic Hood Overview

Hood Overview

1—Hotplate and Aluminum Block
2—VARIAC
3—Glassware Drawer 1
4—Glassware Drawer 2
5—Glassware Drawer 3
6—Common Equipment Drawer

24 CHAPTER 3 ❖ Laboratory Hood Contents

The components of the two drawers of glassware are shown on the following pages.

3.2 Organic Lab Equipment

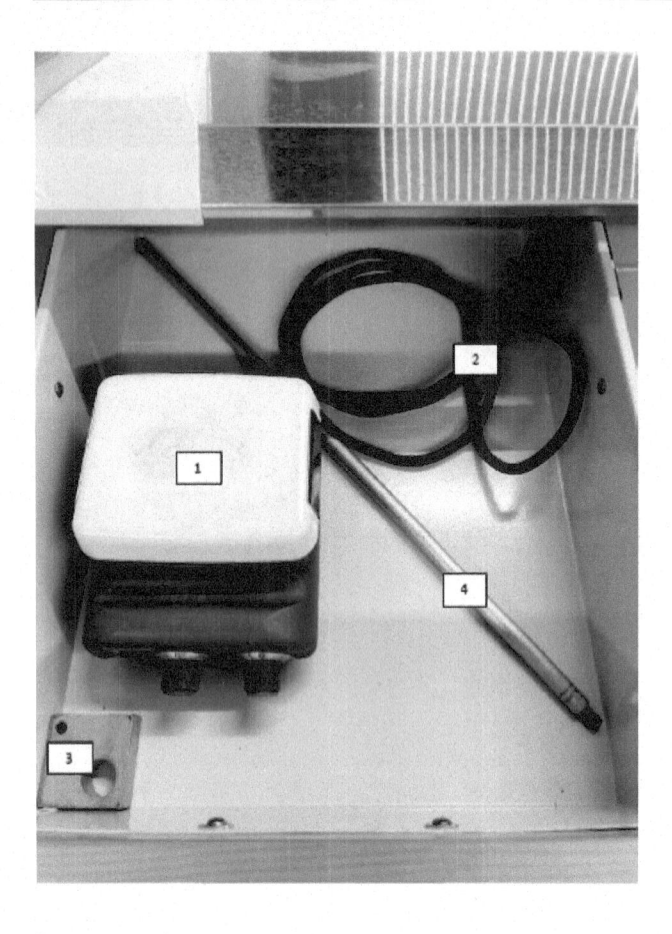

Drawer 1
    1—Hotplate
    2—Hotplate electrical cord
    3—Aluminum Block
    4—Metal Support Rod

CHAPTER 3 ❖ Laboratory Hood Contents   **25**

Drawer 2
1—VARIAC

26 CHAPTER 3 ❖ Laboratory Hood Contents

Organic Glassware Equipment Drawers (Cont.)

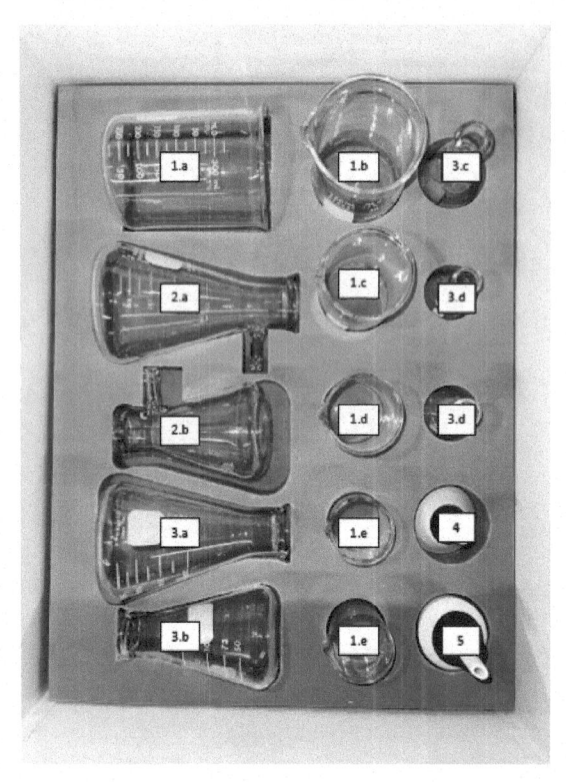

Drawer 3

    1.a—400-mL Beaker
    1.b—250-mL Beaker
    1.c—150-mL Beaker
    1.d—100-mL Beaker
    1.e—50-mL Beaker
    2.a—300-mL Filter Flask
    2.b—250-mL Filter Flask
    3.a—250-mL Erlenmeyer Flask
    3.b—150-mL Erlenmeyer Flask
    3.c—100-mL Erlenmeyer Flask
    3.d—50-mL Erlenmeyer Flask
    4—Hirsch Funnel
    5—Büchner Funnel

Organic Glassware Equipment Drawers (cont.)

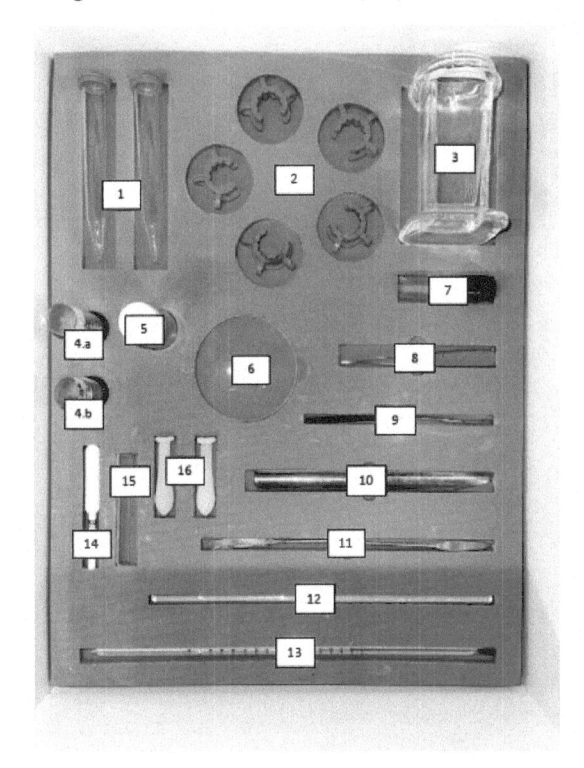

Drawer 4

1—Centrifuge Tubes (2x)
2— Blue Keck Clamps (5x)
3—Coplin Jar
4.a—5-mL Conical Vial
4.b—3-mL Conical Vial
5—Spinvane
6—Watch Glass
7—Macroscale Thermometer Adapter
8—Forceps
9—Microspatula
10—Scoopula
11—Double-sided Spatula
12—Glass Rod
13—Thermometer
14—Teflon Plug with Copper Wire
15—Craig Tube
16—Pipet Bulbs (2x)

28 CHAPTER 3 ❖ Laboratory Hood Contents

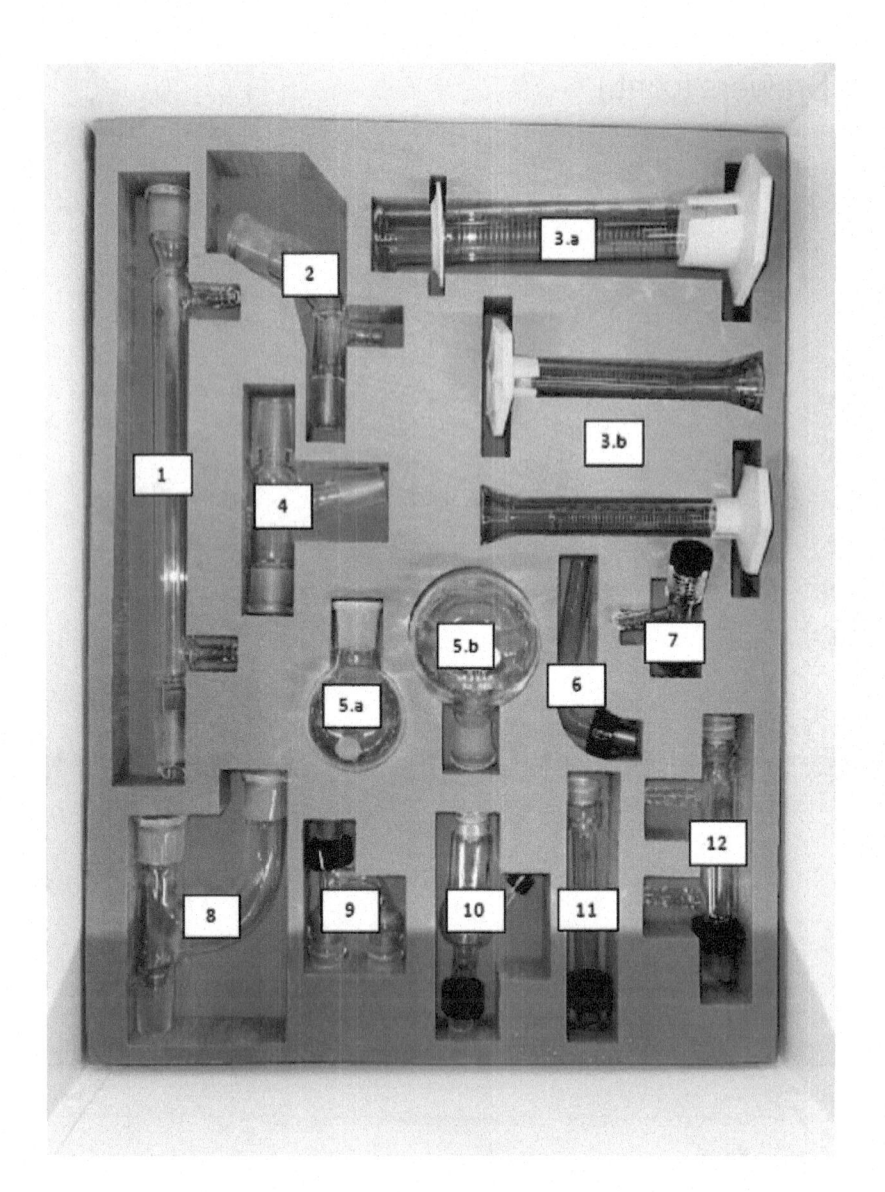

Drawer 5

- 1—Macroscale Water Condenser
- 2—Macroscale Vacuum Adapter
- 3.a—50-mL Graduated Cylinder
- 3.b—10-mL Graduated Cylinder (2x)
- 4—Three Way Adapter
- 5.a—50-mL Round-Bottom Flask
- 5.b—100-mL Round-Bottom Flask
- 6—Microscale Drying Tube
- 7—Microscale Thermometer Adapter
- 8—Microscale Claisen Adapter
- 9—Hickman Still
- 10—Microscale Air Condenser
- 11—Microscale Water Condenser

CHAPTER 3 ❖ Laboratory Hood Contents 29

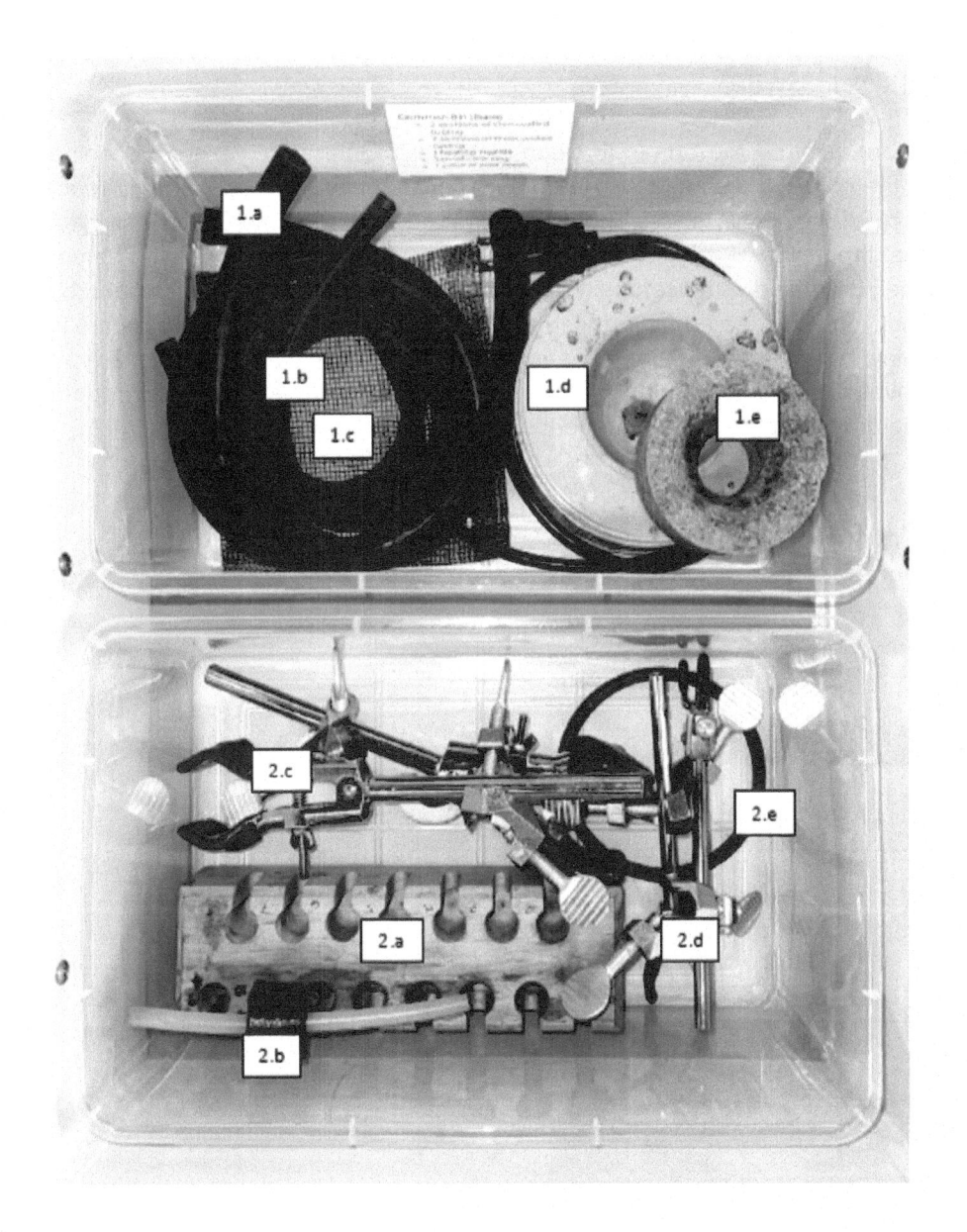

Drawer 6

1.a—Thick-walled Tubing (2x)
1.b—Thin-walled Tubing (2x)
1.c—Wire Mesh
1.d—Heating Mantle
1.e—Cork Ring
2.a—Test Tube Rack
2.b—Rubber Stopper
2.c—Medium Clamp
2.d—Small Clamp
2.e—Iron Ring

3.3 Cleaning and Drying Glassware

Quality organic laboratory work must be performed in clean glassware. Unless the reaction is being performed in aqueous solution, the glassware should also be dry, because many synthetic organic reactions do not work in the presence of water. Glassware should be cleaned with soap and water using an appropriate brush. Make sure that the inside of the glassware is carefully cleaned, then rinsed with deionized water. The glassware can then be rinsed with acetone (~5 mL). Acetone and water are soluble, and by rinsing the wet flask with acetone, you will speed up the drying process. Cleaning and drying glassware is an unavoidable chore in the organic chemistry laboratory experience. The best advice is to clean up as you go along. Many of the periods involve a waiting period. Use this time to clean your glassware. Do not put dirty glassware back into your lab drawer at the end of the period.

3.4 Hood Operation Controls

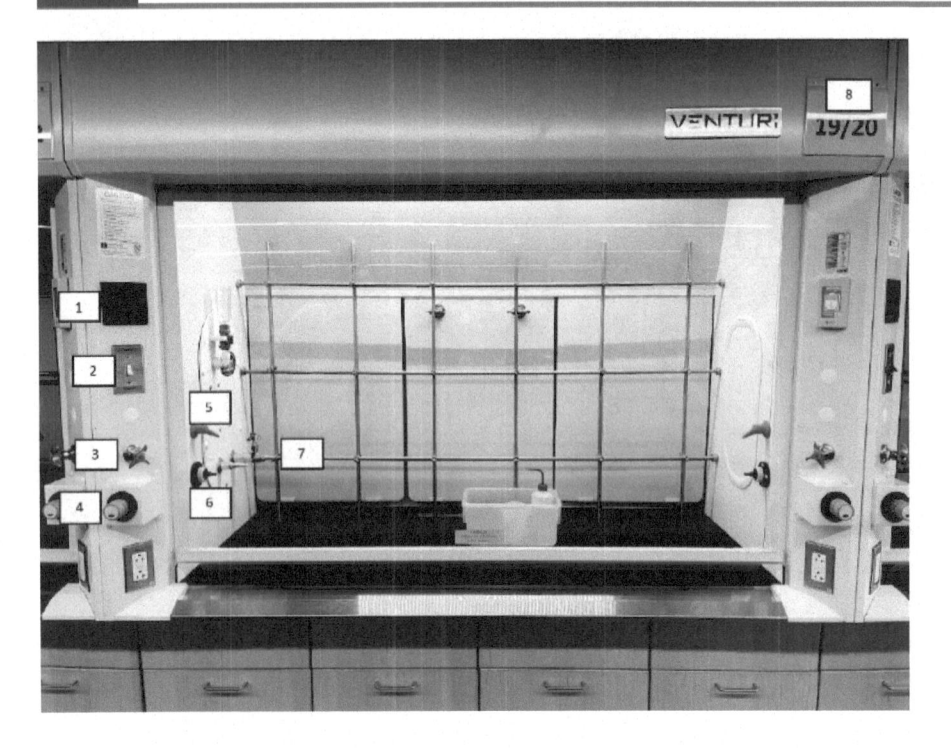

Hood Operation Controls

1—Light Control
2—Eco denser Control
3—Compressed Air Control
4—Vacuum Control
5—Compressed Air Outlet
6—Vacuum Inlet
7—Eco denser Inlet/Outlet
8—Hood Number

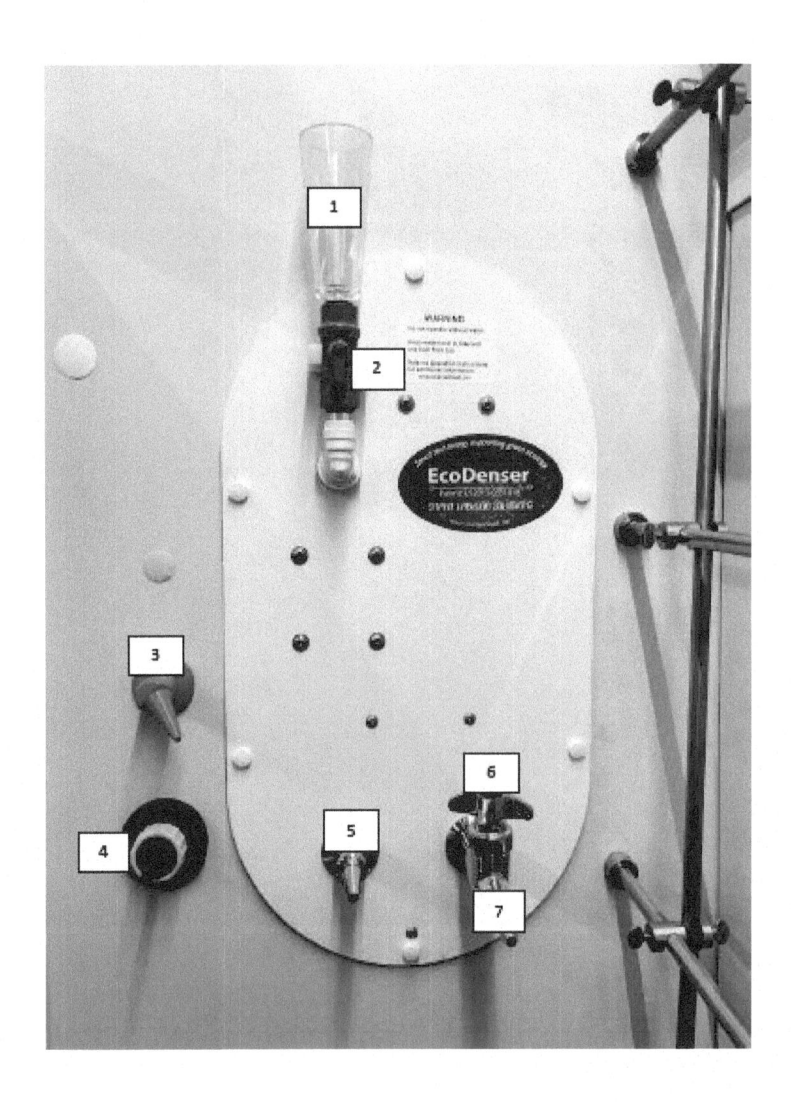

EcoDenser Overview

1—Water Reservoir
2—Reservoir Valve
3—Compressed Air Outlet
4—Vacuum Inlet
5—EcoDenser Inlet
6—EcoDenser Control Valve
7—EcoDenser Outlet

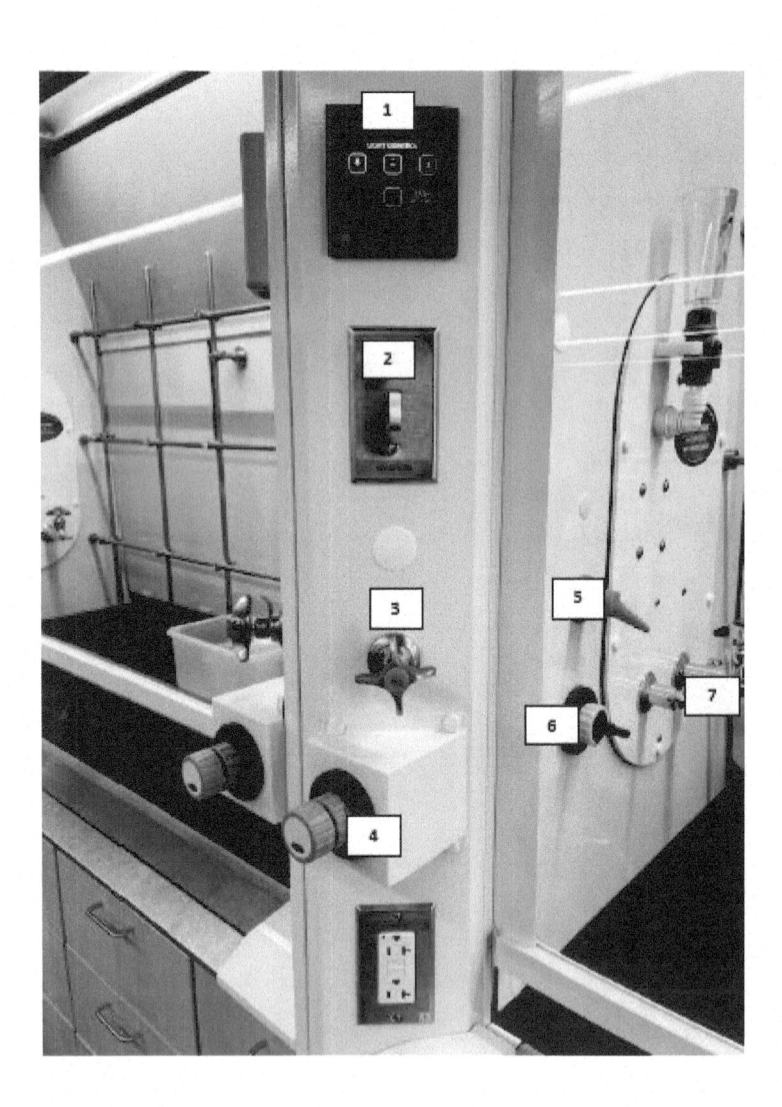

Hood Panel Overview

1—Light Controls (On/Off, Dimmer, Warmth)
2—EcoDenser Control Switch
3—Compressed Air Pump
4—Vacuum Control
5—Compressed Air Outlet
6—Vacuum Inlet
7—EcoDenser Inlet/Outlet

3.5 Hardware Use and Operation

In drawer 6, you will find other laboratory hardware and equipment that you will need to use throughout the semester.

- Clamps and holders for supporting apparatuses
- Metal rings for supporting separatory funnels and heating mantles

A chemical apparatus should always be securely clamped and fixed to a stable support. The metal scaffolding located in the back of your hood is the most used form of support. Clamps of an appropriate size for the apparatus should be chosen and tightened enough to hold the glassware without breaking it. Clamp holders should be used so that the open slot for the clamp faces upward. Most microscale apparatuses are very light and require minimal amounts of clamping, usually near the bottom of the main reaction vial. The hood sash should always be kept at or below the optimal level because it provides protection for the face and top half of the body in the event of an explosion. If the hood sash is open all the way, the fans will not create sufficient air pull to maintain the inrush necessary to contain organic vapors. With the sash pulled down, the hoods are more effective, and you will get into the habit of not leaning over the apparatus when working. Leaning into the hood and putting your head inside is a very unsafe and bad lab practice. It negates all the reasons for operating the hood in the first place. When setting up a chemical apparatus in the hood, it should be placed as far back in the hood as possible where you can still reach it and manipulate it easily.

Heating

Several methods of heating are commonplace in the organic laboratory. It is important that safety comes first regarding the flammability of most organic solvents, coupled with their volatility. Open flames in the organic lab pose the greatest hazard. Bunsen burners should never be used to heat a flammable solvent in an open-air container or if flammable solvents are being used nearby; they can be used only with non-flammable liquids. Always use a piece of wire mesh between the vessel to be heated and the flame. The mesh will help to support the vessel and disperse the heat evenly. This also will lower the risks of cracking the container and of causing severe bumping. Electrical heating mantles are designed for heating round-bottom flasks and must never be used for heating other types of vessels. Each mantle is specific to accept a particular size flask, which should sit snugly in the cavity, touching the concave jacket at all points with no exposed heating areas. The mantles in the organic lab have no direct heating controls and should be connected to a variable heating controller (VARIAC) and never plugged directly into the main power supply. Mantles tend to heat up slowly, so be patient before turning up the power on the VARIAC. When setting up your reaction, you should always allow for the possibility that you might need to remove the heat source when using a heating mantle. The best way to achieve this is to clamp the apparatus at a height that allows the mantle to be supported on an iron ring stand, which can be lowered away without affecting the rest of the apparatus.

Heating Microscale Reactions

Aluminum blocks can be used on top of the hotplate. The aluminum block is bored with a hole that matches the external diameter of tapered reaction vials, allowing stirring to occur normally and for efficient thermal transfer from aluminum.

Magnetic Stirring

Magnetic stirring is the method of choice if you require an extended period of continuous agitation. When placed into your apparatus, the magnetic spinvane interacts with the magnet inside your hot plate to cause stirring. Low settings work best when using a spinvane in a conical vial. Magnetic stirring does not work efficiently in viscous solutions or solutions that contain large amounts of suspended solids. Be careful with your magnetic spinvane as it is easy to lose during the cleaning-up portion of the laboratory period. Loss of the spinvane will result in a loss of points.

Organic Reactions: Setting Up and Chemical Handling

CHAPTER 4

The organic lab course is designed for you to carry out organic reactions in which you will convert one compound into another in a safe and efficient manner. Before coming to lab, it is essential to your success that you read and understand the experiment. Read over the description of the experiment, review the lecture notes, and ascertain that you understand all the underlying chemical principles. While in lab, the typical organic reaction in the lab requires the following:

1. Assembling suitable apparatus for the reaction
2. Adding the correct quantities of reagents and solvents
3. Allowing the reaction to take place under the given set of experimental conditions (temperature, addition rate, and so on)
4. Isolating the product
5. Purifying the product
6. Analyzing the product

4.1 Safe Handling of Chemicals

When handling chemicals, safety always come first. Before starting any procedure or setting up any reaction, you should familiarize yourself with the properties of the chemicals and solvents you will be using, and think about the setup you will need. You should always look at the lab procedure and pre-lab for any chemical warning and safety standards.

Ask yourself:

Are any of the chemicals flammable?

Are any of the chemicals corrosive?

Are any of the chemicals toxic?

Are any of the chemicals moisture- or air-sensitive?

IF YOU ARE IN DOUBT, ALWAYS ASK FIRST!!!

4.2 Measuring and Transferring Chemicals

For a chemical reaction to be successful, it is important to use defined amounts of starting materials to get high yields and results. Do not change the amounts of material to use in the experiment, as it can lead to dangerous situations in the lab. Take care when transporting chemicals around the lab. You should always handle them with care and never take chemicals or reaction apparatus containing chemicals outside of the lab rooms.

Solids

Solids must always be weighed to determine the correct amount to use in a chemical reaction. The accuracy of weight depends on the scale on which the reaction is carried out. Typically, when weighing out 100–300 mg, weighing to the nearest milligram is required. However, if you need a larger scale, such as grams, weighing to the nearest 0.1 g is required. Therefore, you should always use a balance that is appropriate for the accuracy of the required weighing. The analytical balances weigh to the nearest 0.1 mg; they are suitable for weighing things up to 1 g in weight. The top-loading or single-pan balances weigh to the nearest 0.01 g with a very large maximum weight. These balances are suitable for weights in grams.

It is often easier to weigh the chemicals in a suitable container and then transfer the chemicals to the reaction flask. It is very important to use the proper container when weighing out your sample. **Do not use a large weigh boat to measure out something in the milligram quantities.** Rather, if you need to measure out a small quantity, it is best to use a piece of weighing paper. Use a spatula or micro-spatula to transfer the solid to the weighing vessel. You should be careful to avoid spills during the transfer. If you do spill during the transfer, you should wipe up the spill immediately. The most convenient way to transfer a solid that has been weighed out into a reaction vessel is to use a piece of folded weighing paper.

Transfer the solid from the paper to the flask before heading back to your hood. The flask that you are transferring the solid into should be placed inside a beaker. The beaker prevents the flask from tipping over and acts as a trap for any spilled materials.

It is often necessary to weigh the exact amounts specified in the experimental procedure. It is very important to know how much material you have for the reaction. If you obtain 1.520 g of a solid rather than the 1.500 g specified in the procedure, the actual amount weighed is recorded and the theoretical yield will be calculated using that amount.

Liquids

Liquids can be measured by weight or volume, but it is usually easier to measure by volume. The main exception to this idea is that reaction products that are liquids need to be weighed to determine the amount yielded from the reaction. Most of the procedures indicate the amount of liquids to be used in milliliters. Occasionally the quantity is given by weight in grams; in this case you will need to calculate the amount of liquid needed by using the density of the material.

$$\text{Volume} = \text{Weight (g)} / \text{Density (g/mL)}$$

There is various lab equipment available for measuring volume. Graduated pipettes and syringes are the most common place items. The choice of equipment depends on the accuracy needed in the experiment. For example, when you need to heat 25 mL of solvent for a recrystallization, a beaker or Erlenmeyer flask will suffice with the approximate measurement. When more accuracy is needed, it is better to use a graduated cylinder. Always choose one that is the correct size. Do not try to measure 7 mL in a 100 mL graduated cylinder; use a 10 mL cylinder instead. Be careful when pouring liquids from a reagent bottle into a measuring cylinder; use a funnel to minimize spills. You can also use a Pasteur pipette to transfer liquids to measuring containers if they are difficult to pour. Make sure the pipette is clean so that you do not contaminate an entire reagent bottle. Syringes are also useful for measuring small quantities of liquids quickly and accurately. After measuring out your liquid reagent or starting material, it needs to be transferred from the measuring container to the reaction container. Larger volumes of liquid can be poured directly from the measuring container or transferred with a Pasteur pipette. Large volumes of liquids should be poured from the measuring container. Always be sure to use a funnel. Mechanical losses of materials are undesirable in the laboratory and should be avoided. On a microscale, loss of materials can be disastrous to your yield. Small quantities of liquids should always be transferred using pipettes or syringes. To weigh liquids: weigh the empty reaction flask, calculate the volume of liquid needed based on the density. Use a syringe or pipet to measure the liquid and transfer it to the reaction flask. Weigh the reaction flask again to determine the amount of reagent in the flask. The most important thing is to know how much material you started with and that it is in the range that is given in the procedure. As with solids, the theoretical yield should always be calculated from the exact amounts used.

4.3 Filtration

Filtration is a common technique used in almost every organic chemistry lab procedure. Filtration of a suspension to remove the solids is a technique of preparative organic chemistry that is achieved by allowing the liquid to pass through a porous barrier. There are two main filtration techniques in organic chemistry: gravity filtration and suction filtration.

Gravity Filtration

In general, this is a simple technique that applies when you want to isolate the filtered liquid. This technique requires a funnel, a piece of filter paper, and an Erlenmeyer flask for collecting the filtrate. Always use the correct size filter paper for the funnel. You should flute the filter paper when using this method of filtration because it decreases the area of contact between the paper and the funnel. Always support the filter funnel in a metal ring attached to the support stand in your hood. This apparatus is very top-heavy and can be knocked over easily if not supported properly. The solution is then simply poured into the filter paper cone, and the filtrate is collected.

Suction Filtration

Use this type of filtration when you desire to filter the solid material from the suspension. Suction or vacuum filtration is much faster than gravity filtration because the technique relies on reduced pressure in the receiving flask. The receiving flask is an Erlenmeyer flask with a sidearm, often called a Buchner flask. The flask should be clamped securely and attached to the source of vacuum through a suck-back trap using thick-walled tubing. The source of the vacuum in the organic chemistry laboratories is the vacuum port at the hood that is hooked up to a local vacuum pump. The vacuum control knob should be used carefully and only requires two fingers for operation. To open the vacuum port turn the knob counter clockwise about 90°. The knob does not need to be opened all the way to achieve a vacuum suitable for this filtration method. Before starting the filtration, always wet the filter paper with a little solvent and then turn on the vacuum a little to ensure a good seal (the paper should be flat). Carefully pour the contents of the flask with the suspension over the center of the filter paper. When all of the liquid has been removed, release the vacuum by disconnecting the hose at the sidearm, then turn off the vacuum control gently using two fingers to turn the knob clockwise to the closed position.

4.4 Reaction Workup with a Conical Vial

To carry out efficient extractions on the microscale, use a conical vial or centrifuge tube and a Pasteur pipette. To perform this procedure after the reaction is over, clamp the open conical vial into place and add the indicated amount of wash solution. Close the vial or tube with a tight-fitting cap and gently shake the mixture. After carefully shaking the mixture, vent the solution by slowly removing the cap. Allow the mixture to settle and remove the lower layer with a pipette. Exclude all of the air from the pipette by depressing the bulb and inserting the pipette into the bottom of the conical vial. Next, slowly release the bulb, watching the meniscus line carefully so that you remove only the lower layer, then discard the washings and repeat the process as directed. It is important to note the densities of the organic solvent used in the reaction so that you know where the organic layer is when extracting with aqueous solutions. An organic solution with a density of greater than 1 will be on the lower layer of the vial, and an organic solution with a density less than 1 will be on the upper layer.

4.5 Microscale Distillation Apparatus (Simple)

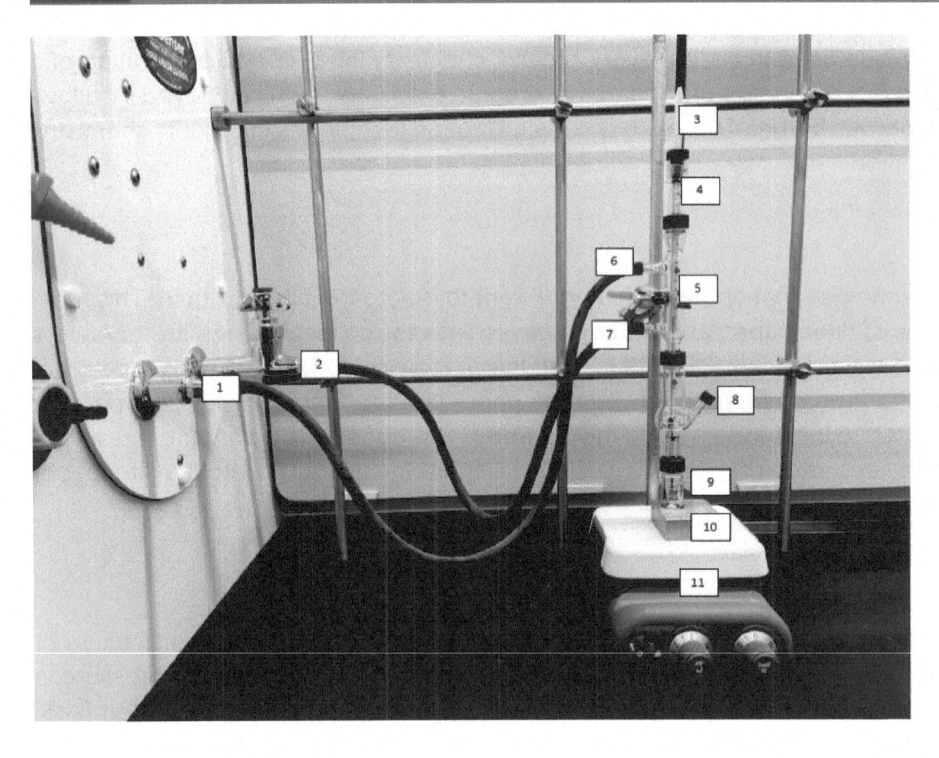

Microscale Distillation Apparatus (Simple Distillation)
1 – Ecodenser Inlet
2 – Ecodenser Outlet
3 – Thermometer
4 – Microscale Thermometer Adapter
5 – Microscale Water Condenser
6 – Water Condenser Outlet
7 – Water Condenser Inlet
8 – Hickman Still
9 – Conical Vial
10 – Aluminum Block
11 – Hotplate

4.6 Microscale Distillation Apparatus (Fractional)

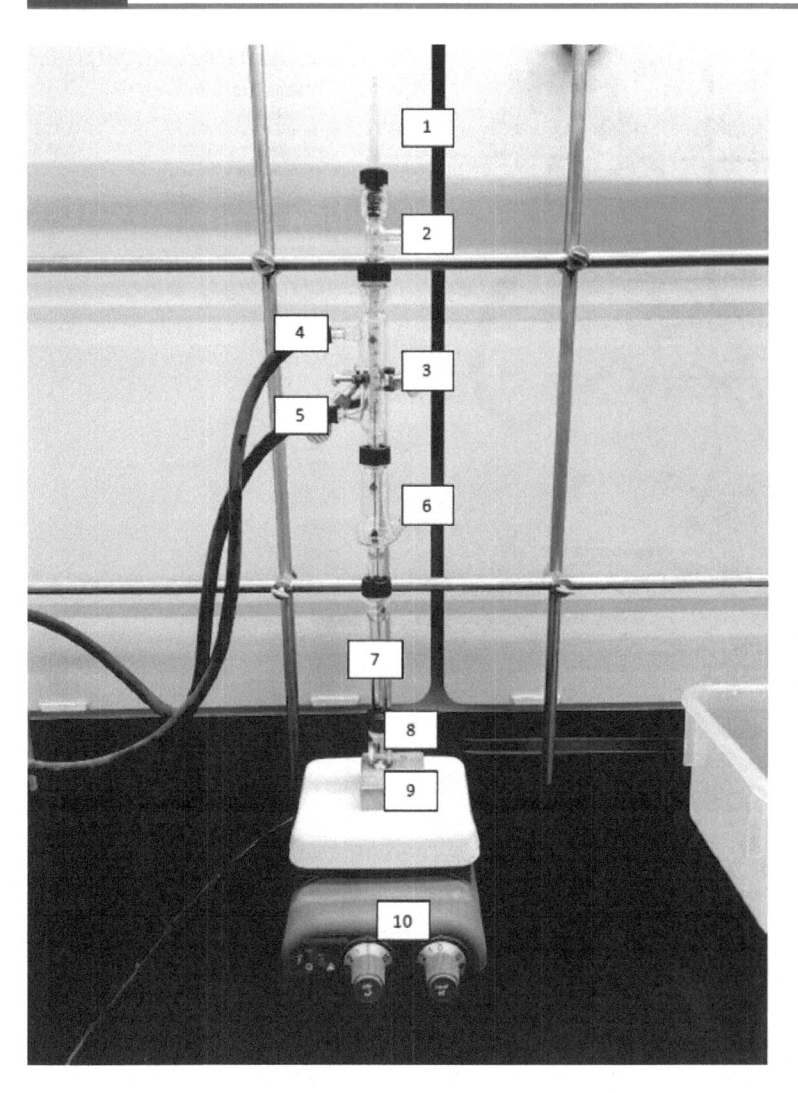

Microscale Distillation Apparatus (Fractional Distillation)
1 – Thermometer
2 – Microscale Thermometer Adapter
3 – Microscale Water Condenser
4 – Water Condenser Outlet
5 – Water Condenser Inlet
6 – Hickman Still
7 – Air Condenser
8 – Conical Vial
9 – Aluminum Block
10 – Hotplate

4.7 Microscale Vacuum Distillation Apparatus

Microscale Vacuum Distillation Apparatus
1 – Vacuum Inlet
2 – Ecodenser Inlet
3 – Ecodenser Outlet
4 – Thermometer
5 – Microscale Thermometer Adapter
6 – Microscale Water Condenser
7 – Water Condenser Outlet
8 – Water Condenser Inlet
9 – Hickman Still
10 – Conical Vial
11 – Aluminum Block
12 – Hotplate
13 – Filter Flask

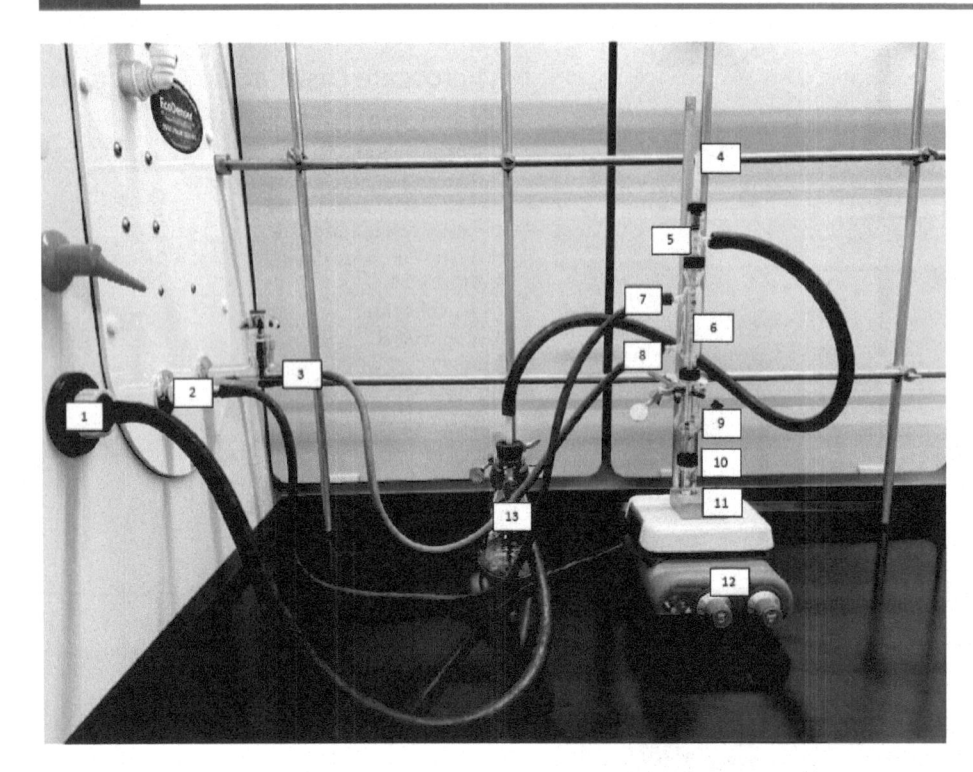

4.8 Reaction Workup with a Separatory Funnel

To carry out efficient extractions on the macroscale, use a separatory funnel supported by an iron ring and stand. To perform this procedure after the reaction is over, pour the reaction mixture into the separatory funnel and add the indicated amount of wash solution. Carefully swirl the contents of the funnel to allow any gas formation to take place and escape. Cap the funnel, and using two hands, carefully shake the funnel with the stopcock in the closed position and supporting the capped end with your hand. After shaking quickly, vent the funnel by turning it upside down and opening the stopcock. Place the separatory funnel back in the iron ring and stand, and carefully drain the lower layer into a clean Erlenmeyer flask. Place the organic layer back in the funnel and repeat the process as directed. It is important to note the densities of the organic solvent used in the reaction so that you know where the organic layer is when extracting with aqueous solutions. An organic solution with a density of greater than 1 will be on the lower layer of the funnel, and an organic solution with a density less than 1 will be on the upper layer.

4.9 Macroscale Distillation Apparatus

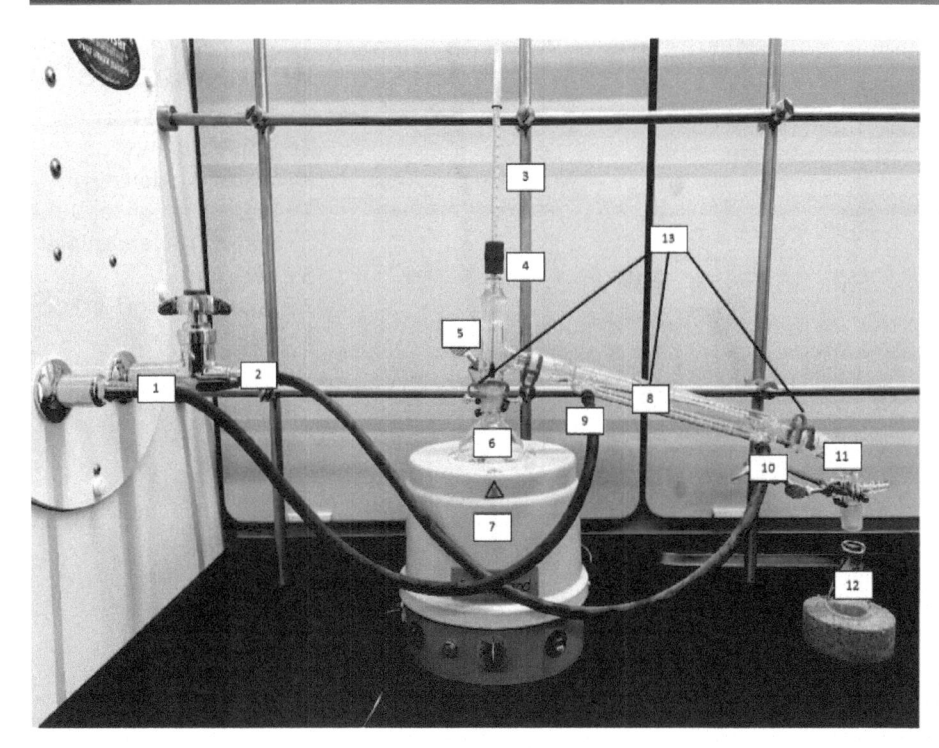

Macroscale Distillation Apparatus
1 – Ecodenser Inlet
2 – Ecodenser Outlet
3 – Thermometer
4 – Macroscale Thermometer Adapter
5 – 3-Way Adapter
6 – Round Bottom Flask
7 – Heating Mantel
8 – Macroscale Water Condenser
9 – Water Condenser Outlet
10 – Water Condenser Inlet
11 – Macroscale Vacuum Adapter
12 – Erlenmeyer Flask
13 – Keck Clips

4.10 Macroscale Reflux Apparatus

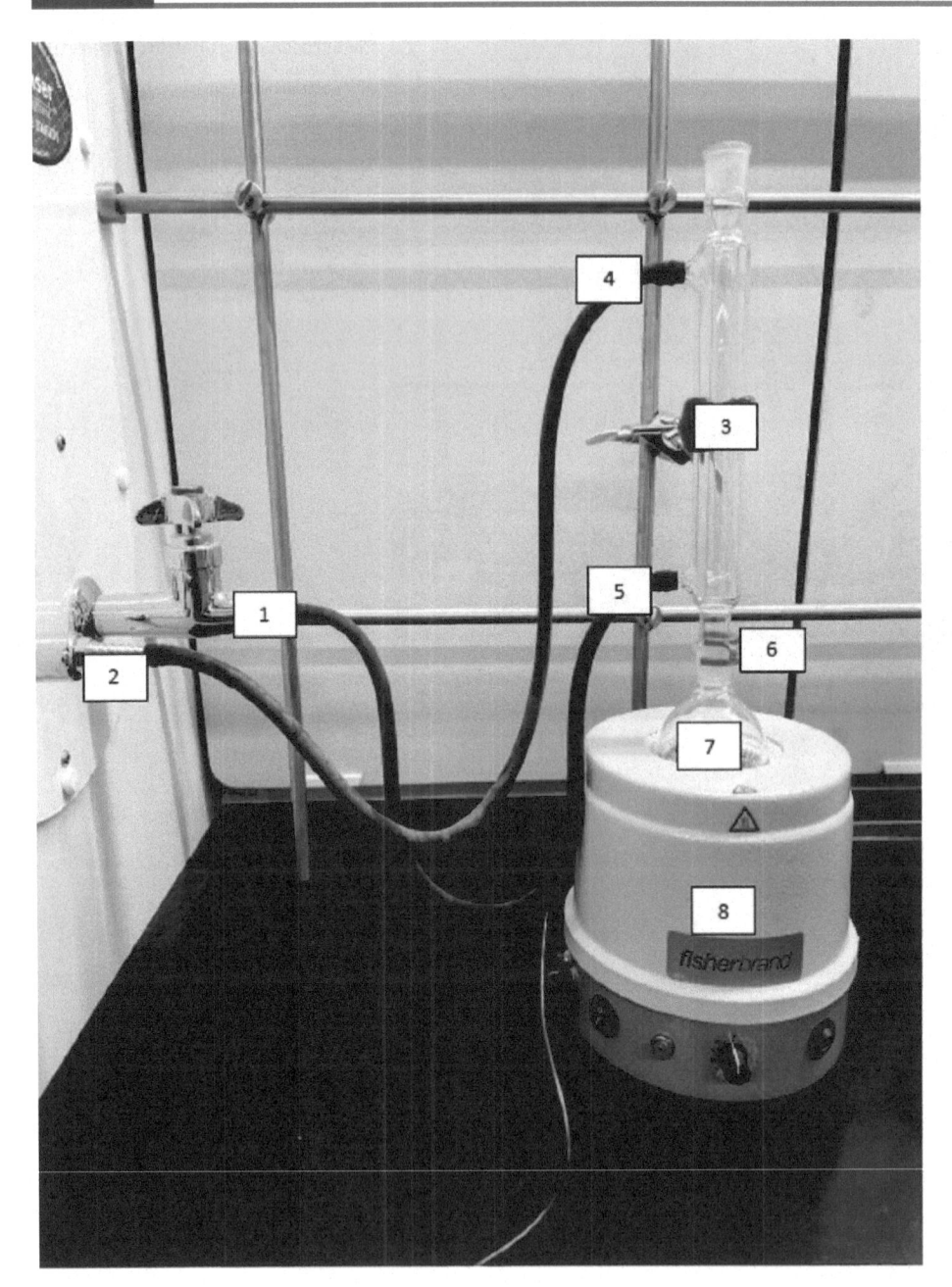

Reflux Apparatus
1 – Ecodenser Outlet
2 – Ecodenser Inlet
3 – Water Condenser
4 – Water Condenser Outlet
5 – Water Condenser Inlet
6 – Keck Clip
7 – Round Bottom Flask
8 – Heating Mantle

Analysis of Organic Compounds

CHAPTER 5

Most compounds synthesized in the organic labs are either solids or liquids, and the physical properties relating to these states are useful in indicating the purity of a compound.

5.1 Melting Point

The melting point of a recrystallized solid is a physical property and can be used to indicate purity and aid in identification of an unknown. In most cases when a compound melts over a narrow melting point range of less than 2 °C (from the initial appearance of drops of liquid within the sample to the sample becoming a liquid), the mixture is believed to be pure.

A broad melting point of greater than 4 °C in most cases indicates an impure compound. An impure compound will also have a depressed melting point when compared to the literature value. In some cases, the sample could be pure in form and then might decompose upon heating while trying to measure the melting point of the component. This is evident by a darkening of the sample or by evolution of a gas repetitive. Dissolution of the compound in residual recrystallization solvent will also give the appearance of a broad melting point. This is commonly encountered if the sample is not dry.

Experimental Procedure for Recording a Melting Point

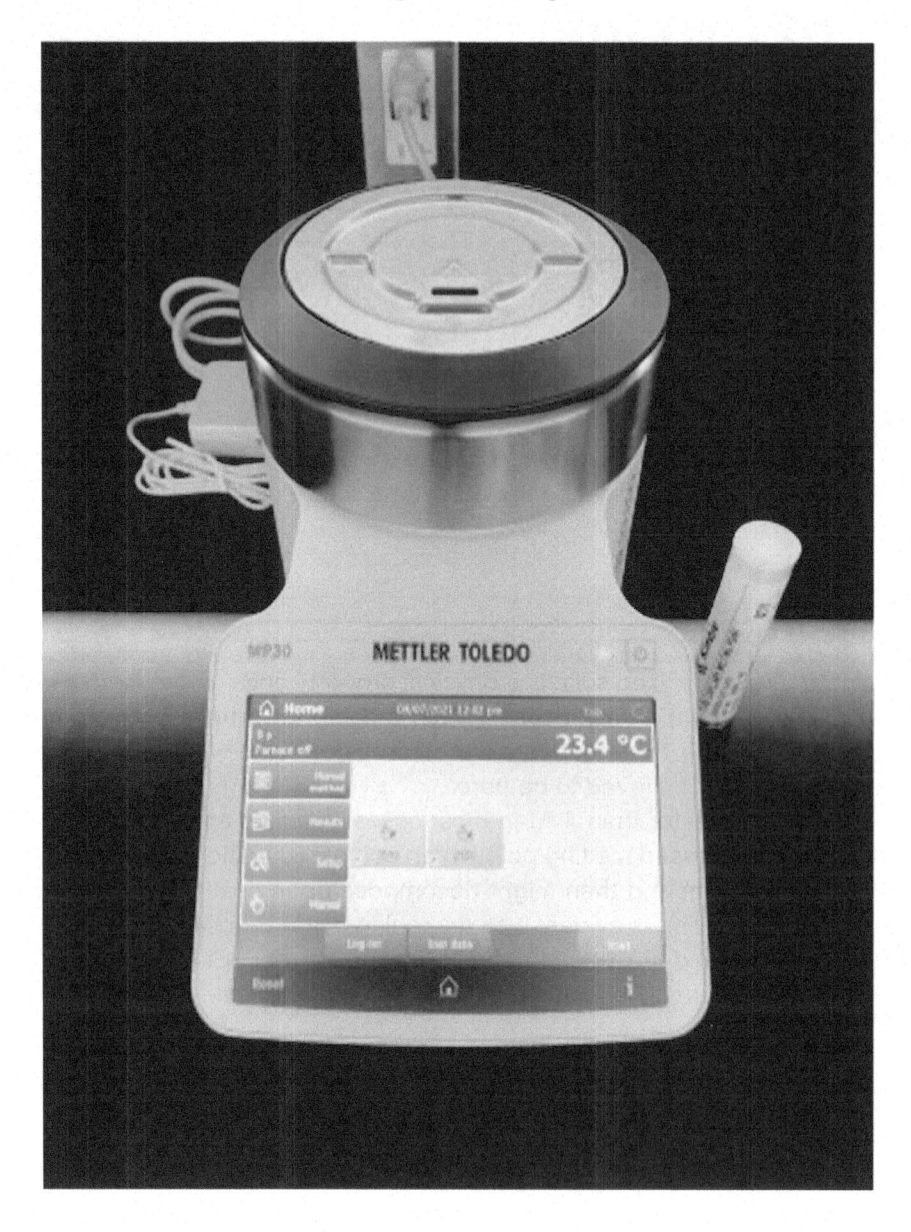

First, place a small amount of the substance to be melted inside a capillary tube that has one end open and the other end closed. Be sure that the sample is dry and in a fine powder. Press the open end of the tube into a small pile of the sample on a clean glass surface, such as a watch glass or small vial. This will cause a plug of the material to become inserted into the mouth of the tube. Insert approximately 3 mm of the sample into the open end of the tube. To move the material to the sealed end, stand a length of the glass tubing on the bench top and drop the tube down with the sealed end first. The force of impact on the bench will cause the solid to transfer down to the sealed end. Then use a melting point apparatus to measure the melting point of the solid in the tube. The melting point apparatus contains a metal heating block that will warm the sample and can melt three sample tubes at a time.

Melting Point How-to-Guide
- Place three capillary tubes in the 3 slots on top of the melting point apparatus.
- After placing your sample(s) in a slot above, choose the course that you are in (2540 or 2550).
- Touch "Start" on the bottom right of the screen. **Do not change any settings on this page.

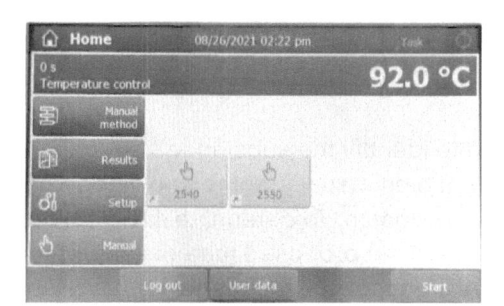

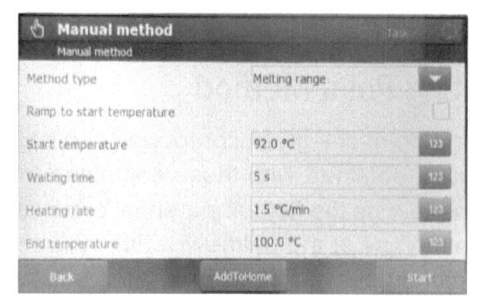

- You should now be able to see the samples that have been placed into the apparatus. Choose "Start" again at the bottom right to start melting point determination.
- Once the test has completed, a results page will appear from which melting point ranges can be recorded. Choose "Home" to start over.

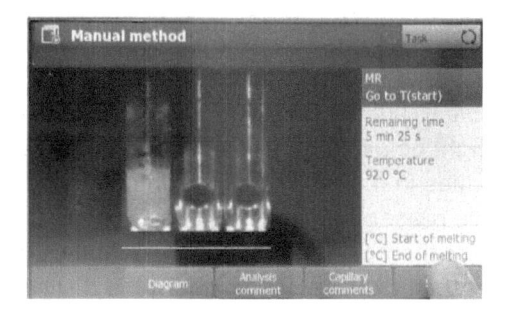

It is assumed that the temperature of the sample will equate with the temperature of the surrounding metal block. The standard procedure involves heating the sample rapidly to within 10 °C of the expected melting point and then to slow down the rate of heating so that the temperature is increased at no more than 2 °C each minute (the slower the better).

If you do not know the melting point that is to be expected, you will have to carry out initial rapid heating to gain approximate melting point, followed by an accurate determination in which the melting point is approached slowly from about 20 °C below the expected value.

The first sign that your sample is about to melt is usually a contraction in volume. This is called a sintering of the sample. After this takes place, the first drop of liquid should be visible. This is considered the commencement of melting (the low value of the melting point range). Melting is complete when the last crystals disappear and become liquid (the high value of the melting point range). After melting the sample, allow it to cool, and dispose of the melting point capillary in the glass waste container. Be careful! The tube could be hot! If you miss any of the above observations, start the process over with a fresh sample. Never melt the same sample twice!

Problems with Melting Points

- mp slightly low small amount of impurities present residual solvent/moisture
- mp slightly high False high: heated faster than 2 °C per min
- Sample darkens and/or releases gas decomposition: mp difficult to characterize
- mp different after 2nd determination sample was no longer crystalline (NO RE-RUNS)

Mixed Melting Point Method

The melting point of a given compound can be used to identify the substance's structure by comparing the melting point obtained with those contained in data tables. Usually, some knowledge of the chemical reactivity helps reduce the field of potential candidates for a match. To determine if two compounds are the same, make a mixture of the unknown with a pure sample of the proposed material in a 1:1 proportion, and record the melting point of the mixture. If the substances are identical, the melting point will be unchanged from what you originally measured for the unknown. However, if they are different, the melting point of the mixture will be depressed compared with that of the original unknown. This is because impurities introduced into the sample will lower and broaden the melting point ranges. This technique is very powerful for determining the identity of unknown solids that have similar melting points.

5.2 Boiling Point

The boiling point of a compound is a physical property that you can use to indicate its purity and identity. Pure liquids will distill without decomposition, and they have a sharp boiling point at a constant temperature.

Boiling points have one problem: they are susceptible to fluctuations in atmospheric pressure and consequently, experimental boiling-point determinations might be a few degrees off from those reported in the literature at standard temperature and pressure. Impurities in liquids can only sometimes be detected by boiling points, depending on the nature of the impurities present. Volatile impurities can cause the boiling point to rise steadily over a certain boiling point range, or the boiling point might fluctuate over a range of values, or the whole boiling point could be much higher than expected throughout the distillation.

5.3 Study Guide—Melting Points

1. Understand what is meant by a melting point range.
2. Understand what is meant by melting point depression and know why and when this occurs.
3. Understand what happens to the melting point range of a pure compound when it becomes contaminated.
4. Given two samples that have the same melting point range, know how to determine whether or not the samples are identical.
5. Understand why it is important to slowly raise the temperature of a melting point apparatus if a melting point determination is to be accurate.
6. Draw a picture on the molecular level of what is taking place during a melting point.

IR Spectroscopy

CHAPTER 6

All organic compounds are known to absorb frequencies of electromagnetic radiation in the infrared region of the spectrum. The infrared region of the electromagnetic spectrum lies at wavelengths lower than those associated with visible light. The absorption of infrared radiation corresponds to energy changes on the order of 2–10 kcal/mol. Radiation in this energy range corresponds to the stretching and bending vibrational frequencies of the bonds in most covalent molecules. In the absorption process, those frequencies of infrared radiation that match the natural vibrational frequencies of the molecule are absorbed, and the energy absorbed increases the amplitude of the vibrational motions of the molecule. Most organic chemists refer to this vibration infrared region of the electromagnetic spectrum by units of wave-numbers. Wavenumbers are expressed in the units of reciprocal centimeters. The vibrational infrared region of the spectrum extends from 4000 cm^{-1} to 650 cm^{-1}.

6.1 Uses of the Infrared Spectrum

Because every type of bond has a different natural frequency of vibration and because the same type of bond in two different compounds is in a different environment, no two molecules of different structure have exactly the same infrared spectrum. The infrared spectrum can be used to identify a molecule because it has a unique fingerprint. If you were to compare the infrared spectra of two compounds thought to be the same, it will establish whether or not they are identical. If the infrared spectra of the two substances coincide peak for peak, in most cases, the two compounds are the same. A second and more important use of the infrared spectrum is that it gives you structural information about a molecule. The absorptions of each type of bond are regularly found only in certain portions of the infrared region.

Table 6.1 – Approximate regions where types of covalent bonds have their stretching vibrations.

O—H	C—H	C≡N	C=O	C—C	C—X
N—H		C≡C	C=C	C—O	
			N=O	C—N	

4000 cm^{-1} — 600 cm^{-1}

The simplest types of vibrational motion in a molecule that are infrared active and give rise to absorptions are the stretching and bending modes.

6.2 What to Look for in Examining Infrared Spectra

The infrared spectrophotometer determines the relative strengths and positions of all of the absorptions in the infrared region. The plot of absorption versus wavenumber is referred to as the infrared spectrum. A typical spectrum is shown below for the molecule pinacolone.

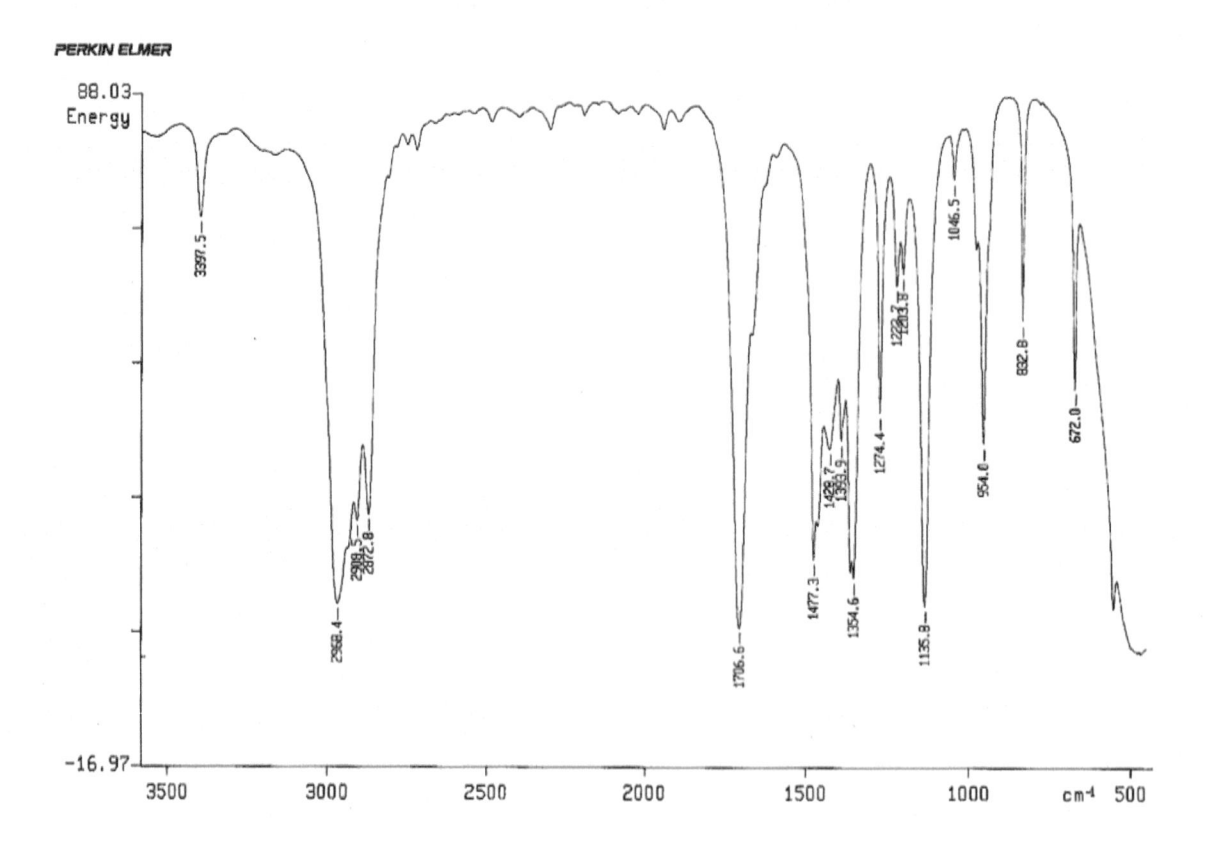

In addition to the characteristic positions of absorptions shown in the spectra, the shape and intensity of the peaks are of major importance. For example, the C=O absorption in the above spectrum is considered to be a strong absorption. As you review the tables and spectra on the following pages, make sure you take note of the shapes and intensities of the peaks. These are as important as the frequency in which the absorption occurs. The notations for peak intensities and shape are strong (s), medium (m), weak (w), broad (b), and sharp (sh). Although the intensities of an absorption often provide useful information about the identity of a peak, be aware that the relative intensities of all of the peaks in the spectrum are dependent on the amount of sample that is used and the instrument itself. Therefore, it is most important to pay attention to relative intensities.

Interpretation of IR Spectra

Infrared spectroscopy provides valuable information about specific patterns of bonding (functional groups) in organic molecules. The data is presented as a two-dimensional plot of frequency of IR radiation absorbed in a particular molecule (X-axis in wavenumbers, cm^{-1}) and the intensity of each absorbance (Y-axis in percent transmittance, %T). A strong peak indicates most of the radiation of a given frequency has been absorbed, whereas weak (w) absor- bances indicate less radiation being absorbed. Different absorbances are characteristic of certain functional groups.

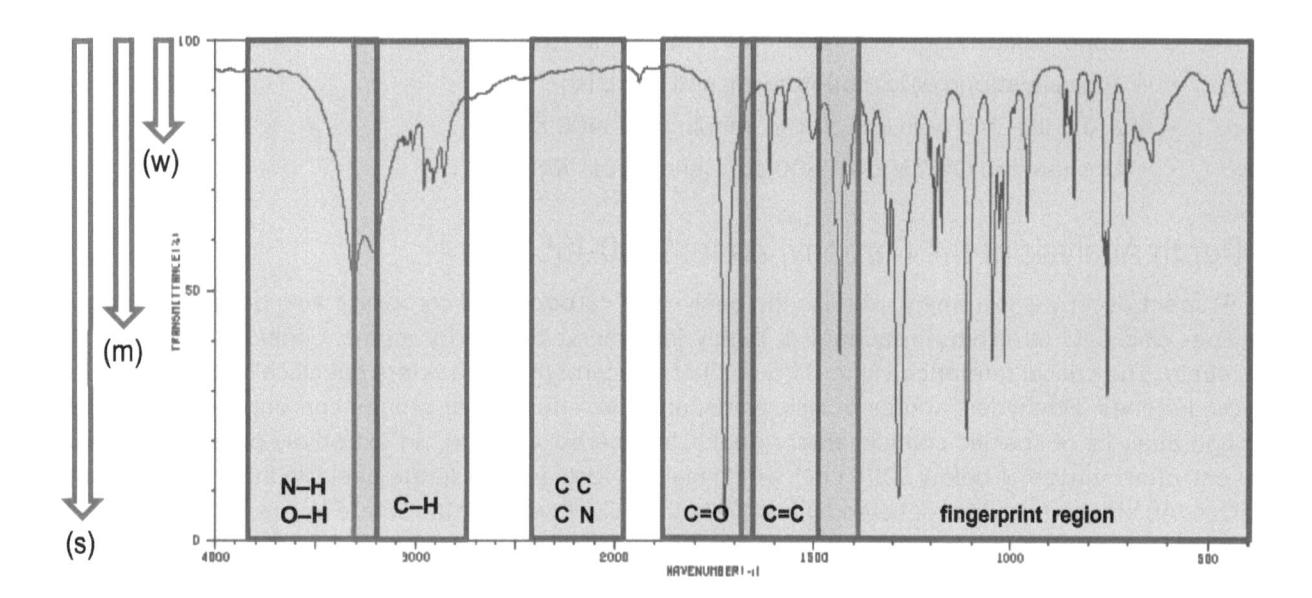

Analyzing the Functional Group Region: 4000-1400 cm^{-1}

Organized and logical IR spectrum analysis begins with decoding the information present in the Functional Group region of the spectrum. The Functional Group region can be separated into five sub-regions, and peaks in these zones can be correlated to a type of chemical bond by comparison to the average center value of that sub-region, referred to as critical reference values below. Though zones are often presented as ranges, these zone boundaries are artificial and can become misleading in some situations; therefore, an approach that focuses on critical reference values is more versatile. When more than one choice of functional group or bond type is possible in a given zone, further analysis of peak shape/intensity, specific frequency "cut-off" values, and the presence (or absence) of complimentary peaks provide more support for confident decision-making. Starting from the left side of the IR spectrum, the five zones are analyzed in order:

- O–H/N–H Zone (critical reference value: 3250 cm^{-1}) - How to differentiate?
  - O–H: typically strong (s) to moderate (m) and broad (br)
  - N–H: typically moderate (m) to weak (w) and sharp (sh)
  - Complimentary Peaks: C=O present?

- C–H Zone (Critical reference value: 3000 cm^{-1}) - How to differentiate?
  - Saturated a.k.a. (sp^3)C–H: below 3000 cm^{-1}
  - Unsaturated a.k.a. (sp^2/sp)C–H: above 3000 cm^{-1}
  - Complimentary Peaks: C=C present?

- ◆ C≡/C≡N Zone (Critical reference value: 2250 cm^{-1}) - How to differentiate?
  - Alkyne a.k.a. C≡C: moderate (m) to weak (w)
  - Nitrile a.k.a. C≡N: Typically moderate (m)
  - Complimentary Peaks: (sp)C–H present?
- ◆ C=O Zone (Critical reference value: 1715 cm^{-1}) - How to differentiate?
  - Typically strong (s) and slightly broad (br)
  - Large range possible: 1800–1650 cm^{-1}
  - Highly influenced by atoms nearby (functional group)
- ◆ C=C Zone (Critical reference value: 1600 cm^{-1}) - How to differentiate?
  - Typically strong (s) to moderate (m) and sharp (sh)
  - Aromatic C=C: below 1600 cm^{-1} (ending at ~1400 cm^{-1})
  - Unsaturated C=C: above 1600 cm^{-1} (ending at ~1680 cm^{-1})

In-Depth Analysis of the Carbonyl Zone: 1850-1650 cm^{-1}

IR spectroscopy is extremely useful in the analysis of carbonyl and carboxylic acid derivatives because the spe- cific C=O stretching frequency is highly influenced by nearby atoms, conjugation, bonds, and ring strain. The critical reference value (1715 cm^{-1}) of the carbonyl zone refers specifically to saturated and acyclic ketones, aldehydes, and carboxylic acids, and these functional groups can only be differentiated through analysis of specific complimentary peaks. In a carboxylic acid, an extremely broad O–H peak is present, often stretching below 3000 cm^{-1}, which makes weak and moderate peaks in this region difficult to analyze. An aldehyde is differentiated by two (2) unique C–H peaks of moderate (m) intensity that occur at approximately 2850 and 2750 cm^{-1}, respectively. Because (sp^2)C–H bonds normally show up above 3000 cm^{-1}, this may be counterintuitive to those new to IR analysis.

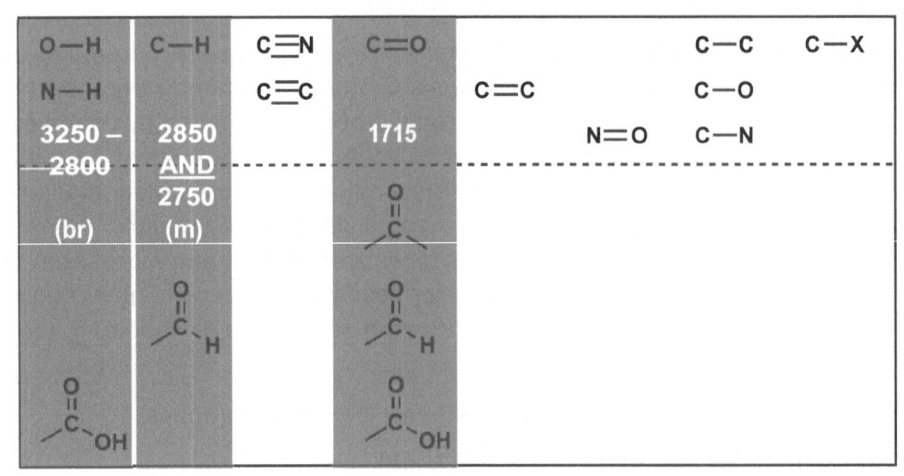

- Carboxylic acid: presence of extremely broad (br) O–H peak
- Aldehyde: presence of moderate (m) C–H peak (2x peaks, below 3000?)
- Ketone: no additional complimentary peak

C=O Zone—Functional Group Effects

The carbonyl bond stretching frequency is greatly affected by atoms directly attached to it, thus different functional groups often have specific and unique C=O peaks that help to identify the presence of these bonds in unknown samples. In a carboxylic amide, the presence of the nitrogen creates a favorable resonance overlap those results in the C=O vibration occurring at a lower frequency (approximately −30 cm^{-1}) than those found in ketones. The competition of resonance and inductive effects result in a carboxylic ester displaying an increased carbonyl stretching frequency (approximately +30 cm^{-1}) relative to a "normal" carbonyl, and the presence of a chloride or bromide in a carboxylic acid halide result in this frequency increasing even further (+90 cm^{-1}). In a carboxylic anhydride, the symmetric and asymmetric stretching of the two carbonyl groups close in space result in a characteristic set of two (2) peaks at 1825 and 1765 cm^{-1}. Interestingly, the average of those peaks (1795 cm^{-1}) is similar to the single carbonyl stretch frequency of the carboxylic acid halide, to which it is related in chemical reactivity.

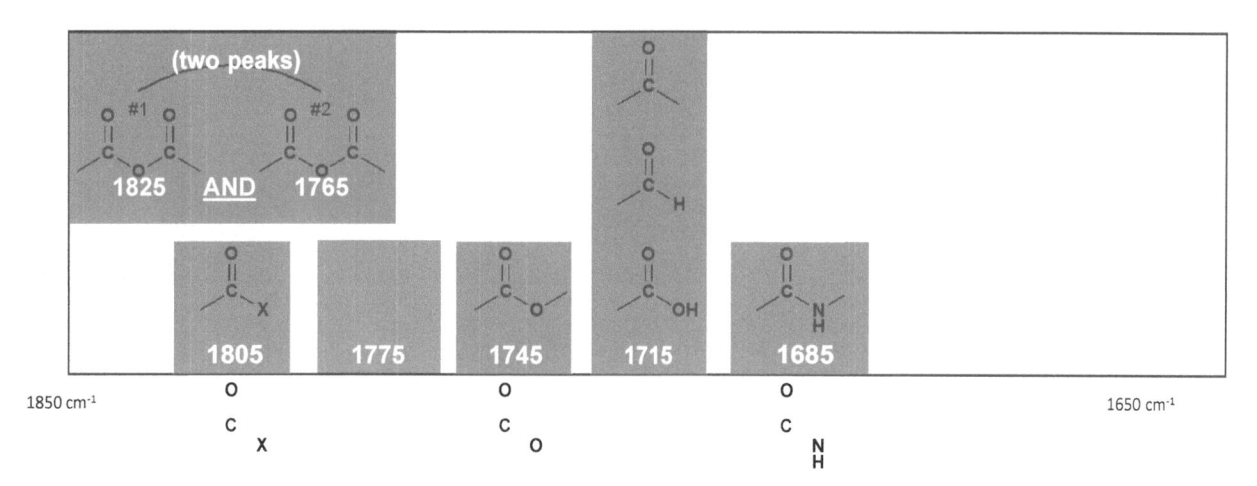

Functional Group Effects Summary

- "Normal" C=O: ketone/aldehyde/carboxylic acid
- Amide decreases vibrational frequency -30 cm^{-1}
- Ester increases vibrational energy +30 cm^{-1}
- Acyl halides increase vibrational energy +90 cm^{-1}
- Anhydrides vibrate at two discrete frequencies with an average like acyl halides

C=O Zone—Conjugation Effects

When a carbonyl group is attached to a carbon of a double (or triple) bond or aromatic ring, these unsaturated carbonyls experience a reduction of the stretching frequency (−30 cm^{-1}) attributed to an increase in resonance overlap. This resonance effect can be combined with the functional group effects discussed above. For instance, the expected C=O stretch of an unsaturated ester may be estimated the following way:

Estimate the carbonyl stretching frequency of methyl methacrylate.

"normal" carbonyl + ester functional group + unsaturated/aromatic = estimated C=O of an unsaturated ester (1715 cm^{-1})(+30 cm^{-1})(-30 cm^{-1})(1715 cm^{-1}

The effect of the ester functional group is "cancelled out" by the presence of the C=C, resulting in a frequency that is closer to "normal" than an ester would typically exist. However, when the experimental value for methyl methacrylate is obtained (1726 cm^{-1}), the degree of error in these estimation methods is revealed. Instead of elaborating more complex and specific rules for estimate calculation, a chemist may simply choose to qualify all his or her estimates with ±10 cm^{-1} of acceptable error whenever a comparison between an estimate and an experimental value is made. When a molecule contains a carbonyl that is unsaturated on both sides, the stretching frequency is further reduced (–60 cm^{-1}) compared to a "normal" carbonyl; however, since a carbonyl with this connectivity can only be a ketone by definition, further discussion of functional group effects is not needed.

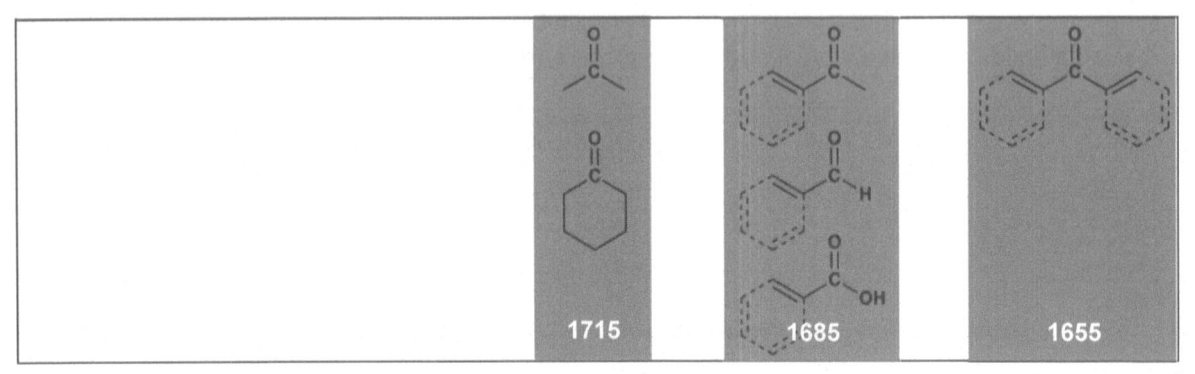

Conjugation Effects Summary

- "Normal" C=O: ketone/aldehyde/carboxylic Acid
- Conjugation on one side decreases vibrational frequency –30 cm-1
- Conjugation on both sides of the carbonyl –60 cm^{-1}

C=O Zone—Ring Strain Effects

Both cyclohexanone and acetone exhibit a 1715 cm^{-1} carbonyl stretching frequency consistent with the "normal" carbonyl definition described in this analysis, which is consistent with other experimental observations that atoms in a six-membered ring are relatively free of angle strain. However, decreasing ring size is related to increasing stretching frequency of a carbonyl if the carbon of the C=O is part of the ring. The effects of ring strain and functional groups can be combined as above, and the expected C=O stretch of a four-membered amide (beta-lactam) may be estimated the following way:

Estimate the carbonyl stretching frequency of 2-azetidinone.

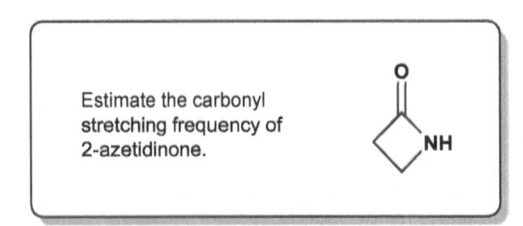

"normal" carbonyl + amide functional group + 4-membered ring = estimated C=O of a 4-membered amide (1715 cm^{-1})(+30cm^1)(+60 cm^{-1}) (1745 cm^{-1})

The effect of the amide functional group counteracts the strain present at the carbonyl present in the four-membered ring, resulting in a frequency that is surprisingly closer to an ester than an amide. Again, when the experimental value for 2-azetidinone is obtained (1723 cm^{-1}), the simplifications used in this method result in a slightly larger error than before. Instead of being disturbed by this difference in the prediction, it is helpful to appreciate that 3- and 4-membered rings may have effects on stretching frequency that are more difficult to estimate due to their highly-strained structures. Interestingly, the difference between a 6- and 7-membered ring is within the previously discussed acceptable error of ±10 cm^{-1}, implying that a seven-membered ring may not be significantly more strained at the carbonyl carbon than cyclohexanone.

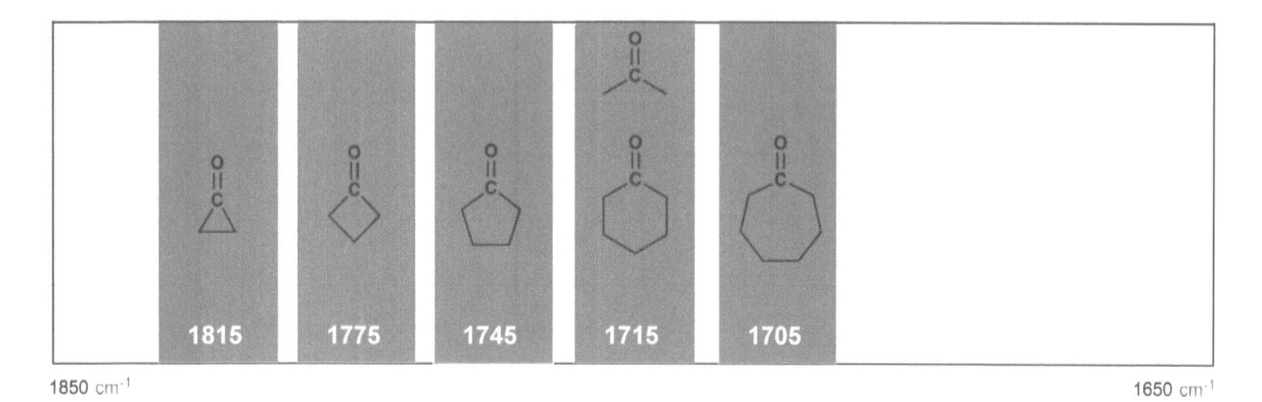

Ring Strain Effects Summary

- "Normal" C=O: cyclohexane and acetone are unstrained
- Shrinking the 6-membered ring increases vibrational energy +30 cm^{-1} (per -CH$_2$- unit)
- Expanding the ring from 6 to 7 does not deviate the vibration outside of "normal"

The Difference between Estimation and Experimental Values

Using this system of estimation, a sensible expectation of what types of bonds may or may not be present in a structure can be generated. In chemistry problem-solving, there should always be room to reject any of these assumptions and pursue more in-depth analyses, and in real-life, problems most often do not fit so neatly into neat categories. The "tweaks" for functional group, conjugation, and ring strain (±30 or 60 cm^{-1}) and acceptable error (±10 cm^{-1}) that are described above are simple approximations that allow for the greatest problem-solving benefit from the minimum number of rules and values to remember. However, all of this flexibility disappears when a chemist is comparing an actual experimental result to a known, literature value. In this situation, an IR peaks should match within ±3 cm^{-1} (and typically less), or otherwise be met with scrutiny. The enormous benefit of IR spectroscopy (and other spectral methods) is that experimental data obtained anywhere in the world should agree to this level of accuracy.

Analyzing the Fingerprint Region: 1600–400 cm^{-1}

Although the Functional Group (4000–1400 cm^{-1}) region can interpreted by looking at specific frequency values and correlating those data to expected stretching frequencies of key functional groups, the Fingerprint Region (1600–400 cm^{-1}) is more difficult to correlate to specific bonding patterns. However, the Fingerprint Region is useful to unambiguously identify an unknown sample so long as a reference spectrum of the compound is available to compare. Two different spectra of the same compound (ortho-dichlorobenzene) are presented below, yet they appear dissimilar to the untrained eye as a result of differences in baseline and scaling of the axes.

54   CHAPTER 6 ❖ IR Spectroscopy

O-dichlorobenzene

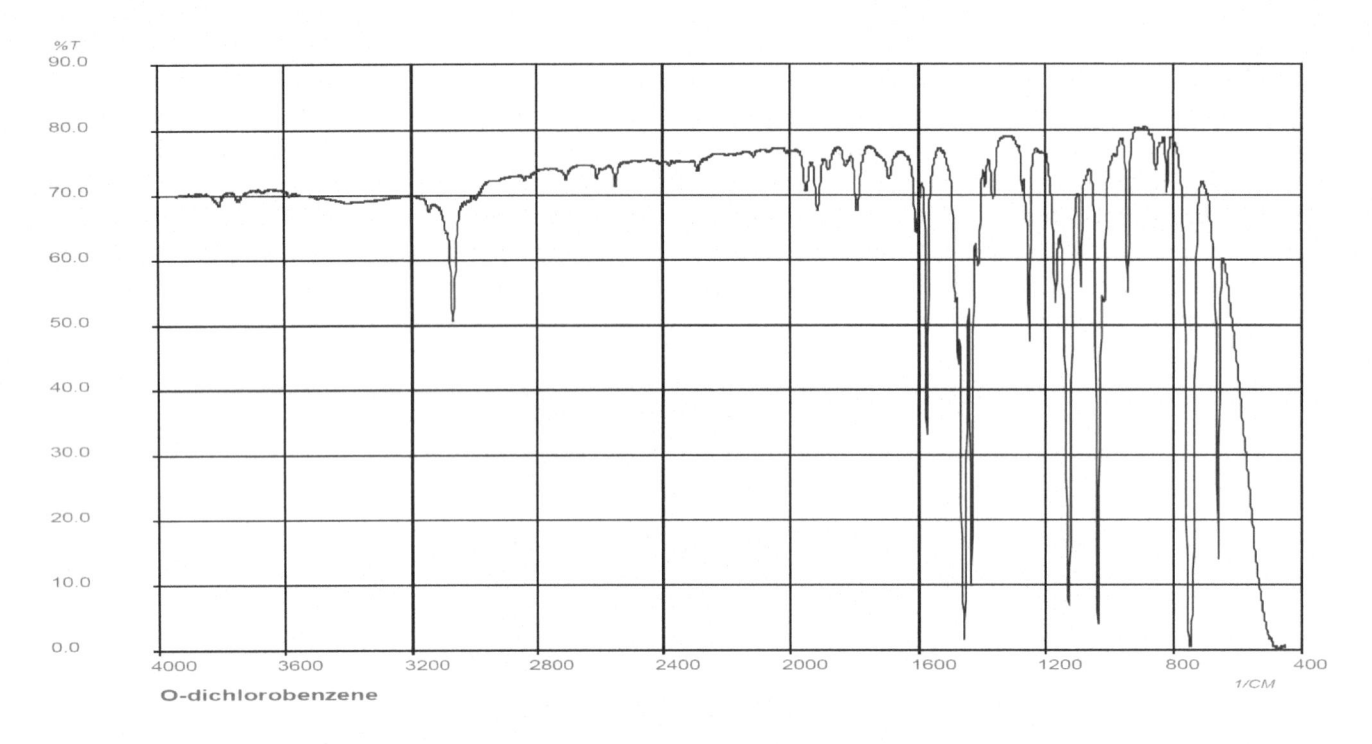

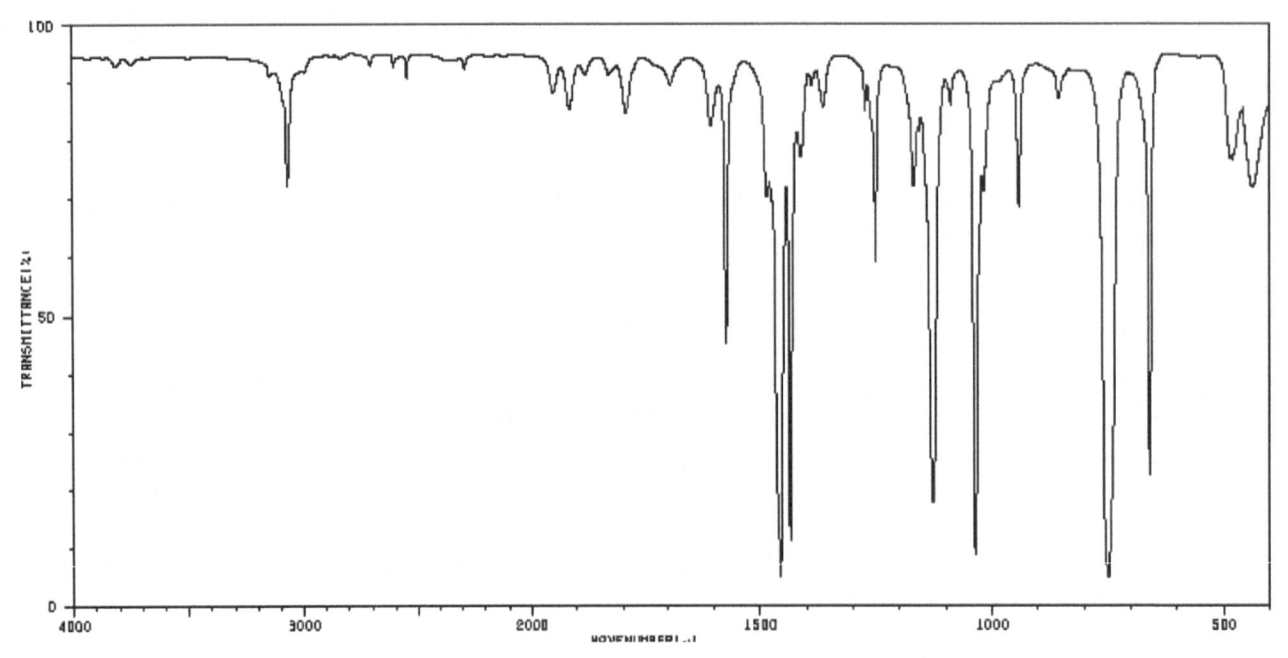

Upon closer examination, there are very strong similarities between the two spectra if a careful and orderly catalog of peaks is constructed. In this example, nine peaks have been labeled (a-i) to illustrate the similarity, though all peaks in this region should match in the following ways:

- Each and every peak of the sample spectrum is found in the reference spectrum
- To be considered a match, the peaks should be different by no more than ±3 cm^{-1}
- The relative intensity of each peak is the same between the two spectra: from largest to smallest, (b) and (h) followed by (f), (e), (c), (i), (a), (d), and (g)
- No "extra" peaks are present in either spectrum

CHAPTER 6 ❖ IR Spectroscopy 55

O-dichlorobenzene

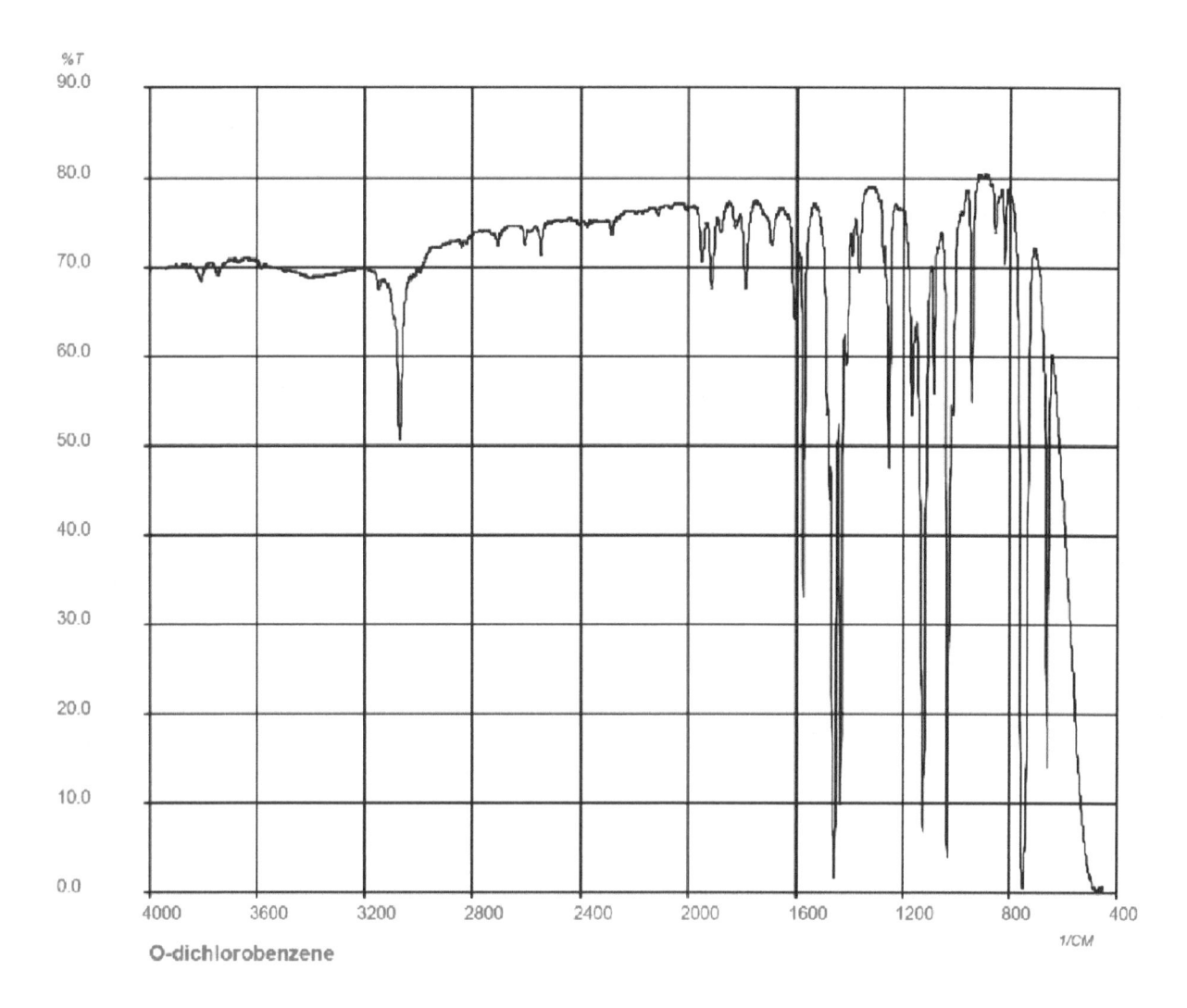

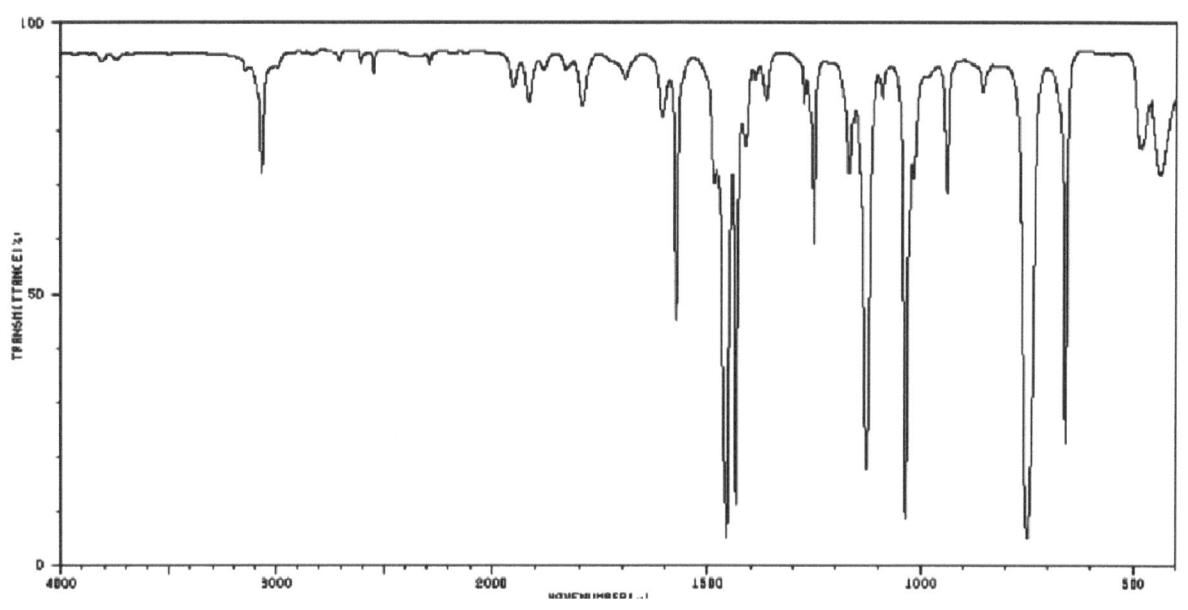

With this approach, compounds with very similar structures and functional groups can be differentiated, if reference spectra are available

6.3 Summary: Analyzing an IR Spectrum

In analyzing a spectrum of an unknown, concentrate first on establishing the prescence (or absence) of a few major functional groups. Ask yourself:

1. Are there any alcohols or amines present?
2. What type of C–H bonds are present? (sp^3, sp^2, sp)
3. Are there any triple bonds present for a nitrile or alkyne?
4. Are there any carbonyl groups present? What type of carbonyl is present based on the absorption freqeuncy?
5. Are there any double bonds or aromatic rings present?
6. Are there any nitro groups present?

IR Functional Groups

alcohol	alkane	ketone	aldehyde
R*–Ö–H (hydroxyl group); butanol	R*–R' (alkyl group); butane	R*–C(=O)–R* ; 2-butanone	R–C(=O)–H ; butanal

primary amine	alkene	carboxylic ester	nitro
R*–N̈H–H (1° amino); n-butylamine	R₂C=CR₂ (olefin); trans-2-butene	R–C(=O)–O–R* (ester); ethyl butanoate	R*–N⁺(=O)(O⁻) ; nitrobutane

secondary amine	aromatic hydrocarbon	carboxylic amide	ether
R*–N̈H–R* (2° amino); diisopropylamine	Ar–R (arene, aryl group); 1-phenylbutane	R–C(=O)–NR₂ (carboxamide or amide); butanamide	R*–Ö–R* ; diethyl ether

carboxylic acid	alkyne	anhydride	tertiary amine
R–C(=O)–O–H ; butanoic acid	R–C≡C–R (acetylene); 2-butyne	R–C(=O)–O–C(=O)–R ; acetic anhydride	R*–N̈(R*)–R* (3° amino); triethylamine

compound class	nitrile	acyl halide	halo
[essential Lewis structure] (alternate name); [example] example name	R*–C≡N: (cyano group); butanenitrile	R–C(=O)–X (carboxylic acid halide, alkanoyl halide, acid halide); butanoyl chloride	R*–X: (halide) (bromo, bromide); 1-bromopropane

Developed by Christopher Callam and Noel M. Paul ©

LEGEND
R = any C (except C=O) or H
R• = any C (except C=O) but never H

6.4 Prelab

Written Prelab: There is no written prelab for the IR Unknown Experiments Part 1, Part 2 or Part 3.

6.5 How to Take an IR—Operation Instructions

Note - Your teaching assistant will run a background scan prior to the start of lab with no salt plates in the instrument. The background scan should only be performed once at the start of the lab period.

1. Clean the salt plates using DCM and drying carefully with a Kim-Wipe.
2. Apply 1 drop of your assigned unknown sample to one of the salt plates using a pipet without rubber bulb attached, then sandwich the sample between the plates and place in metal salt plate holder.
3. Insert sample holder into slot in the instrument. The IR cover sash can remain open during all scans.
4. Click the scan icon in the upper right corner of the screen.
5. After scanning, the sample can be removed and the next person can begin sample prep while the spectrum is being processed and printed.
6. Click the labels icon.
    - If some labels are not visible move them by dragging with a mouse.
    - If labels are missing insert them by right clicking on the peak, and clicking insert peak label.
7. Click Text and place the text box at the top left corner of the spectrum. Add the following text:
   TA INITIALS - ROOM NUMBER - YOUR NAME - YOUR UNKNOWN # / COMPOUND NAME
8. Right click on the spectrum and then click print. Pick up the printed IR from the "window" (431 CE).
   DO NOT CLICK FILE>PRINT TO PRINT!

6.6 IR Unknown Narrative

For IR Unknown Part 1, write a narrative that includes how to use the instrument and your unknown number. Don't forget to include your name, the experiment name, date and time (and any other important information) in the appropriate location on each page of your laboratory notebook.

6.7 Data Submission

For each part of the IR Unknown Experiments Part 1, Part 2 or Part 3 you will submit your answers in the labeled assignments on Carmen.

Submissions are due as listed in the Course Schedule, and late submissions will be penalized −5 pts per day late.

Awareness Counts! Students will be held accountable for submission mistakes, so be sure to careful check your selection.

Failure to submit your answers will result in a zero for that part of the assignment.

Part 2 and Part 3 of the IR Unknown experiment are due at a later date; please check the Course Schedule. All spectra for Part 2 and Part 3 are provided on Carmen course website, you will not have to take them during lab. Your Postlab submissions should be submitted to Carmen course website for Part 2 and Part 3 prior to the deadlines listed in the Course Schedule. Potential structures for each part of the experiment can be found on the following pages.

6.8 Digital Lab Report

There are no digital lab reports for the IR Unknown experiments.

6.9 IR Unknown Structures Part 1

cyclohexanone   allyl alcohol   toluene   diethylamine   ethyl cyanoacetate

6.10 IR Unknown Structures Part 2

6.11 IR Unknown Structures Part 3

CHAPTER 6 ❖ IR Spectroscopy   61

IR Spectroscopy Reference Table

name	structure	IR (cm⁻¹)	
1° alkyl (methyl)	R—CH₃	colspan=2 rowspan=7	
2° alkyl (methylene)	RCH₂R'		
3° alkyl (methine)	R₃C—H		
quaternary alkyl	R₄C		
allylic	(allyl structure)	alkyl C–H stretch 3000 – 2850 (s)	
benzylic	(benzyl structure)		
α to carbonyl	(α-carbonyl structure)		
amine	R₂CH—NH₂ (R—NH₂)		N–H stretch 3500 – 3250 (sh m-w) (2 peaks for RNH₂, 1 peak for R₂NH)
alkyne	R—C≡C—H	C–H stretch 3330 – 3260 (s)	C≡C stretch 2260 – 2100 (m-w)
chloroalkane	R₂CH—Cl		800 – 700 (m-w)
bromoalkane	R₂CH—Br		700 – 600 (m-w)
iodoalkane	R₂CH—I		600 – 500 (m-w)
ether	R₂CH—OR'		1300 – 1000 (s)
alcohol	R₂CH—OH (R—OH)		O–H stretch 3650 – 3200 (br m-s)
α to nitro	(nitro structure)		NO₂ stretch 1600 – 1500 (s) AND 1400 – 1300 (s)
terminal alkene	(terminal alkene structure)	C–H stretch 3100 – 3000 (s)	C=C stretch 1680 – 1600 (m-w)
internal alkene	(internal alkene structure)		
aryl	(aryl structure)	C–H stretch 3150 – 3050 (s)	C=C stretch 1600 – 1400 (m-w)
amide	(amide structure)	N–H stretch 3400 – 3100 (br)	C=O stretch 1690 – 1650 (s)
aldehyde	(aldehyde structure)	C–H stretch 2900 – 2800 (m) AND 2800 – 2700 (m)	C=O stretch 1740 – 1720 (s)
ketone	(ketone structure)		C=O stretch 1725 – 1705 (s)
carboxylic acid	(carboxylic acid structure)	O–H stretch 3300 – 2500 (br)	C=O stretch 1725 – 1700 (s)
carboxylic ester	(ester structure)	C–O stretch 1300 – 1000 (s)	C=O stretch 1750 – 1735 (s)
anhydride	(anhydride structure)		C=O stretch 1850 – 1800 (s) AND 1790 – 1740 (s)
acyl halide	(acyl halide structure)		C=O stretch 1815 – 1790 (s)
nitrile	R—C≡N		C≡N stretch 2260 – 2240 (m)
thiol	R—SH		S–H stretch 2550 – 2600 (br m-s)

Recrystallization

CHAPTER 7

Recrystallization is a purification procedure for organic solids.

7.1 A Review of Intermolecular Forces

Noncovalent interactions (also known as intermolecular forces) are the electrostatic attractions present between molecules with complete valences or octets. Although many specific descriptions of the forces exist, they can be simplified into three types of relationships:

- London Dispersion Interactions—attraction of transient induced dipoles in greasy hydrocarbon molecules
- Dipolar Interactions—directional attraction of polarized electron clouds in molecules with electronegative atoms
- Hydrogen Bonding Interactions—directional attraction of a hydrogen attached to one N or O (H-bond donor) with a lone pair of a different N or O (H-bond acceptor) within one molecule (intramolecular) or between two molecules (intermolecular).

All are types of van der Waals interactions (though H-Bonding often violates these van der Waals radii), all are weaker than covalent bonding interactions, and all are critical to explain the observed "bulk" properties of a substance or mixture of substances.

A Molecular View of the three types of intermolecular forces is shown here:

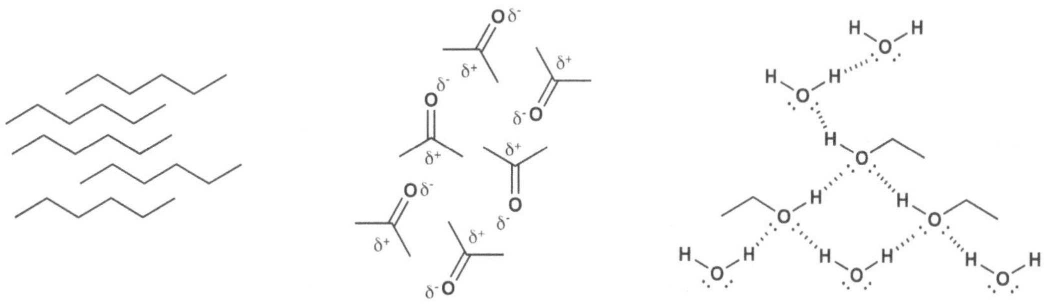

London dispersion forces
in hexane
(weakest*)

dipolar interactions
in acetone
(weaker*)

hydrogen bonding
in water-ethanol mixture
(weak*)

How to represent LDF?
carbon chains drawn close
together
(no formal notation)

How to represent dipolar interactions?
dipoles labeled (partial/delta charges or dipole
arrow) and molecules oriented to bring
opposite charges close together

How to represent H-bonding?
draw out O-H (or N-H) Lewis structure and
connect donor H's and acceptor atoms
with dashed or dotted lines

* in comparison to covalent bonding

The solubility and crystal forming tendencies of molecules can all be explained by an understanding of these interactions at the molecular level.

7.2 Principles of Recrystallization

Crystallization is the method of choice for purification of an organic solid. The process of crystallization involves five main steps.

1. Dissolution
2. Filtration (if necessary)
3. Crystallization
4. Collecting the crystals
5. Drying the crystals

The most common method of purifying solid organic compounds is recrystallization, which is based on a large difference in the solubility of a compound in a hot solvent versus the same solvent when it is cold. In this technique, an impure solid compound is dissolved in a hot solvent and then allowed to slowly crystallize out as the solution cools. As the compound crystallizes from the solution, the molecules of the other compounds dissolved in solution are excluded from the growing crystal lattice, yielding a pure solid.

Crystallization of a solid is not the same as precipitation of a solid. In crystallization, there is a slow, selective formation of the crystal framework, resulting in a pure compound. In precipitation, there is a rapid formation of a solid from a solution that usually produces an amorphous solid containing many trapped impurities within the solid's crystal framework. For this reason, experimental procedures that produce a solid product by precipitation always include a final recrystallization step to yield the pure compound.

Summary of Recrystallization Flow Chart

| IMPURE COMPOUNDS
desired compound and impurities from reaction | → | 1. Dissolution in minimal HOT solvent
2. Crystallization on slow cooling on cork ring.
3. Cooling in ice bath
4. Filtration, washing with cold solvent and collection by suction filtration | → | PURE CRYSTAL OF COMPOUND

FILTRATE (MOTHER LIQUOR)
soluble impurities |

General Method for Recrystallization

1. Place the crude substance to be recrystallized in an Erlenmeyer flask. In a separate Erlenmeyer flask, heat the crystallization solvent on the hot plate. Be sure to include a boiling stick to prevent bumping. Add hot solvent in small portions to the Erlenmeyer containing the crude material and place this material on the hot plate to keep it warm. Add enough hot solvent to dissolve all the crude material. Be careful not to add too much solvent. It is best to err on the side of too little solvent rather than too much.

2. Once all the compound is completely dissolved in the hot solvent, remove the flask from the hot plate and set it on a cork ring to cool SLOWLY to room temperature. Once the solution achieves room temperature, crystallization should begin. If crystallization does not begin, scratch the inside of the container with a glass rod at the liquid-air interface. Once crystallization has started, it is best not to disturb the container. This will allow large crystals to form. Slow, undisturbed cooling will guarantee the formation of large crystals, which are easily separated by filtration and easily washed free of adhering impurities.

3. Once the flask has cooled to room temperature without disturbance and crystal formation is evident, it can be cooled in an ice bath to maximize the amount of product that comes out of solution

4. Once crystallization is complete, the crystals need to be filtered away from the cold mother liquor, washed with ice-cold solvent, and dried.

7.3 Dissolving the Sample

The first goal in performing a recrystallization is to select a suitable solvent to dissolve the impure substance. The ideal solvent for a crystallization should:

- not react with the compound
- be volatile so that it is easy to remove from the crystals
- have a boiling point lower than the melting point of the compound to be purified
- be non-toxic
- impurities should be either fully soluble or fully insoluble at all temperatures
- most important—the compound to be purified should be very soluble in hot solvent and insoluble in cold solvent
- **most important**—the impurities to be separated are either soluble or insoluble at all temperatures

In most cases in the laboratory course, you will know which solvent to use based on laboratory resources or literature based on previous synthesis. Choosing a solvent for crystallization is often difficult, and requires trial and error to find the perfect and best solvent for recrystallization. The general rule is "like dissolves like." For the crystallization of a non-polar compound, a non-polar solvent such as hexane, pentane, or petroleum ether would be used. Compounds that contain polar functional groups such as alcohols and amines generally are crystallized better from a polar solvent such as ethanol.

If the crystallization solvent is not known, carry out a preliminary solubility test by dissolving a small amount of the solid in a small test tube and add a few drops of cold solvent. If the compound dissolves in the cold solvent, try again with a different solvent and a fresh tube of solid. If the substance is insoluble in the cold solvent, warm the tube and try to dissolve the compound. If the solvent does dissolve upon warming, you probably have a good solvent for crystallization. If the substance does not dissolve upon heating, try another solvent.

Once you have found a suitable solvent, try to dissolve the impure solid for purification. Before starting, it is a good idea to weigh the solid so that you can calculate the percent recovery for the crystallization process. Once the compound is dissolved in the hot solvent, inspect the solution for any minor insoluble impurities. If there are insoluble impurities present, filter the solution to remove these materials. This material might be an insoluble impurity or a by-product, or simply might be pieces of extraneous materials (dust, glass, paper, sand, and so on). The solution should be filtered quickly using gravity filtration while it is still hot.

7.4 Tricks of Recrystallization

Sometimes during the crystallization, colored impurities will be present. Most of the time, the impurities will remain in solution as your materials crystallize and can be filtered off. If you find that the colored materials are crystallizing with your compound, those impurities can be removed. After dissolution of the material in the hot solvent, add a small portion of decolorizing charcoal, stir the hot solution for several minutes, and carry out a hot gravity filtration. The activated charcoal will absorb the colored molecules that are in solution. You need to ensure that all of the charcoal is removed from the solution, which might require a second gravity filtration while hot. To rinse the flask, you can use a small amount of hot crystallization solvent.

After the material is dissolved and free of insoluble material, allow the flask to cool slowly on the bench top. The rate at which the compound cools will determine the size of the crystals. If the solution cools down too quickly, the crystals will be small. Quick cooling will favor the formation of a lot of small crystals, and slow cooling encourages the growth of fewer, but much larger, crystals.

The best method for yielding large crystals is to allow the hot solution to cool to room temperature by placing it on the bench top. Leave it undisturbed, resting on a cork ring or wooden block. Once some crystal formation is evident at room temperature, it is best to cool the solution in an ice bath. This will allow formation of the maximum number of crystals.

If you have no crystal formation, induce crystallization by one of the following methods. Add a seed crystal of the original material and scratch the side of the flask with a glass rod at the interface of the liquid and air. This serves to produce micro-fragments of glass that induce crystallization. If crystal formation cannot be induced by one of these methods, evaporate some of the solvent on a hot plate and then allow the solution to cool again. The final common problem in crystallization is called "oiling out." This usually occurs when the compound is very impure or when its melting point is lower than the boiling point of the solvent. Even if the oil eventually solidifies, the compound will not be in pure form. This problem is generally solved by heating the solution again to re-dissolve the oil, and adding a little more solvent to the flask. Slower cooling also favors the formation of crystals rather than oils.

The last step of the process requires vacuum or suction filtration to separate the mother liquor. To completely transfer, you can always use some ice-cold recrystallization solvent. Remember that the mother liquor from the crystallization still might contain a significant amount of your desired compound. A second batch of crystals can be isolated in some cases.

When the amount to crystallize is between 10–100 mg of organic compound, you should use special techniques and precautions to minimize the loss of materials. Normal conditions as described above will not work well because of the loss of material during the filtration steps. The most common method for small scale recrystallization is to use a Craig tube.

7.5 Prelab

Written Prelab: Record the following in your lab notebook:

- Your Name and Date
- Experiment Title
- Table of molecular structures and properties including:
  - molecular weight (MW)
  - boiling point (bp)
  - melting point (mp)
  - density (d) for liquids
- References for your property data and experiment
- A brief plan of procedure, which means "enough detail that you could perform the experiment without your laboratory manual"

compound name	structure	MW	bp	mp	d
sulfanilamide					
ethanol (95%)					

compound name	structure	MW	bp	mp	d
benzoic acid					
water					

Electronic Prelab: Prior to the beginning of your laboratory section, login to our Chemistry 2540 Carmen page and complete the prelab quiz in the labeled experimental module. Prelab assignments are due as listed on the Course Schedule.

7.6 Microscale Recrystallization of Sulfanilamide—Procedure

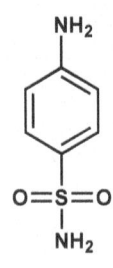

sulfanilamide

1. **Mass of Sulfanilamide by Difference:** Weigh the vial provided to 4 decimal places (without the cap). At your hood, loosen the solid by scraping the black cap vial provided with a micro-spatula and transfer the solid to a Craig tube. Re-weigh the vial to 4 decimal places (without the cap) to determine the mass of solid transferred to the Craig tube.

2. **Microscale Recrystallization:** In a small Erlenmeyer flask, heat ~15–20 mL of 95% ethanol on a hot plate (be sure to include a boiling stick to prevent bumping). Once the ethanol is boiling, add the liquid in small portions to the Craig tube until all of the solid dissolves.

    You should place the Craig tube in the top of the clamped Erlenmeyer flask so that it stays warm and secure while adding solvent.

    Be careful not to add too much solvent. It is best to err on the side of too little solvent rather than too much. You should stir the material with your microspatula to aid in the dissolution.

3. **Cool and Crystallize:** Once all of the compound is dissolved in the 95% ethanol, remove the Craig Tube from the flask and place it in your test tube rack to cool SLOWLY to room temperature. Once the solution reaches room temperature, crystallization should begin.

    If crystallization does not begin, scratch the inside of the container with a glass rod at the liquid-air interface. Once crystallization has started, it is best not to disturb the container to promote large crystal formation.

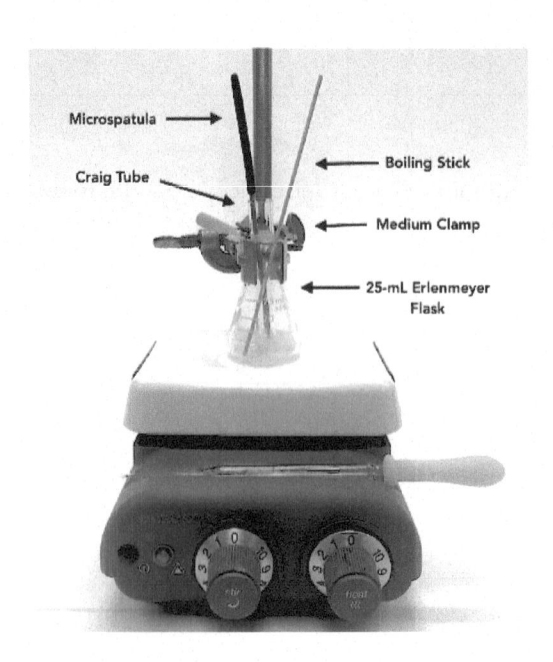

Craig Tube Filtration. *Craig tube assembly with Teflon plug for centrifugation. Make sure the tube is counterbalanced when placed in the centrifuge. To remove all the solvent, you will need to centrifuge the mixture for a few minutes.*

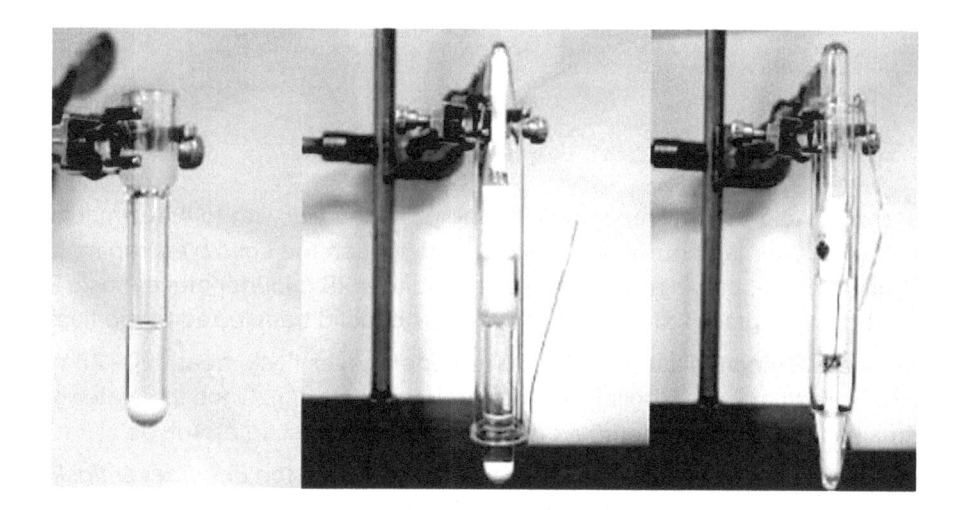

4. **Ice-Water Bath:** Once the Craig Tube has cooled to room temperature and crystal formation is evident, it can be cooled in an ice bath.

    Cooling in an ice bath will maximize the amount of pure compound that comes out of solution.

5. **Centrifuge:** Once crystallization is complete, remove the solvent by centrifugation. Transfer the crystals using a paper funnel from the Craig tube to the pre-weighed vial.

6. **Recovered Yield:** Calculate the percent recovery of purified sulfanilamide from the crude sample using the following formula.

    % Recovery Calculation:

$$\% \text{ Recovery} = \frac{final\ mass}{starting\ mass} \times 100\%$$

7. **Characterization:** Record the melting point of the purified sulfanilamide.

Waste Disposal

The 95% ethanol from the recrystallization must be disposed of in the organic solvent waste beaker.

7.7 Semi-microscale Recrystallization of Benzoic Acid—Procedure

benzoic acid

1. **Mass of Benzoic Acid by Difference:** Weigh the provided vial with to 4 decimal places and record the information in your lab notebook. At your hood, loosen the solid by scraping the black cap vial provided with a micro-spatula and transfer the solid to a 25 mL Erlenmeyer flask. Re-weigh the vial with cap to 4 decimal places to determine the mass of solid transferred to the flask.

2. **Semi-microscale Recrystallization:** In a 50 mL Erlenmeyer flask, heat ~20–25 mL of water on a hot plate (be sure to include a boiling stick to prevent bumping). Once the water is boiling, add the liquid in small portions to the Erlenmeyer flask until all of the solid dissolves.

   Once the initial portion of solvent is added you can place the Erlenmeyer flask on the hot plate to keep it warm while the remainder of the solvent needed to dissolve the solids is added. Be sure to have both flasks clamped during the process. Be careful not to add too much solvent. It is best to err on the side of too little solvent rather than too much. You should stir the material with your micro spatula to aid in the dissolution.

3. **Cool and Crystallize:** Once all of the compound is dissolved in the water, remove the flask from the hotplate and place it in on the bench top in your hood to cool SLOWLY to room temperature. Once the solution reaches room temperature, crystallization should begin.

   If crystallization does not begin, scratch the inside of the container with a glass rod at the liquid-air interface. Once crystallization has started, it is best not to disturb the container to promote large crystal formation.

4. **Ice-Water Bath:** Once the flask has cooled to room temperature and crystal formation is evident, it can be cooled in an ice bath.

   Cooling in an ice bath will maximize the amount of pure compound that comes out of solution.

5. **Vacuum Filtration:** Once crystallization is complete, isolate the crystals by vacuum filtration equipped with a Hirsch filter funnel.

   Before filtering the crystals be sure to secure the filter paper by turning on the vacuum and wetting the filter paper with a small portion of cold water. To aid in the transfer of the crystals you can wash them from the Erlenmeyer flask to the Hirsch funnel using cold water.

6. Transfer the crystals using a paper funnel to a pre-weighed sample vial with cap. Determine the mass of the purified solid by difference.

7. **Recovered Yield:** Calculate the percent recovery of purified benzoic acid from the crude sample using the following formula.

   % Recovery Calculation:

   $$\% \, Recovery = \frac{final \, mass}{starting \, mass} \times 100\%$$

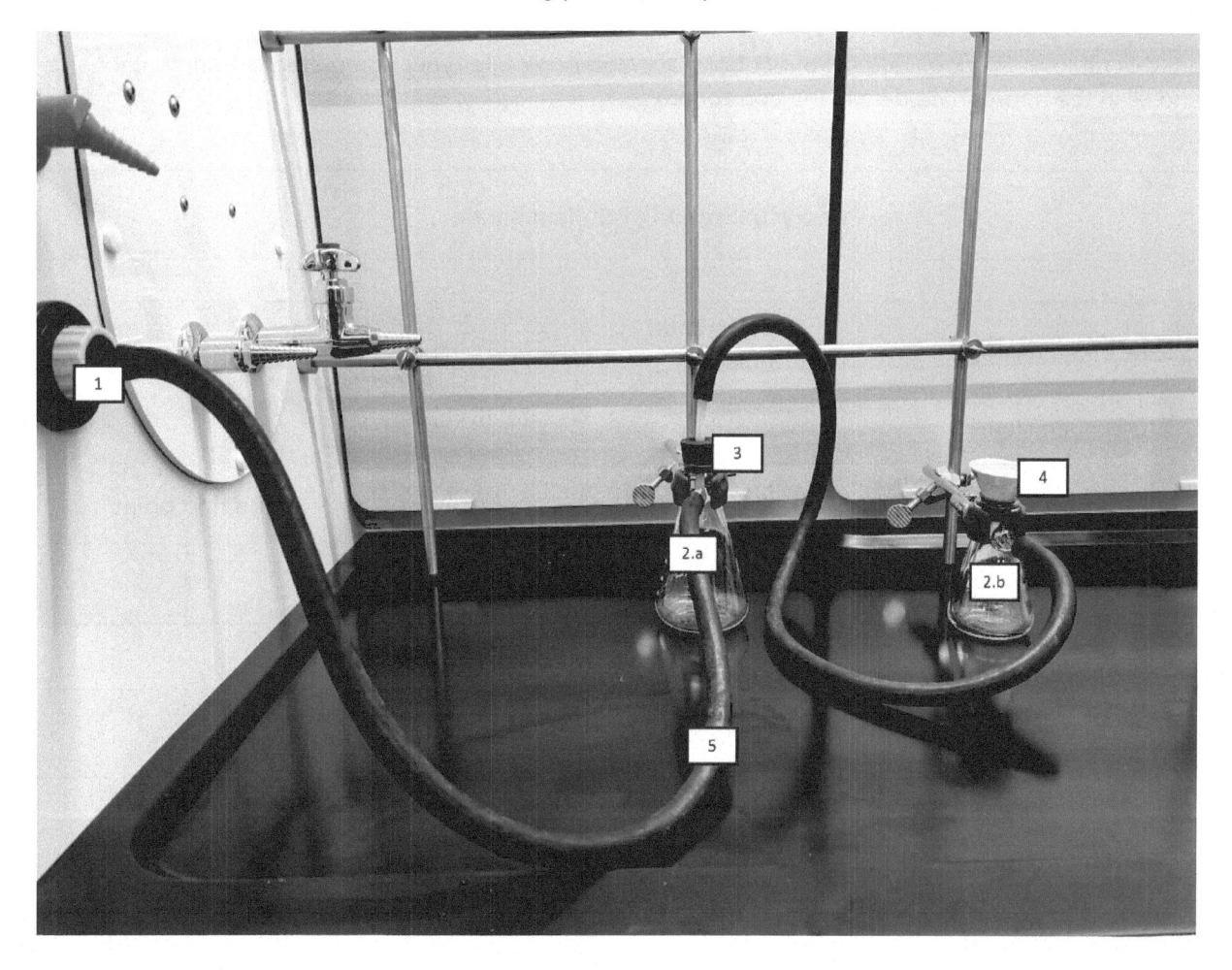

8. **Characterization:** Record the melting point of the purified benzoic acid.

Vacuum Filtration Apparatus
- 1 – Vacuum Inlet
- 2.a – 300 mL Filter Flask
- 2.b – 250 mL Filter Flask
- 3 – Rubber Stopper with Stem
- 4 – Hirsch Funnel
- 5 – Thick Wall Tubing

Waste Disposal

The filtrate (water) from the recrystallization can be disposed of down the drain.

7.8 Postlab Data Submission

Prepare this table of *Postlab Data* in your *Laboratory Notebook* after your completed experimental narrative, and fill in the appropriate data in the correct box:

Recrystallization of Sulfanilamide

starting materials	experimental mass (g)		
crude sulfanilamide			
product	**experimental mass (g)**	**% recovery**	**melting point**
recrystallized sulfanilamide			

Recrystallization of Benzoic Acid

starting materials	experimental mass (g)		
crude benzoic acid			
product	**experimental mass (g)**	**% recovery**	**melting point**
recrystallized benzoic acid			

Login to our Chemistry 2540 Carmen page and complete any listed postlab assignments in the labeled experimental module. Postlab assignments are due as listed on the Course Schedule.

7.9 Digital Lab Report Guidelines

Login to our Chemistry 2540 Carmen page and download a copy of the appropriate *Digital Lab Report Template* for this experiment in the labeled experimental module. Follow the instructions listed in the *Digital Lab Report Template* with regard to the preparation of ChemDraw drawings, Formal Procedure section, and the answers to Concept Questions. Submit your completed Digital Lab Report as a Microsoft Word Document (.doc or .docx file only) or Adobe PDF to the Chemistry 2540 experiment assignment. Digital Lab Reports are due as listed on the Course Schedule, and late submissions will be penalized −10 pts per day late.

7.10 Practice Problems

1. Select the following compounds that could potentially be purified by crystallization. You will need to consult a reference that lists the physical properties of the compounds below to answer this question.

naphthalene	benzoic acid	triethyl amine
benzene	ethanol	benzil
sulfanilamide	tetraphenylcyclopentadienone	benzaldehyde

2. What are five characteristics of a good recrystallization solvent for a given compound?

3. After completing your crystallization, how can you determine whether or not the process has purified the sample?

4. If your sample is still wet with trace amounts of solvent after the recrystallization process, what will the melting point look like?

5. The lab manual discusses differences between an observed melting point and the literature melting point to determine if the sample is pure vs. impure. How will the observed melting point be different from the literature melting point if the product is impure?

6. What are some common explanations for the melting point indicating that a product is impure? (i.e., what are common explanations for the presence of impurities?)

7. Draw a flow chart to determine a good recrystallization solvent.

8. You have proven benzoic acid can form a stable and selective crystal lattice. Draw additional molecules of benzoic acid and hypothesize the intermolecular interactions that are most important for providing a stable and selective crystal structure.

benzoic acid

9. Consider the structure of water. Why is it a good solvent to dissolve benzoic acid?

10. Order the 3 intermolecular forces from strongest to weakest. Describe the proper way to depict each intermolecular force.

7.11 Study Guide—Recrystallization

1. Know and understand the characteristics of a good recrystallization solvent.
2. Know how to develop a strategy for determining a good recrystallization solvent if you had an impure organic solid to purify.
3. Be able to identify and understand whether or not a recrystallization has actually purified an impure sample.
4. Understand how to conduct a recrystallization in a Craig tube and when this method is used.
5. Understand how to purify organic compounds that contain both soluble and insoluble impurities by recrystallization.
6. Draw a picture on the molecular level of what is taking place during crystallization.

CHAPTER 8

Extraction

Extraction is a method used to separate compounds based on their relative solubilities in two different immiscible liquids.

Organic chemists commonly face the task of separating an organic compound from a mixture of compounds, often derived from natural sources or the side products of a synthetic reaction. The most common method used is a process in which one molecule selectively dissolves, or extracts, one or more of the compounds from the mixture.

A solid-liquid extraction involves the removal of soluble compounds from a solid matrix into a liquid solvent, such as brewing tea in water. In a liquid-liquid extraction, which is more common, compounds move from one liquid solvent to another liquid solvent. Using this extraction method, a compound can easily be separated from impurities in a solution by extracting the compound from the original, or first solvent, and into a second solvent. The key for liquid-liquid extraction is that the component must be more soluble in the second solvent than in the first solvent, and the impurities must be insoluble in the second solvent. More important, however, is that the two solvents must be immiscible so that they produce two layers when mixed together.

One solvent is commonly water, which is polar in nature, and the second solvent should be nonpolar and usually organic. The choice of organic solvent used varies more, and there are a wide range of choices available. Dichloromethane is one of the most commonly used solvents because it fulfills all of the requirements for an extraction solvent: immiscibility with water, different density than water, good solubility characteristics, low reactivity with organic compounds, and high volatility (so that it can be easily removed from the organic component by evaporation). Extraction solvents fall into two groups: those that are less dense than water and those that are denser. Those organic solvents which are less dense than water are pentane, hexanes, petroleum ether, ethyl acetate, diethyl ether, benzene, and toluene. Dichloromethane falls into the second category of being denser than water. Dichloromethane's greatest drawback is its tendency to form emulsions in some extraction scenarios.

Once both solvents have been added, they are mixed together to maximize the surface area between them. When two immiscible solvents are placed into a container, two liquid layers are formed; the liquid with the greater density is at the bottom. The layers are then allowed to separate, and the molecules partition into the layers in which they are more soluble. When the two layers are separated, this completes the separation of the desired compounds from the impurities.

8.1 Solubility

To produce and carry out an effective extraction process, you must understand the solubility characteristics of commonly encountered chemicals in the organic lab.

To understand solubility, the main rule that applies is "like dissolves like."

Water Solubility

Molecules that are soluble in water are as follows: There are three classes of molecule that are water soluble:

1. Most inorganic salts (NaCl, MgCl$_2$, KI, etc.) and inorganic acids (H$_2$SO$_4$, HCl, etc).
2. Very polar organic molecules that are dominated by a large amount of polar functional groups (-OH, -NH, -SH) on their carbon skeleton backbone. These molecules can hydrogen-bond well with water.
3. Salts of organic molecules that have a charge (sodium benzoate, pyridinium hydrochloride).

Organic Solubility

Neutral organic molecules are soluble in organic solvents. Depending on the solvent and the nature of the substrate, solubilities will vary. In general, most simple organic molecules that are neutral are soluble in common organic solvents such as diethyl ether or dichloromethane.

8.2 Partition Coefficients and Extraction

The physical chemistry behind the principle of extraction is based on the theory that when organic compound X is placed in a container with two immiscible liquids, such as water and dichloromethane, some of the compound will be soluble in the water layer and some of the compound will be soluble in the organic layer. Molecule X will partition itself between the water and the dichloromethane. The ratio of concentrations of X in each phase is known as the partition coefficient, or the distribution coefficient. It is a constant (K) defined as:

$$K = \text{Concentration in organic layer/concentration in water}$$

Suppose, for example, we assume that the concentration in dichloromethane and solubility in dichloromethane is approximately the same. Assume that the solubility of X in dichloromethane is 50 g/100 mL and in water it is 5 g/100 mL at the same temperature.

$$K = (50 \text{ g}/100 \text{ mL}) / (5 \text{ g}/100 \text{ mL}) = 10$$

Now we can use this coefficient to know how much of the material we can extract from water using dichloromethane. Suppose we have 100 mL of water containing 5 g of X and we extract it with 100 mL of dichloromethane. How much of X will we extract?

$$10 = (X \text{ g}/100 \text{ mL}) / ((5 - X) \text{ g}/100 \text{ mL})$$
$$X = 4.55 \text{ g}$$

Therefore, we can extract 4.55 g of X from 100 mL of water using 100 mL of dichloromethane. The remaining 0.45 g of X will remain in the water layer. The process allowed us to extract 91 percent of the material. Note that we can improve this by dividing our one 100 mL extraction into two 50 mL portions of dichloromethane and carrying out the extraction process twice with fresh solvent each time.

Calculation:

First Extraction: $10 = (X\ g/50\ mL) / ((5 - X)\ g/100\ mL)$
$X = 4.17\ g$

Second Extraction: $10 = (X\ g/50\ mL) / ((0.83 - X)\ g/100\ mL)$
$X = 0.69\ g$

Total = 4.17 + 0.69 = 4.86 = 97% Extraction

The important conclusion from this exercise in the theory of extraction is that it is more efficient to carry out two or three small extractions with organic solvent than one large one. A greater number of even smaller extractions would be more efficient than one, provided that the extraction coefficient is greater than 4. A double or triple extraction will remove most of the compounds from the water layer.

If the partition coefficient is less than 1, very little of the compound will be extracted simply by shaking the two liquids together. The partition coefficient can be changed by adding an inorganic salt such as sodium chloride to the aqueous solution. The theory behind this is that the organic compound will be less soluble in sodium chloride solution than in water itself, and therefore the partition coefficient between the organic solvent and aqueous solvent will have a much larger value and will increase the efficiency of the process.

8.3 Techniques of Extraction

Three types of apparatus can be used in the organic laboratory for extractions: 5-mL conical vial, centrifuge tubes, and separatory funnels. A 5-mL conical vial is used for microscale reactions on combined volumes of less than 4 mL, centrifuge tubes can handle up to 10 mL of combined volume, and separatory funnels are available in many different sizes. They are commonly used for combined volumes of 100–1000 mL.

Using a Separatory Funnel for an Extraction—(Lower Layer Organic)

*Check to make sure the separatory funnel is fully operational. You should make sure before using it that the stopcock is lightly greased, that there are no leaks from the stopcock or glass stopper, and that the funnel drains liquids properly.

1. With the separatory supported by an iron ring stand, place the aqueous phase to be extracted into the separatory funnel and add dichloromethane. Gently swirl the funnel with the cap off to allow any gas evolution to take place. Cap the funnel and gently shake with a rocking motion. Be sure to vent the funnel between shakings.
2. After the initial mixing, carefully set the funnel back in the ring stand and remove the cap. Allow the phases to separate completely so that you can detect two distinct layers in the funnel.
3. Carefully drain the lower organic layer out of the funnel into a clean Erlenmeyer flask. Make sure to drain the bottom layer slowly to prevent a vortex from forming.
4. Pour the top aqueous layer out of the top of the funnel into a separate flask.

Using Separatory Funnel for an Extraction—(Upper Layer Organic)

1. With the separatory supported by an iron ring stand, place the aqueous phase to be extracted into the separatory funnel and add dichloromethane. Gently swirl the funnel with the cap off to allow any gas evolution to take place. Cap the funnel and gently shake with a rocking motion. Be sure to vent the funnel between shakings.

2. After the initial mixing, carefully set the funnel back in the ring stand and remove the cap. Allow the phases to separate completely so that you can detect two distinct layers in the funnel.
3. Carefully drain the lower aqueous layer out of the funnel into a clean Erlenmeyer flask. Make sure to drain the bottom layer slowly to prevent a vortex from forming.
4. Pour the top organic layer out of the top of the funnel into a separate flask.

It sometimes is very easy to tell which layer in the separatory funnel is organic and which is the aqueous by knowing the relative volumes or densities of the solvents. During other extractions, it can be problematic to determine which layer is which, due to the presence of intense colors or other substances with different densities. You can easily determine which layer is which by adding a little water and seeing with which layer the added water combines. The other possible option is to dispense a few drops of the lower layer onto a watch glass and add a few drops of water to see if they are miscible. When carrying out several extractions, it is always a good idea to save everything until the product has been isolated and identified.

Often the two solvents will not separate completely after shaking, because of the formation of an emulsion at the interface between them. An emulsion is a suspension of small droplets of one liquid in another liquid. Emulsions are generally opaque or cloudy in color and often make it look as if there is a third layer present in the separation. The small droplets cause the separation to take place very slowly. You can use several procedures to remove the emulsions, such as centrifugation on a microscale, or adding a small amount of saturated NaCl and swirling the contents.

The simplest and easiest understanding of solubility is based on the idea of "like dissolves like." Nonpolar Compounds are more polar in nonpolar solvents than in polar solvents. Or, stated another way, ionic and polar compounds are more soluble in polar solvents. These solubility differences allow you to separate nonpolar organic compounds from ionic or polar compounds easily. For example, at the end of a reaction the by-product is an ionic inorganic salt along with the desired nonpolar organic. In this case, the salts can be separated from the organic by washing the organic solvent containing the compound with water. Extraction is very effective when you need to separate two organic compounds where one of the compounds in the mixture can be chemically converted to an ionic form. The ionic form is soluble in water, and all of the other organic molecules will partition to the organic phase. Ionic forms of some organic compounds can be produced by reacting them with aqueous acid or bases. Reacting organic acid with bases such as sodium hydroxide converts them to water-soluble anions. Reacting organic bases with dilute aqueous acid solution such as HCl converts them to water-soluble cations.

8.4 Acid-Base Chemistry

Chemistry is arguably the story of electrons and their interactions with matter and energy. Organic chemists have taken the outcomes of experiments that describe the stability of electrons in a number of molecular environments (Lewis structures, functional groups) and used these data to develop a powerful perspective of electronic reactivity as both the motivating factor and starting point for predicting the outcome of nearly any chemical reaction. As one of the oldest and most well-studied methods of quantitating electronic stability, a mastery of acid-base chemistry (ABC) will equip a chemical scientist with a powerful set of problem solving tools.

Brønsted-Lowry Acid-Base Chemistry

In Brønsted-Lowry Acid Base Chemistry, an **acid** is a molecule that can donate a proton, a **base** is a molecule that can accept a proton, and they react together to form a **conjugate base** (the deprotonated form of the acid) and a **conjugate acid** (the protonated form of the base).

$$A-H + BH \longrightarrow A:^{\ominus} + HB-H^{\oplus}$$

Since the ability of any particular molecule to donate or accept a proton is dependent upon its structure, a more specific set of structural descriptions becomes critical to understand the complex equilibria of acid base chemistry that simmers below the surface of almost all organic reactions.

Structurally, a Brønsted-Lowry acid can be any atom (or atom in a molecule) that has a shared or bonding pair of electrons between itself and a hydrogen atom, and this **sigma bond** is most clearly represented by a single line between the acidic atom and the hydrogen. The **formal charge** of this acidic atom is most often positive (+1) or neutral (0) and is rarely negative (−1), though the **overall charge** of the molecule may be negative, as observed in bicarbonate, bisulfate,etc.).

$$A-H \qquad \overset{\oplus}{H B}-H$$
neutral acid ⠀⠀⠀⠀ cationic conjugate acid

$$\overset{\oplus}{A}-H \qquad B-H$$
cationic acid ⠀⠀⠀⠀ neutral conjugate acid

By contrast, a Brønsted-Lowry base can be any atom (or atom in a molecule) with an unshared or non-bonding pair of electrons, and this **lone pair** of electrons is most clearly represented as two dots near the basic atom. The formal charge of this basic atom is most often negative or neutral (rarely positive), however, the presence of a negative formal charge alone does not signify guaranteed reactivity: anions such as nitrate, bromide, chloride, and even sulfate are quite stable and unreactive as bases for structural reasons that will be explored more deeply below.

$$\overset{\ominus}{A}: \qquad BH$$
anionic conjugate base ⠀⠀⠀⠀ neutral base

$$A: \qquad \overset{\ominus}{BH_2}$$
neutral conjugate base ⠀⠀⠀⠀ anionic base

Quantitating Acid Strength (K_a and pK_a)

"Strong acid and strong base goes to weak acid and weak base" has evolved as the mantra of Brønsted-Lowry acid-base chemistry but offers a view that is too simplistic for wide application. Proton transfer mechanisms of acid base reactions are both fast and reversible (since hydrogens are always on the outside of organic molecules, they are almost always accessible) and are best described as equilibria where protons are in never-ending transit in a sea of competing lone pairs. Furthermore, there are no absolutes in acid-base chemistry, and as tempting as the terms may be to use, even a vast list of memorized "strong" and "weak" acids and bases are sometimes powerless to differentiate reactivities when structures appear too similar.

A structural definition of acid strength is also valuable in gaining a useful problem solving perspective, and the absolutes of "strong" and "weak" might be modified to better emphasize the equilibrium nature of acid-base reactions. Thus, a "stronger" acid is an atom (in a molecule) whose sigma bond to hydrogen is more polarized and more easily dissociated, and upon reaction, the resulting conjugate base's new lone pair is more diffuse (delocalized) and more difficult to reprotonate. Conversely, a "stronger" base is an atom (in a molecule) whose lone pair is more focused (localized) and bond-like, making it capable of attracting a proton, and upon reaction, the resulting conjugate acid's new sigma bond to hydrogen is more difficult to dissociate. The reaction of a strong(er) acid and a strong(er) base can be represented mechanistically the following way:

$$A-H + B\overset{\frown}{H} \rightleftharpoons [A\cdots H\cdots :B]^{\ddagger} \rightleftharpoons A:^{\ominus} + B-H^{\oplus}$$

even when the A-H bond is barely stretched, the proton is easy to dissociate $-\Delta H$

where the two **mechanism arrows** (atom-to-bond and bond-to-atom) denote a basic lone pair that is attracted to an acidic proton, as well as the dissociation of the acid's sigma bond and release of electrons to the conjugate base, the **transition state** (TS‡, in brackets) shows the ease at which the transfer takes places using longer (very dissociated) and shorter (very formed) partial bonds, and **unsymmetrical equilibrium** arrows describe a favored product side of the equilibrium reaction. The reaction of strong(er) acid and a strong(er) base is accompanied by a release of enthalpy (-ΔH), which provides an energetic view of the proton transfer.

The mechanism of a disfavored acid-base equilibrium can also be described structurally using a similar approach, though in reality, it is the reaction of a strong(er) acid and a strong(er) base written in reverse. A "weak(er)" acid is an atom (in a molecule) whose sigma bond to hydrogen is more difficult to dissociate, and upon reaction, the resulting conjugate base's new lone pair is more focused (localized) and easy to reprotonate. A "weak(er)" base is an atom (in a molecule) whose lone pair is more diffuse (delocalized) and has more difficulty attracting a proton, and upon reaction, the resulting conjugate acid's new sigma bond to hydrogen is more polarized and more easily dissociated. The reaction of a weak(er) acid and/or a weak(er) base can be represented using the same mechanism and equilibrium:

$$A-H + B\overset{\frown}{H} \rightleftharpoons [A\cdots H\cdots :B]^{\ddagger} \rightleftharpoons A:^{\ominus} + B-H^{\oplus}$$

even when the A-H bond is greatly streched, the proton is resistant to dissociate $+\Delta H$

where the two **mechanism arrows** (atom-to-bond and bond-to-atom) denote a lone pair that is attracted to a proton, and the dissociation of the acid's sigma bond to release electrons to the conjugate base, however here the **transition state** (TS‡, in brackets) shows the reluctance of the more stable bond to break, and the more stable lone pair to form a bond, and the **unsymmetrical equilibrium arrows** describe a favored reactant side of the equilibrium reaction. The reaction of a weak(er) acid and a weak(er) base is enthalpically unfavorable (+ΔH) and the proton transfer will result in a less stable arrangement of atoms and electrons results.

A convenient descriptor of any acid's relative strength called pKa has been used by chemists for years to gauge the likelihood that a particular proton will dissociate under specific reaction conditions, but understanding the nature of this quantity requires a particular perspective of acid-base reactions. Any acid (or conjugate acid) can be exposed to water, and the concentration of hydronium (pH) of the resulting equilibrium solution can be determined by experimental methods.

$$A-H + H_2O \overset{K_{eq}}{\rightleftharpoons} A:^{\ominus} + H_3O^{\oplus}$$

$$HB-H^{\oplus} + H_2O \overset{K_{eq}}{\rightleftharpoons} BH + H_3O^{\oplus}$$

K_{eq} describes the equilibrium of a 1:1 mixture in an inert solvent

Since known concentrations of acid are added, and the conjugate base (or base) is produced in a 1:1 ratio with hydronium, the equilibrium constant for the dissociation of the proton, defined as K_{eq}, can be determined. Although it is customary to include products over reactants when deriving equilibrium constants, water as the solvent is present is such excess ("bulk" water), that its concentration is nearly a constant (55 mol L^{-1} or 55 M) and unaffected by the equilibrium, so its term is removed from equation. With the removal of water from the equilibrium equation, the expression becomes the acid dissociation constant, K_a. Strong acids dissociate completely in water and result in large K_a values. Table 7.1 includes a range of acids with K_a values greater than 1, and weak acids with K_a values of 10^{-5} to 10^{-10}, and an essentially non-acidic molecule with a K_a value less than 10^{-48}. Since the K_a-values obtained from these equilibrium measurements can be extremely large or small, it is useful to convert these numbers into more convenient pK_a-values for comparison.

$$K_{eq} = \frac{[A:^{\ominus}][H_3O^{\oplus}]}{[A-H][H_2O]} = \frac{[B:][H_3O^{\oplus}]}{[B-H^{\oplus}][H_2O]}$$

since water is in excess, its term can be removed

$$K_a = \frac{K_{eq}}{[H_2O]} = \frac{[A:^{\ominus}][H_3O^{\oplus}]}{[A-H]} = \frac{[B:][H_3O^{\oplus}]}{[B-H^{\oplus}]} \quad pK_a = -\log K_a = -\log \frac{[A:^{\ominus}][H_3O^{\oplus}]}{[A-H]} = -\log \frac{[B:][H_3O^{\oplus}]}{[B-H^{\oplus}]}$$

The pK_a values are used throughout organic chemistry to determine whether acid-base reactions occur by comparing the strength of the acid and conjugate acid. The product side of the equilibrium is favored when the acid is stronger than the conjugate acid (the acid has a lower pK_a value). Reactant side of the equilibrium is favored when the acid is weaker than the conjugate acid (the acid has a higher pK_a value).

The results of these Ka and pKa determinations have provided a perspective on the magnitude to which these equilibria are favored. Consider a strong acid (such as hydrochloric acid, HCl) in the equations below:

Hydrogen Chloride in "Bulk" Water

$$HCl + H_2O \xrightleftharpoons{K_a(HCl)} Cl^{\ominus} + H_3O^{\oplus}$$
$$[1] \qquad\qquad\qquad\qquad [10,000] \quad [10,000]$$

$$\frac{[Cl^{\ominus}][H_3O^{\oplus}]}{[HCl]} = \frac{[10,000][10,000]}{[1]} = 100,000,000 = 1 \times 10^8 = K_a(HCl)$$

$$-\log \frac{[Cl^{\ominus}][H_3O^{\oplus}]}{[HCl]} = -\log\left(\frac{[10,000][10,000]}{[1]}\right) = -\log(100,000,000) = -\log(1 \times 10^8) = -8 = -\log K_a(HCl) = pK_a(HCl)$$

The Ka and pKa-values of 1 × 10^8 and −8, respectively, result from measuring a pH equating to a 10,000-to-1 ratio of dissociated acid to unionized hydrochloric acid; to put it another way, the "odds" of finding an

Table 8.1 – The Acidity of Common Laboratory Molecules at 25 °C.

acid		base		K_a	pK_a
name	formula	formula	name		
perchloric acid	$HClO_4$	ClO_4^-	perchlorate	1×10^{10}	−10
hydroiodic acid	HI	I^-	iodide	3.2×10^9	−10
hydrobromic acid	HBr	Br^-	bromide	1×10^9	−9
hydrochloric acid	HCl	Cl^-	chloride	1.3×10^8	−8
sulfuric acid	H_2SO_4	HSO_4^-	bisulfate	1.0×10^3	−3
hydronium ion	H_3O^+	H_2O	water	5.0×10^1	−1
nitric acid	HNO_3	NO_4^-	nitrate	2.4×10^1	−2
oxalic acid	$HO_2C_2O_2H$	$HO_2C_2O_2^-$	hydrogen oxalate	5.4×10^{-2}	1
sulfurous acid	H_2SO_3	HSO_3^-	bisulfite	1.3×10^{-2}	2
bisulfate	HSO_4^-	SO_4^{2-}	sulfate	1.0×10^{-2}	2
phosphoric acid	H_3PO_4	H_2PO	dihydrogen phosphate	7.1×10^{-3}	2
nitrous acid	HNO_2	NO_2^-	nitrite	7.2×10^{-4}	3
hydrofluoric acid	HF	F^-	fluoride	6.6×10^{-4}	3
formic acid	HCO_2H	HCO_2^-	formate	1.8×10^{-4}	4
hydrogen selenide	H_2Se	HSe^-	hydroselenide	1.3×10^{-4}	4
benzoic acid	C_6H_5COOH	$C_6H_5COO^-$	benzoate	6.3×10^{-5}	4
hydrogen oxalate	$HO_2C_2O^{2-}$	$O_2C_2O_2^{2-}$	oxalate	5.4×10^{-5}	4
hydrazoic acid	HN_3	N_3^-	azide	2.5×10^{-5}	5
acetic acid	CH_3COOH	CH_3COO^-	acetate	1.8×10^{-5}	5
carbonic acid	H_2CO_3	HCO_3^-	bicarbonate	4.4×10^{-7}	6
hydrogen sulfide	H_2S	HS^-	hydrosulfide	1.1×10^{-7}	7
dihydrogen phosphate	$H_2PO_4^-$	HPO_4^{2-}	hydrogen phosphate	6.3×10^{-8}	7
bisulfite	HSO_3^-	SO_3^{2-}	sulfite	6.2×10^{-8}	7
hypochlorous acid	$HClO$	ClO^-	hypochlorite	2.9×10^{-8}	8
hydrocyanic acid	HCN	^-CN	cyanide	6.2×10^{-10}	9
ammonium	NH_4^+	NH_3	ammonia	5.8×10^{-10}	9
boric acid	H_3BO_3	$H_2BO_3^-$	dihydrogen borate	5.8×10^{-10}	9
bicarbonate	HCO_3	CO_3^{2-}	carbonate	4.7×10^{-11}	10
hydrogen phosphate	HPO_4^{2-}	PO_4^{3-}	phosphate	4.2×10^{-13}	12
dihydrogen borate	$H_2BO_3^-$	HBO_3^{2-}	hydrogen borate	1.8×10^{-13}	13
hydrosulfide	HS^-	S^{2-}	sulfide	1.3×10^{-13}	13

acid		base		K_a	pK_a
name	formula	formula	name		
hydrogen borate	HBO_3^{2-}	BO_3^{3-}	borate	1.6×10^{-14}	14
water	H_2O	HO^-	hydroxide	1.8×10^{-16}	16
methanol	CH_3OH	CH_3O^-	methoxide	3.2×10^{-16}	16
hydrogen	H_2	H^-	hydride	1×10^{-36}	36
ammonia	NH_3	NH_2^-	azanide/amide	1×10^{-38}	38
methane	CH_4	$^-CH_3$	methide	1×10^{-48}	48

unionized molecule of hydrochloric acid are 1 in 10,000. In this way, a "strong acid" can be quantitatively described as a solution with a very high probability of coming in contact with a proton dissociated from the acid.

A carboxylic acid (acetic acid, CH_3CO_2H) can also be analyzed using the same logic to reveal a perspective of how a weaker acid looks in solution:

Acetic Acid in "Bulk" Water

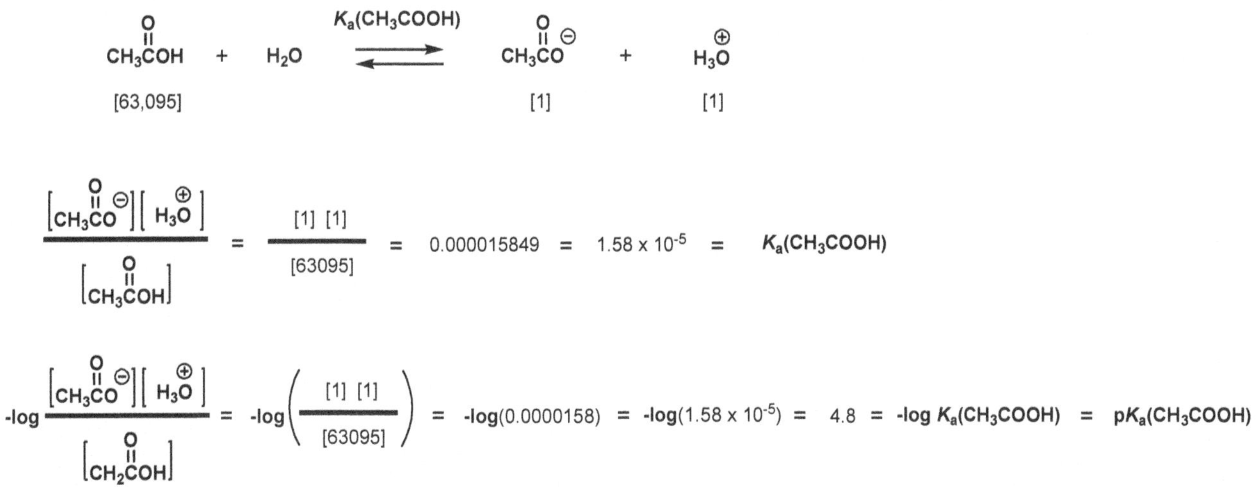

$$CH_3COH + H_2O \underset{}{\overset{K_a(CH_3COOH)}{\rightleftharpoons}} CH_3CO^- + H_3O^+$$

[63,095]   [1]   [1]

$$\frac{[CH_3CO^-][H_3O^+]}{[CH_3COH]} = \frac{[1][1]}{[63095]} = 0.000015849 = 1.58 \times 10^{-5} = K_a(CH_3COOH)$$

$$-\log\frac{[CH_3CO^-][H_3O^+]}{[CH_2COH]} = -\log\left(\frac{[1][1]}{[63095]}\right) = -\log(0.0000158) = -\log(1.58 \times 10^{-5}) = 4.8 = -\log K_a(CH_3COOH) = pK_a(CH_3COOH)$$

The K_a and pK_a-values of 1.58×10^{-5} and 4.8, respectively, result from measuring a pH equating to a 1-to-63,000 ratio of dissociated acid to un-ionized acetic acid molecule, demonstrating that a weak acid can be quantitatively described as a solution with a low probability of detecting a proton dissociated from the acid.

To highlight how these calculations provide a perspective on the staggeringly the small dissociations of extremely weak acids, the hypothetical dissociation of an alkane hydrogen (2-methylpropane or isobutane) can be examined froma calculated set of values:

Methane in "Bulk" Water

$$(CH_3)_3CH + H_2O \xrightleftharpoons[]{K_a((CH_3)_3CH)} (CH_3)_3C^{\ominus} + H_3O^{\oplus}$$

[100,000,000,000,000,000,000,000,000,000,000,000,000,000,000,000,000]   [1]   [1]

OR

[1 × 10⁻⁵³]

$$\frac{[(CH_3)_3C^{\ominus}][H_3O^{\oplus}]}{[(CH_3)_3CH]} = \frac{[1][1]}{[1 \times 10^{53}]} = 1 \times 10^{-53} = K_a((CH_3)_3CH)$$

$$-\log \frac{[(CH_3)_3C^{\ominus}][H_3O^{\oplus}]}{[(CH_3)_3CH_3]} = -\log\left(\frac{[1][1]}{[1 \times 10^{53}]}\right) = -\log(1 \times 10^{-53}) = 53 = -\log K_a((CH_3)_3CH) = pK_a((CH_3)_3CH)$$

The K_a and pK_a-values of 1×10^{-53} and 53, respectively, describe a solution where the odds of finding a proton resulting from the dissociation of an alkane C-H are mind-bendingly low, only one chance in 100,000,000,000,000,000,000,000,000,000,000,000,000,000,000,000,000 or 1-in-10^{53}, which is really very, very, very, very unlikely.

Predicting the Acid Strength, Base Strength, and Chemical Reactivity

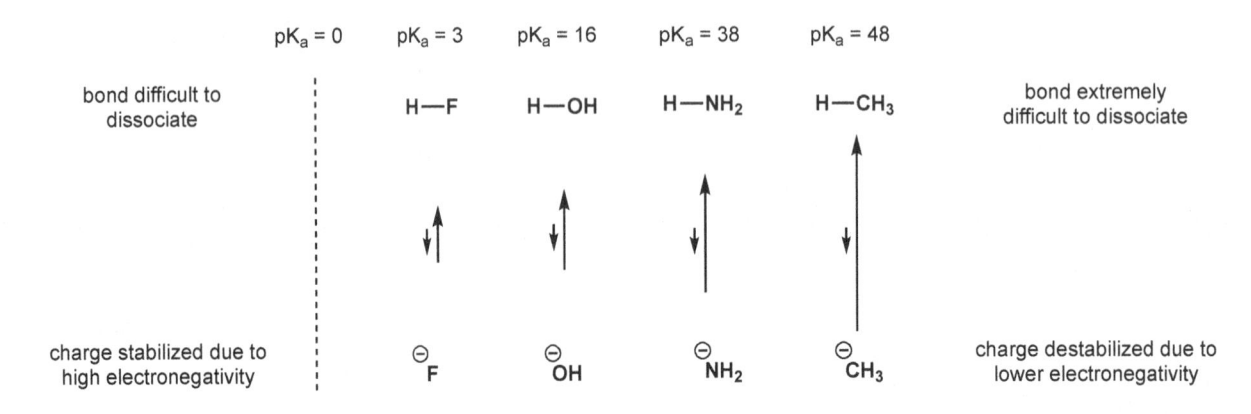

	$pK_a = 0$	$pK_a = 3$	$pK_a = 16$	$pK_a = 38$	$pK_a = 48$	
bond difficult to dissociate		H—F	H—OH	H—NH₂	H—CH₃	bond extremely difficult to dissociate
charge stabilized due to high electronegativity		$F^{\ominus}$	$OH^{\ominus}$	$NH_2^{\ominus}$	$CH_3^{\ominus}$	charge destabilized due to lower electronegativity

An overwhelming amount of experimental and theoretical evidence has provided pK_a as a tool to assess the effect of various atoms in different structural arrangements acting to stabilize electron density that allows an acidic bond in a molecule to dissociate. Predicting the favored side of an acid-base reaction is then possible by examining the reactants and products and selecting the side of the reaction that has the better stabilized electron lone pair, which may or may not be negatively charged. The four factors that influence the ability of a molecule to stabilize a negative charge are, in order of decreasing importance: elemental, resonance, hybridization, and inductive effects:

Elemental effects are best described due to an atom's relative position on the periodic table.

♦ Larger atoms can stabilize a negative charge better because they spread the charge out over a greater area, and a more diffuse charge is easier to stabilize in solution.

♦ More electronegative atoms can better stabilize a negative charge through the influence of effective nuclear charge and valence electron energy levels.

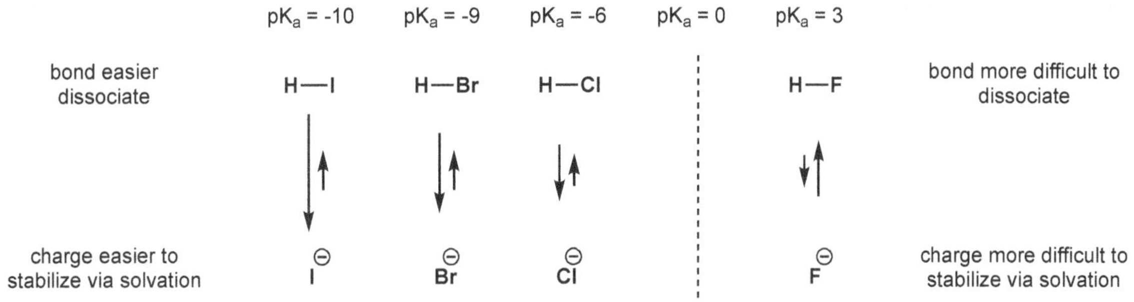

	pKa = -10	pKa = -9	pKa = -6	pKa = 0	pKa = 3	
bond easier dissociate	H—I	H—Br	H—Cl		H—F	bond more difficult to dissociate
	↓↑	↓↑	↓↑		↓↑	
charge easier to stabilize via solvation	I⁻	Br⁻	Cl⁻		F⁻	charge more difficult to stabilize via solvation

Resonance effects enable molecules to spread the negative charge out over a greater area thus making it more stable.

◆ Resonance with one or more electronegative atom is increasingly favorable

	pKa = -3	pKa = -1.3	pKa = 0	pKa = 5	pKa = 10	pKa = 16	
bond easy to dissociate	HO–S(=O)(=O)–OH	O=N⁺(O⁻)–OH	CH₃C(=O)–OH	C₆H₅–OH	CH₃CH₂–OH		bond difficult to dissociate
	↓↑	↓↑	↓↑	↓↑	↓↑		
	HO–S(=O)(=O)–O⁻	O=N⁺(O⁻)–O⁻	CH₃C(=O)–O⁻	C₆H₅–O⁻	CH₃CH₂–O⁻		charge less stabilized due to less delocalization

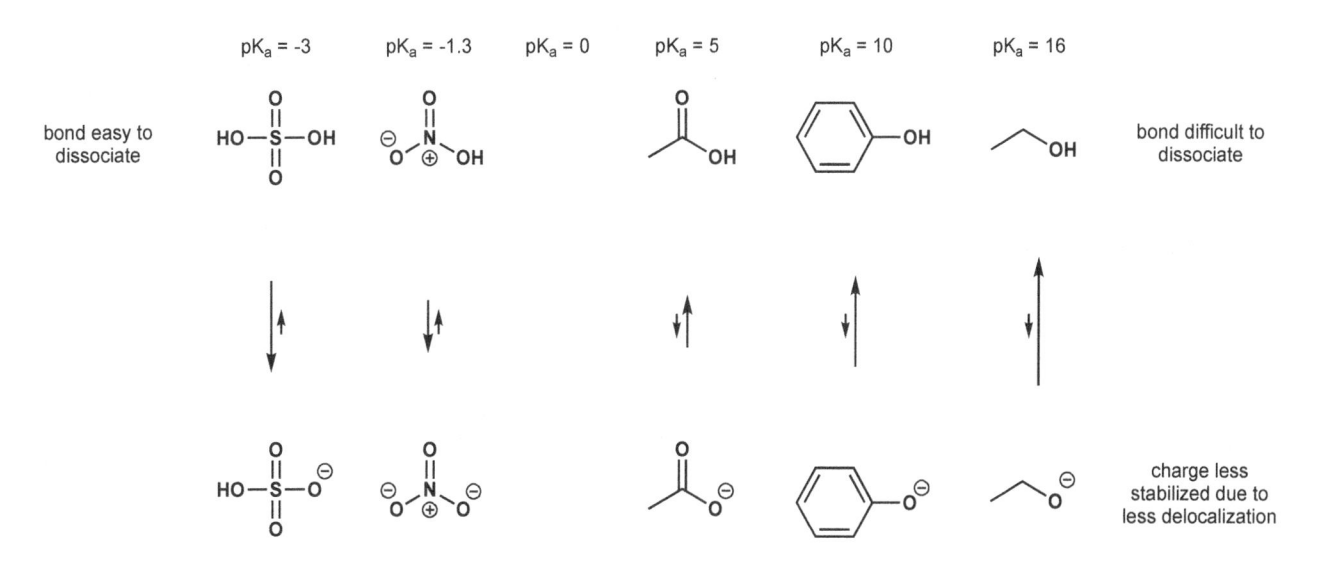

◆ The acidity of a carbon atom is greatly influenced by resonance and electronegativity

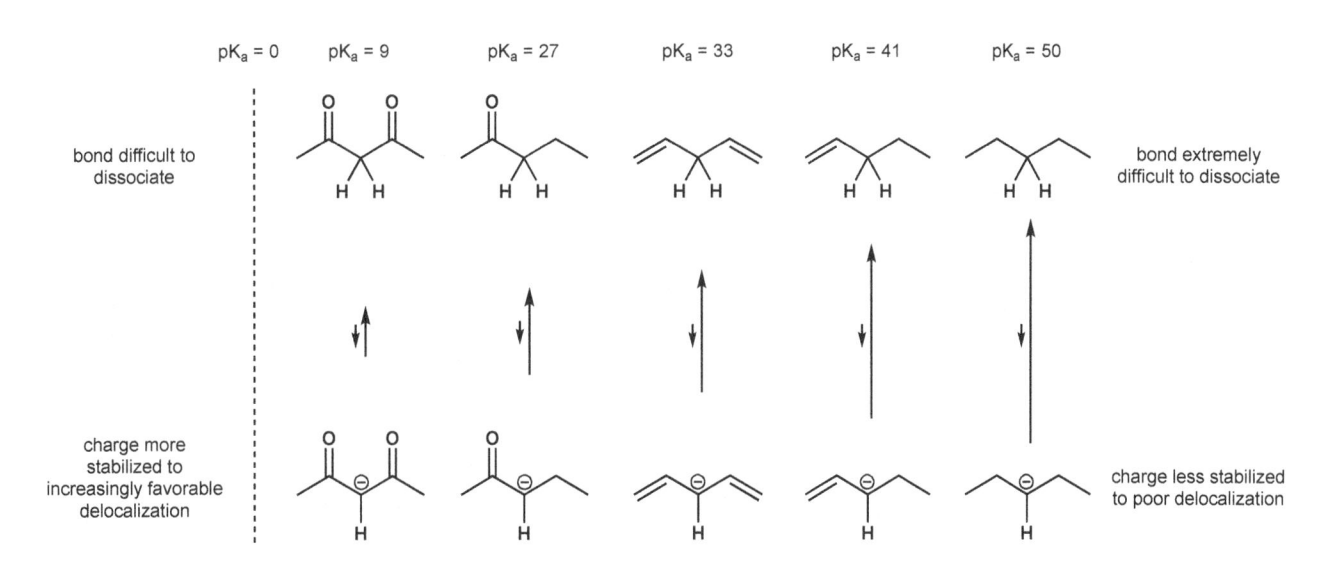

	pKa = 0	pKa = 9	pKa = 27	pKa = 33	pKa = 41	pKa = 50	
bond difficult to dissociate		CH₃C(=O)CH₂C(=O)CH₃	CH₃C(=O)CH₂CH₃	CH₂=CHCH₂CH=CH₂	CH₂=CHCH₂CH₂CH₃	CH₃CH₂CH₂CH₂CH₃	bond extremely difficult to dissociate
		↓↑	↓↑	↓↑	↓↑	↓↑	
charge more stabilized to increasingly favorable delocalization		CH₃C(=O)CH⁻C(=O)CH₃	CH₃C(=O)CH⁻CH₃	CH₂=CHCH⁻CH=CH₂	CH₂=CHCH⁻CH₂CH₃	CH₃CH₂CH⁻CH₂CH₃	charge less stabilized to poor delocalization

Hybridization/Orbital effects are observed when comparing the same atom with the same charge but only differing in the number of pi-bonds. Lone pairs are more stable in orbitals with a higher % s-character.

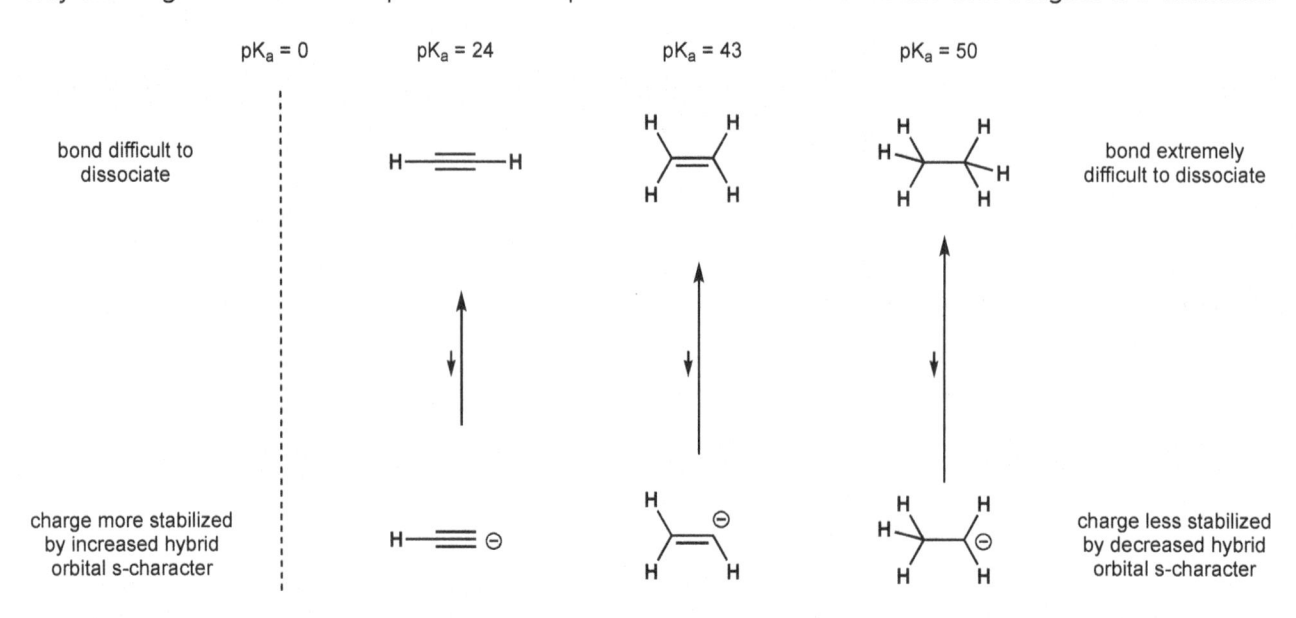

pK_a = 0 | pK_a = 24 | pK_a = 43 | pK_a = 50

bond difficult to dissociate | | | | bond extremely difficult to dissociate

charge more stabilized by increased hybrid orbital s-character | | | | charge less stabilized by decreased hybrid orbital s-character

Inductive/Hyperconjugation effects are when atoms near those bearing a charge stabilize or destabilize due to their electronegativity.

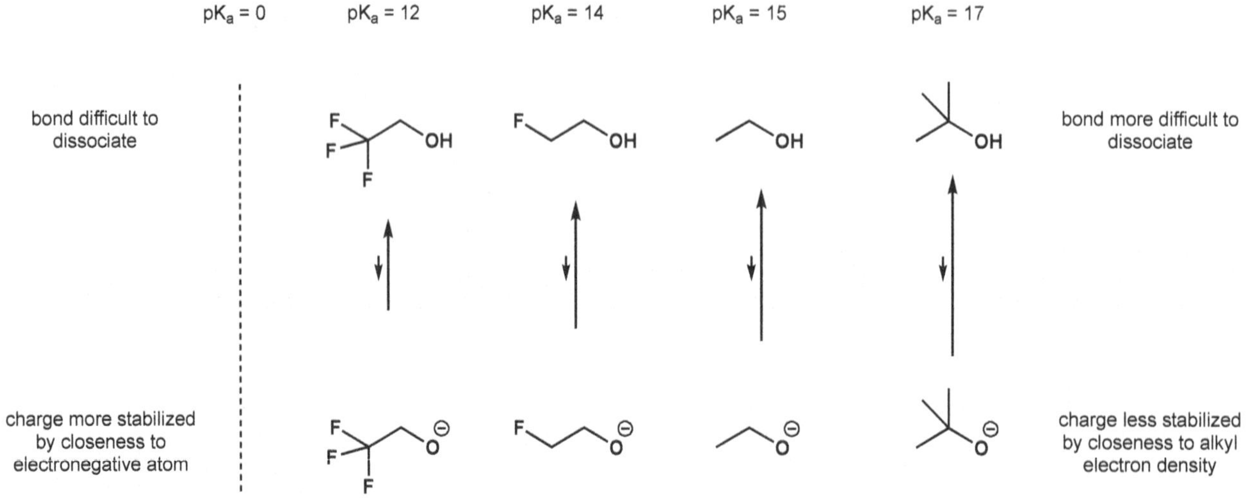

pK_a = 0 | pK_a = 12 | pK_a = 14 | pK_a = 15 | pK_a = 17

bond difficult to dissociate | | | | | bond more difficult to dissociate

charge more stabilized by closeness to electronegative atom | | | | | charge less stabilized by closeness to alkyl electron density

Solving Acid-Base Problems

Using the ideas and experimental data discussed, the equilibrium of acid-base reactions can be predicted either quantitatively, using available pK_a data, or qualitatively using an understanding of electronic stability.

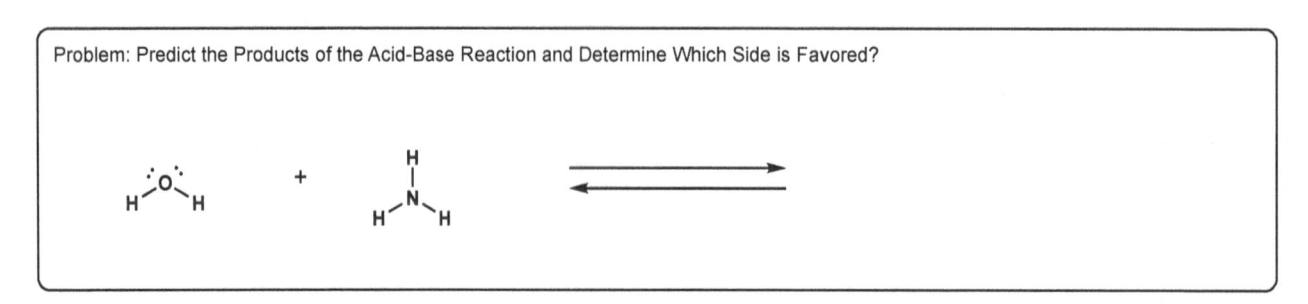

Problem: Predict the Products of the Acid-Base Reaction and Determine Which Side is Favored?

Water and ammonia (and many nitrogen and oxygen-containing organic compounds) are described as amphoteric, or capable of behaving as an acid or a base; thus it is important to consider both patterns of reactivity when deciding on a favored side of any acid-base equilibrium. In Analysis #1, water has accepted a proton from ammonia to produce a hydronium ion and an amide ion (note: this is not the carboxylic acid derivative). To quantitatively solve this problem, the pK_a values of the acid and conjugate acid are compared, and it is determined that the products side of the reaction as written contains the stronger acid (smaller pK_a). Favoring the product side of the equilibrium is intuitively incorrect since the stronger acid should be more dissociated and therefore, the equilibrium lies toward the reactants side (weaker acid is favored).

Analysis #1: Water as the "Base" and Ammonia as the "Acid"

ABC Role	A—H	B:		A:	B—H
pKa value	38				-1
	weaker acid FAVORED SIDE!	more stable base (more EN and neutral)		less stable base (less EN and Charged)	stronger acid

To answer the question without the use of pK_a values, consider the "base perspective" and compare the relative stability of the base and conjugate base in the equilibrium as drawn. For the base (water), the electron lone pair is held by oxygen and the molecule is overall neutral in charge, yet for the conjugate base (amide), the lone pair is on nitrogen, which is less electronegative, and the molecule is overall negatively charged. Both of these factors for the amide conjugate base suggest it has a higher reactivity and is less stable, thus the favored side of this equilibrium is the reactant side.

ABC Role	B:	A—H		B—H	A:
pKa value		16		9	
	more stable base	weaker acid FAVORED SIDE!		less stable base (less EN and Charged)	stronger acid

Assigning the roles of acid and base and choosing the correct proton to consider in the equilibrium can be even more difficult when more complex organic molecules are involved. Consider the reaction of acetic acid with sodium hydroxide:

Problem: Predict the Products of the Acid-Base Reaction and Determine Which Side is Favored?

CH₃COOH + NaOH ⇌

To best analyze this problem, expand the Lewis structures around the atoms of interest. Likewise, represent the bond between a Main Group Element (H, C, N, O, X, etc.) and a Metal (Li, Na, K, Mg, etc.) ionically to generate a very predictive picture of reactivity.

[Reaction scheme: H₃C-C(=O)-O-H + Na⁺ + ⁻:O-H ⇌]

A base's role is to donate electrons, so the hydroxide anion becomes an excellent first guess for the role of the base. Although acetic acid contains two unique types of hydrogens that could serve as the acid, the O-H bond is a strong choice to dissociate first, due to the expectation that the electronegativity of oxygen will help to stabilize the resulting conjugate base when it is formed. The products of the reaction are the acetate ion and water. (Note: the sodium counter-ion is represented as "free" in this equation but in reality, it will stay closely associated with whatever anionic species is present in solution.)

Analysis #1: Hydroxide as the "Base" and Acetic Acid O-H as the "Acid"

[Reaction scheme showing acetic acid + Na⁺ + OH⁻ ⇌ acetate⁻ + Na⁺ + H₂O]

ABC Role	A—H	B:⁻	A:⁻	B—H
pKa value	5			16
	stronger acid	(less stable base)	(more stable base) resonance effects	weaker acid FAVORED SIDE!
	[1]			[100,000,000,000]

Quantitatively, the pK_a values for the acid and conjugate acid can be applied, and in doing so, the product side of the equilibrium can be considered favored due to the O-H of water being the weaker of the two choices of acid in this equilibrium. The degree to which this equilibrium is favored can be roughly calculated by subtracting the pK_a of the conjugate acid from the pK_a of the acid, resulting in a $pK_{reaction}$ as follows:

$$pK_a(\textbf{A-H}) - pK_a(\textbf{B-H}) = pK_{(reaction)}$$

$$pK_a(CH_3CO_2H) - pK_a(H_2O) = pK_{(reaction)}$$

$$(5) - (16) = -11$$

The $pK_{reaction}$ of −11 can be interpreted to mean the product side this reaction of is favored 100,000,000,000-to-1 or 10¹¹-to-1; this equilibrium is quite favored on the product side.

An interesting and common stumbling block occurs if these pK_a values are not readily available in print or from memory. How can the favored side of an equilibrium be determined using only molecular structures? The answer lies in the taking the "base perspective" by comparing the electrons of the base and conjugate base, and choosing the more stable of the two as the favored side of the equilibrium. By considering the importance of elemental, resonance, hybridization/orbital, and inductive/hyperconjugation effects, a confident and informed choice is always possible. For this reaction, the comparison between hydroxide and acetate is a relatively straightforward one. Because the anion is centered on oxygen in both cases, the stabilization due to elemental effects (size or electronegativity) is the same. The critical difference between these anions is that the negative charge on acetate is stabilized by resonance with another oxygen while hydroxide is has no resonance stabilization. Additional hybridization and inductive effects could be considered, but in this case, they are not needed since the effect of resonance stabilization is more important than those lesser effects. Therefore, without the use of the pK_a values, the product side of the equilibrium is chosen as favored due to the presence of the more stable acetate conjugate base.

Analysis #1: Hydroxide as the "Base" and Acetic Acid O-H as the "Acid"

ABC Role	A—H	B:⁻	A:⁻	B—H
pKa value	5			16
	stronger acid	(less stable base)	(more stable base) resonance effects	weaker acid FAVORED SIDE!
	[1]			[100,000,000,000]

Other acid-base equilibria are possible, and although none are more favorable than the one discussed in Analysis #1, examination of these situations may help avoid poor decision-making in future examples. In Analysis #2, hydroxide is still playing the role of base, but instead of the O-H bond, a C-H bond is playing the role of acid. Although the carbon anion of the conjugate base is in resonance with oxygen, stability of this anion is much lower than that of acetate because of elemental effects (carbon is not as electronegative as oxygen). Furthermore, when a hydroxide base approaches acetic acid, it always has a "choice" of protons to remove: the more acidic O-H proton will always react faster and preferentially with the base, making the product side of the equilibrium in Analysis #2 impossible to favor.

Analysis #2: Hydroxide as the "Base" and Acetic Acid C-H as the "Acid"

ABC Role	A—H	B:⁻	A:⁻	B—H
	potential acid		carbon anion conjugate base? unstabilize compared to acetate and formation is very unlikely in the presence of any O-H NOT FAVORED!	

In Analysis #3, the roles of acetic acid and hydroxide are reversed, and although the protonated acetic acid conjugate base is possible to form in the presence of stronger acids, the product side of this equilibrium is greatly disfavored due to the very poor acidity of hydroxide correlated to the very, very unstable conjugate base oxide (O^{2-}).

Analysis #3: Acetic Acid as the "Base" and Hydroxide as the "Acid"

ABC Role	BH	A:⁻	⁺HB—H	:B:⁻²
	potential base	anion? typically poor choice as acid	potential conjugate acid	oxygen dianion? very unlikely and very unstable! NOT FAVORED!

When there exists more than one choice of proton to deprotonate, it is helpful to draw many possible analyses, and then choose the favored equilibrium based on the comparative stability of the possible bases. Until the logic of Analysis #1 is second nature, it is helpful to assemble a list of "red flags" to avoid making the wrong conclusions when working acid-base problems: 1) formal charges are useful but far from the most important factor in determining acid or base stability or reactivity, 2) negatively-charged atoms almost never play the role of acid and positively-charged atoms almost never play the role of base because, 3) dianions and dictations are so disfavored, they are almost never needed to describe chemical reactions in solution.

8.5 Acid/Base Example

Organic compounds can be separated from impurities and other organic molecules based upon their acidity. Organic acids such as phenols, and sulfonic and carboxylic acids, are easily converted into their sodium salts (water soluble) by reaction with sodium bicarbonate or sodium hydroxide. Also, organic bases such as amines are converted into water-soluble hydrochloride salts by reaction with hydrochloric acid. The overall plan for the separation of an organic mixture into acidic, basic, and neutral composition is shown in the following figures.

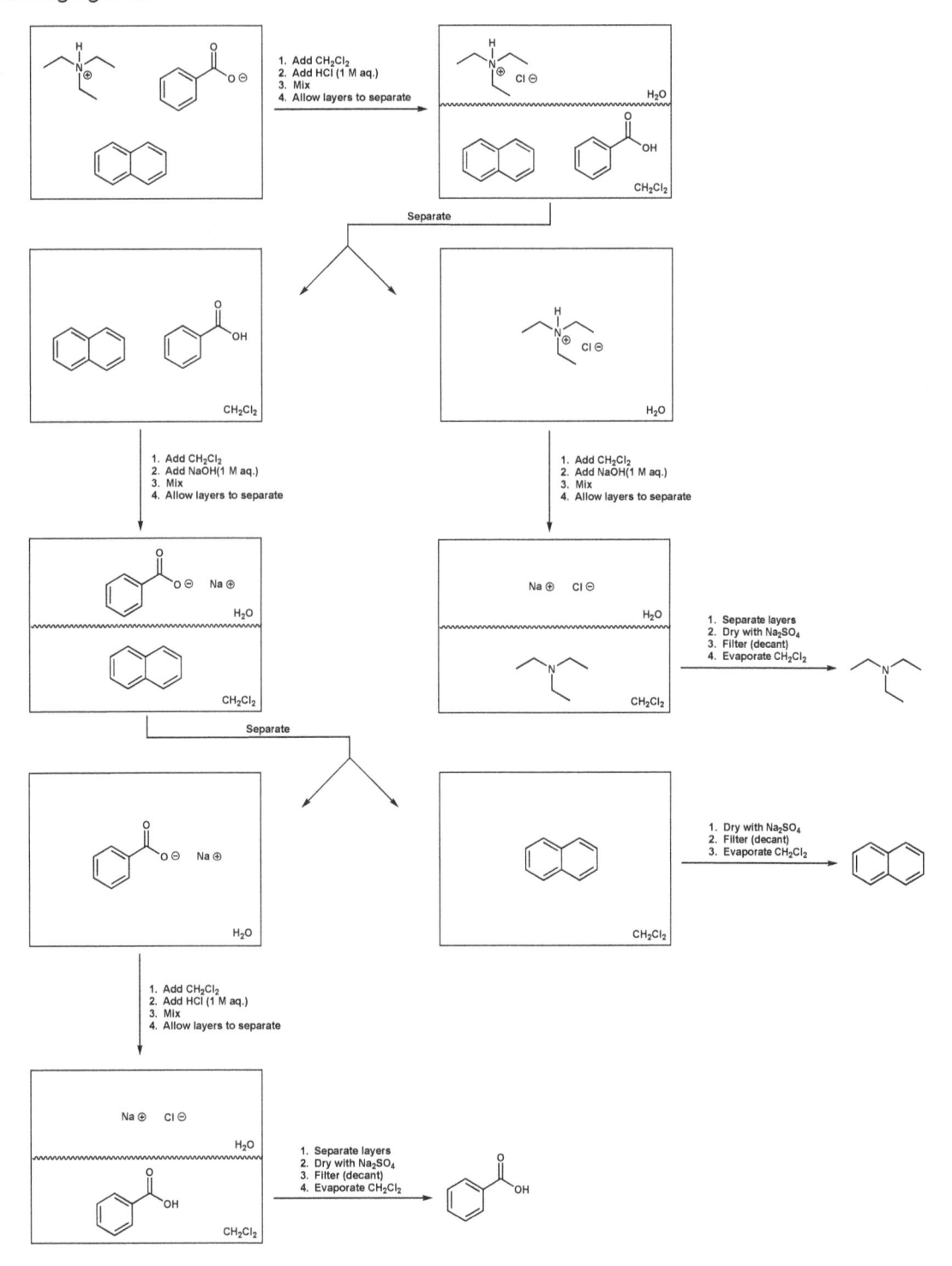

Since the formation of the conjugate acids and conjugate bases is reversible, it is a simple task to regenerate the carboxylic acid or amines. By acidifying the base extract containing the carboxylate, the carboxylic acids are regenerated.

By basifying the acid extracts containing the ammonium ion, the organic amines are regenerated.

Organic carboxylic acids can be de-protonated easily using a base such as aqueous sodium bicarbonate. The conjugate base of the carboxylic acid, since it is charged, has high solubility in water but very low solubility in organic solvents such as dichloromethane. The initial carboxylic acid, on the other hand, is very soluble in the organic solvents such as dichloromethane, but has a very low solubility in water. The same principle holds true for almost all organic compounds.

Organic amines can be protonated by aqueous acids, such as a 5% aqueous hydrochloric acid. These species form positively charged ammonium species (conjugate acid). The ammonium species is highly soluble in water but has very low solubility in organic solvents such as dichloromethane. This difference in solubility can be used to separate organic amines from other types of organic compounds.

These Extraction Principles Can Be Used to Separate Mixtures of Organic Compounds

Remember that the extent to which an acid-base reaction proceeds correlates directly to the relative acidity and basicity of the reactants and products. Reactions occur in a fashion so that stronger acids and bases react to produce weaker conjugate bases and acids.

$$pK_a = -\log K_a$$

Stronger acids have small pK_a and their conjugate bases are inherently weaker. The position of an acid base equilibrium can then be predicted using the pK_a of the acids involved. The equilibrium always lies to the side of the equation with the larger pK_a. Stronger acids will react with the conjugate bases of weaker acids. Take the following example into account:

Reaction 1

Phenol (pKa = 10) + NaOH ⇌ Sodium phenoxide + H₂O (pKa = 15.7)

Equilibrium lies to the right.

Reaction 2

Benzoic acid (pKa = 4.5) + NaOH ⇌ Sodium benzoate + H₂O (pKa = 15.7)

Equilibrium lies to the right.

Reaction 3

Phenol (pKa = 10) + NaHCO₃ ⇌ Sodium phenoxide + H₂CO₃ (pKa = 6)

Equilibrium lies to the left.

Reaction 4

Benzoic acid (pKa = 4.5) + NaHCO₃ ⇌ Sodium benzoate + H₂CO₃ (pKa = 6)

Equilibrium lies to the right.

Examination of the *pK*$_a$ indicates that NaOH can be used to deprotonate a phenol and a carboxylic acid from a non-polar solvent because the equilibrium lies to the right of the equation forming the ion, which is highly water soluble. On the other hand, sodium bicarbonate is a weaker base and will not deprotonate a phenol but will deprotonate a carboxylic acid.

8.6 Alkaloids

Alkaloids are a class of nitrogen-containing organic molecules that are synthesized by a variety of plant and animal species. Compounds like strychnine, mescaline, and atropine are hypothesized to play a role in plant defense from herbivores, while the alkaloids dopamine, serotonin, and adrenaline are synthesized by animals from dietary amino acids and serve a critical role in neuron signaling in the brain and peripheral nervous system. Human beings have also discovered how to harness, as well as abuse the powerful psychoactive properties of compounds like morphine, nicotine, cocaine, and of course caffeine.

Figure 8.1 Common plant and animal derived alkaloids.

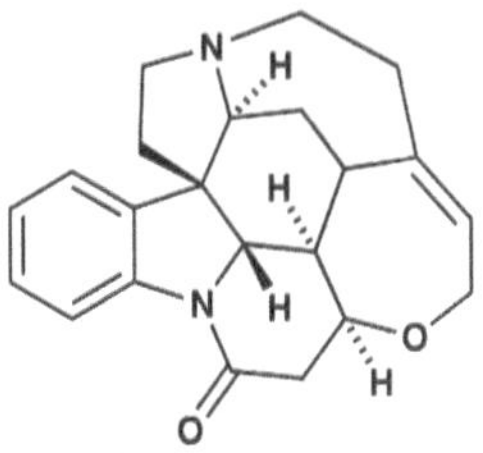

strychnine

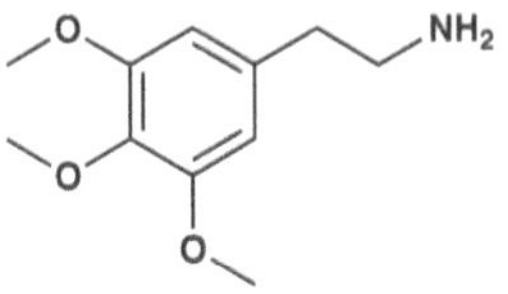

mescaline

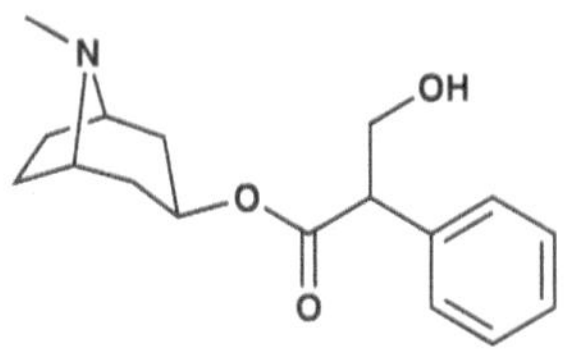

atropine

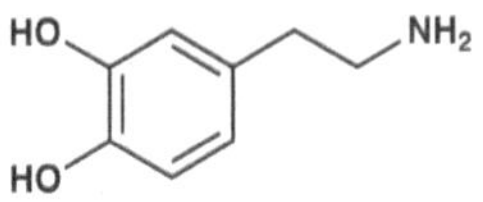

dopamine

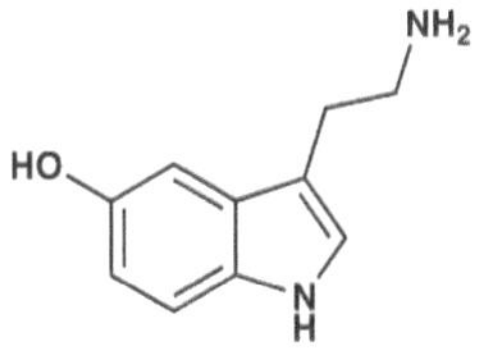

serotonin

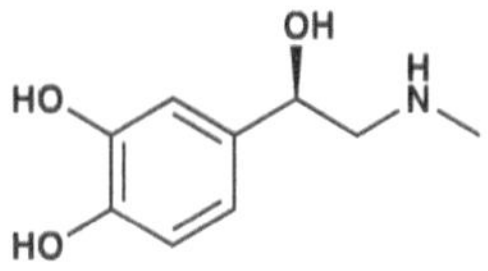

adrenaline

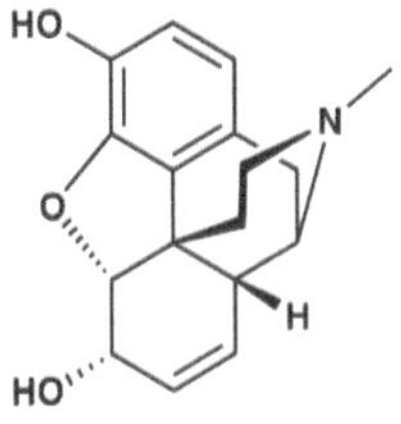

morphine

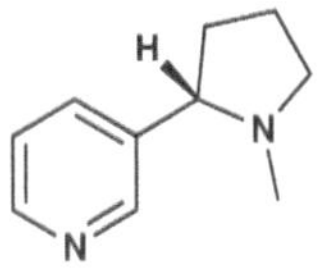

nicotine

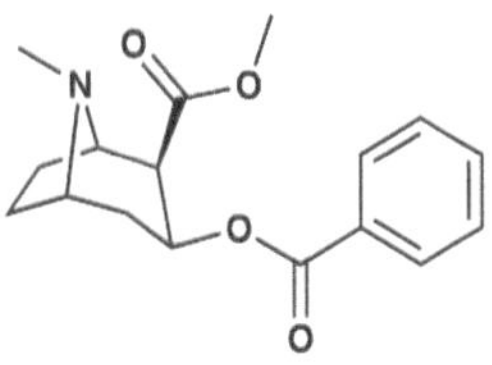

cocaine

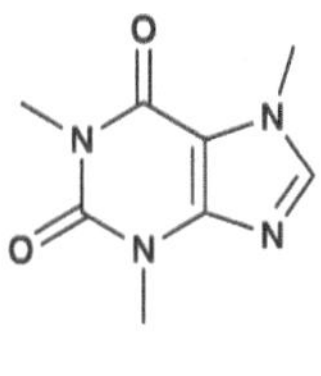

caffeine

Caffeine is a bitter-tasting, white crystalline xanthine alkaloid that acts as a central nervous stimulant through inhibition of adenosine receptors in the brain. When ingested, caffeine increases heart rate and respiration, induces alertness, and acts as a diuretic. Caffeine's molecular structure, including its size, and its type and arrangement of functional groups, is responsible for its physiological effects. The structurally-related molecules theophylline and theobromine, found in tea and cocoa, respectively, are also potent psychoactive compounds hypothesized to be responsible for the reinforcing effects of tea and chocolate consumption. The structures of these compounds are also responsible for their controversial health investigations. Health concerns surrounding caffeine are fueled by the molecules superficial structural similarity to the purine nucleobases guanine and adenine present in DNA. To date, no conclusive evidence exists to suggest negative health effects of caffeine consumption; to the contrary, new evidence supports caffeine's performance enhancing abilities, its protective anti-tooth decay activity, and its potent antioxidant characteristics. The goal of this laboratory experiment is to extract caffeine from a common beverage (coffee, tea, soda, etc.). Since caffeine possesses large differences in solubility between water and other solvents, the technique of extraction becomes a viable way to separate caffeine from water soluble molecules. Caffeine is soluble in water at a concentration of 21.7 mg mL^{-1} 25 °C and 670 mg mL^{-1} at 100 °C. Caffeine's solubility in dichloromethane is 1400 mg mL^{-1}.

Because of this increased solubility of caffeine in dichloromethane, the partition coefficient for the extractions will favor the caffeine dissolving in the organic layer.

Figure 8.2 Caffeine, related xanthines, and other structurally-related purine molecules.

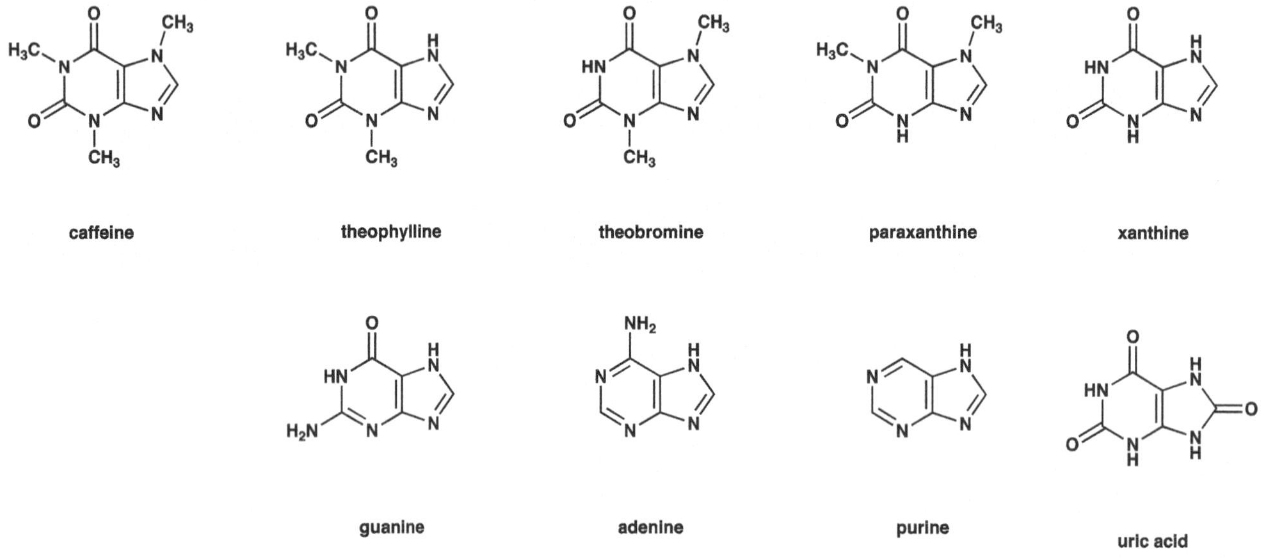

8.7 Extraction Scheme for Caffeine from Tea Leaves

Figure 8.3 Extraction of Caffeine

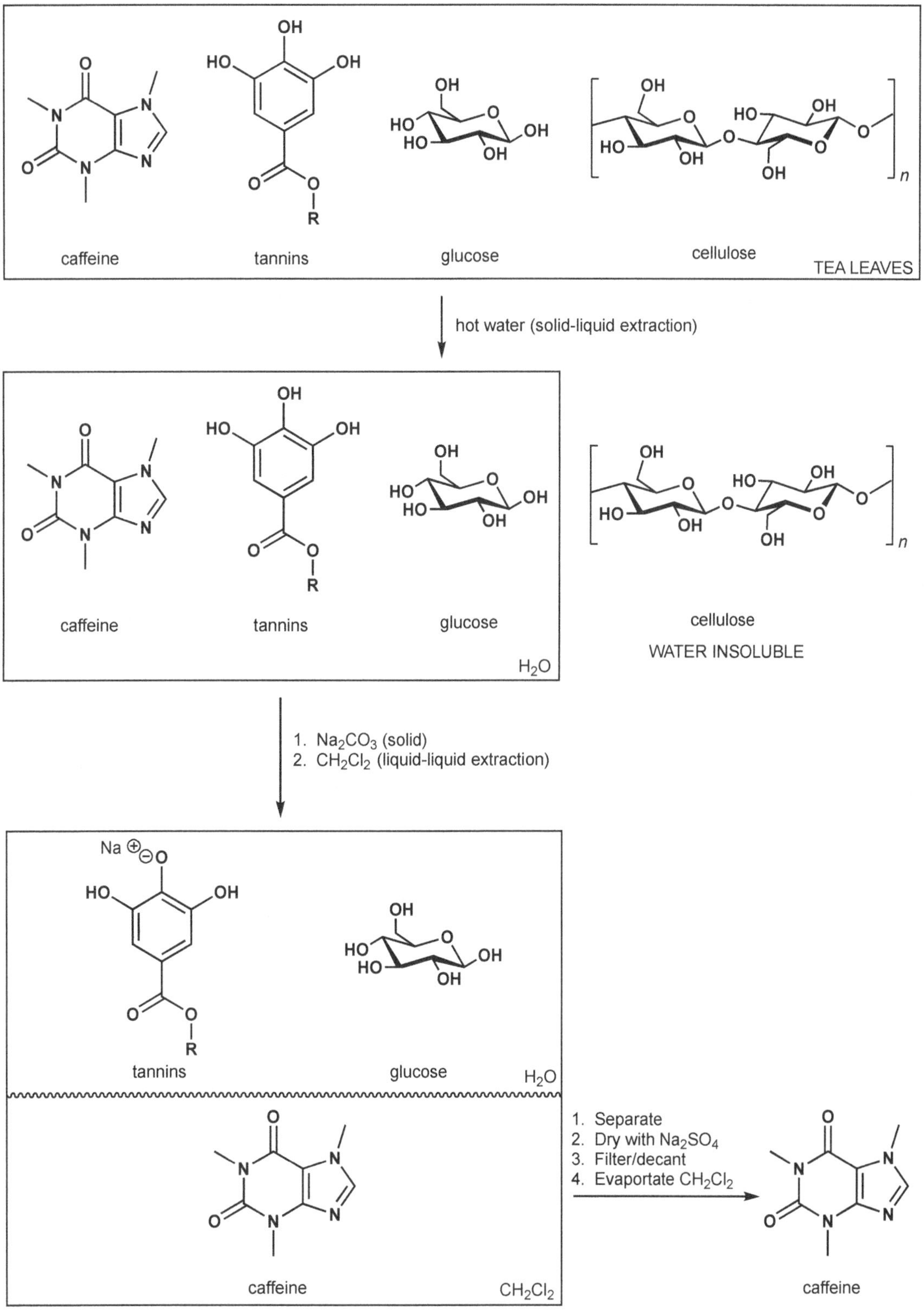

8.8 Prelab

Written Prelab: Record the following in your lab notebook:

- Your Name and Date
- Experiment Title
- Table of molecular structures and properties including:
  - molecular weight (MW)
  - boiling point (bp)
  - melting point (mp)
  - density (d) for liquids
- References for your property data and experiment
- A brief plan of procedure, which means "enough detail that you could perform the experiment without your laboratory manual"

compound name	structure	MW	bp	mp	d
caffeine					
glucose					
sodium carbonate					
dichloromethane					

Electronic Prelab: Prior to the beginning of your laboratory section, login to our Chemistry 2540 Carmen page and complete the prelabs in the labeled experimental module.

8.9 Extraction of Caffeine from Tea—Procedure

1. Transfer the mixture of prepped tea and sodium carbonate into two centrifuge tubes, approximately half of the mixture in each tube.

    In order to aide in the dissolution of sodium carbonate in tea, shake the vial prior to the transfer.

2. **Extraction:** To each centrifuge tube, add 3 mL of dichloromethane (CH_2Cl_2), cap, and invert gently 2–3 times. Make sure to vent to avoid pressure buildup.

3. **Extraction:** With a Pasteur pipette, remove the lower CH_2Cl_2 layer from each tube, and combine the extracts into a 50-mL beaker.

4. In order to complete two additional extractions per tube, repeat Steps 2 and 3 two more times. Make sure to place all extracts in the same 50-mL beaker.

    If during any of the extractions, an emulsion forms (the liquids become dispersed in each other and are not separating as indicated by tiny bubbles where the interface between the aqueous and organic layers meet), simply let the tube stand for a few minutes after gently stirring with the tip of your pipet at the interface.

5. **Drying:** Add a small amount of sodium sulfate (about 3–4 microspatulas) to the combined CH_2Cl_2 extracts in the beaker. Swirl the beaker to disperse the sodium sulfate throughout the extract, and allow the mixture to stand undisturbed for a couple of minutes.

    Sodium sulfate is a drying agent that will absorb any water left behind from the extraction. All of the colored water droplets should "stick" to the sodium sulfate when you have added enough. Additionally, freely flowing granules of sodium sulfate will indicate a thoroughly dried solution.

6. **Separation:** Carefully pipet the dried CH_2Cl_2 into a pre-weighed 50-mL or 100-mL round-bottom flask. Evaporate the CH_2Cl_2 6. under reduced pressure using the Buchi rotory evaporator (rotovap). Determine the mass of the crude caffeine.

    Be sure to rinse the beaker with a small portion of CH_2Cl_2 and transfer it to the evaporating flask. Quantitatively transferring the solution will ensure that no caffeine is left behind in transfer.

7. **Transfer:** Add 1 mL of CH_2Cl_2 to the round bottom flask containing the crude caffeine. Swirl the solution around the flask to dissolve the solid. Use a pipet to transfer the solution to a Craig tube. Rinse the round bottom flask with 0.5 mL of CH_2Cl_2 and transfer this liquid to the same Craig Tube. Add a boiling stick to the Craig tube.

8. **Evaporation:** In a small Erlenmeyer flask, heat ~15–20 mL of isopropyl alcohol on a hot plate (be sure to include a boiling stick to prevent bumping). Clamp the Craig tube above the warming liquid to aid in the evaporation of the CH_2Cl_2 Once the CH_2Cl_2 is evaporated the solid crude caffeine will be visible in the bottom of the Craig tube. Be sure to push the solid down with the boiling stick once to ensure all of the CH_2Cl_2 has evaporated.

9. **Microscale Recrystallization:** Add small quantities of the boiling isopropanol to the Craig tube to dissolve the crude caffeine. The Craig tube should be clamped in the top of the Erlenmeyer flask so that it stays warm and secure during the addition of the recrystallization solvent. Be careful not to add too much solvent.

    You should place the Craig tube in the top of the clamped Erlenmeyer flask so that it stays warm and secure while adding solvent at all times. Be careful not to add too much solvent. It is best to err on the side of too little solvent rather than too much. You should stir the material with your microspatula to aid in the dissolution.

10. **Cool and crystallize:** Once all the compound is dissolved in the isopropyl alcohol, remove the Craig Tube from the flask and place it in your test tube rack to cool SLOWLY to room temperature. Once the solution achieves room temperature, crystallization should begin.

If crystallization does not begin, scratch the inside of the container with a glass rod at the liquid-air interface. Once crystallization has started, it is best not to disturb the craig tube to promote large crystal formation.

11. **Ice water bath:** Once crystal formation is evident, it can be cooled in an ice bath. Cooling in an ice bath will maximize the amount of pure compound that comes out of solution.
12. **Centrifuge:** Once crystallization is complete, remove the solvent and isolate the crystals by centrifugation of the Craig Tube for ~2 minutes.
13. **Recovered yield:** Use mass by difference with a black capped vial with cap to determine the mass of your purified caffeine.

    Record the mass to 3 decimal places.
14. **Calculations:** Calculate percent recovery of caffeine in your tea based on the reported commercial concentration of caffeine.

    Calculate your percent recovery of caffeine from tea:

    pure caffeine crystals / expected caffeine content (0.100 g) × 100 = % recovery (from tea)

    Calculate your percent recovery of caffeine from crude caffeine solid:

    pure caffeine crystals / crude caffeine solid × 100 = % recovery (from crude)
15. Record the melting point of your purified caffeine.

Waste Disposal

The isopropyl alcohol mother liquor from the recrystallization must be disposed of in the organic solvent waste beaker.

8.10 Postlab Data Submission

Prepare this table of Postlab Data in your Laboratory Notebook after your completed experimental narrative, and fill
in the appropriate data in the correct box:

\multicolumn{5}{c}{Extraction of Caffeine}
starting materials	experimental mass (g)			
caffeine in tea				
product	experimental mass (g)	% recovery (from tea)	% recovery (from crude)	melting point
crude caffeine				
recrystallized caffeine				

Login to our Chemistry 2540 Carmen page and complete any listed postlab assignments in the labeled experimental module. Postlab assignments are due as listed on the Course Schedule.

8.11 Digital Lab Report Guidelines

Login to our Chemistry 2540 Carmen page and download a copy of the appropriate *Digital Lab Report Template* for this experiment in the labeled experimental module. Follow the instructions listed in the *Digital Lab Report Template* with regard to the preparation of ChemDraw drawings, Formal Procedure section, and the answers to Concept Questions. Submit your completed Digital Lab Report as a Microsoft Word Document (.doc or .docx file only) or Adobe PDF to the Chemistry 2540 experiment assignment. Digital Lab Reports are due as listed on the Course Schedule, and late submissions will be penalized –10 pts per day late.

8.12 Practice Problems

1. *Acid/Base Reactions.* Provide the products for the following acid/base reactions. Label the acid, base, conjugate acid, and conjugate base. Depict the electron movement using arrows. Draw an arrow to depict which side of the equilibrium is favored and provide an explanation by comparing the stability of the base vs. conjugate base.

2. *Extraction Flow Chart Practice.* Propose a step-by-step procedure for the separation of pyridine and decalin using the same format as the flow chart shown in the lab manual.

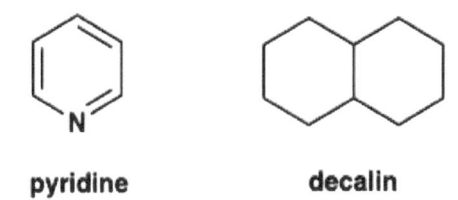

pyridine   **decalin**

3. Fluorine is the most electronegative element on the periodic table, and molecules that contain multiple fluorine atoms have been shown to possess some interesting properties. For example, the molecule hexafluorobenzene will not dissolve in organic solvents or in water. With this information in hand and the basic principle of extraction "like dissolves like," answer the following questions.

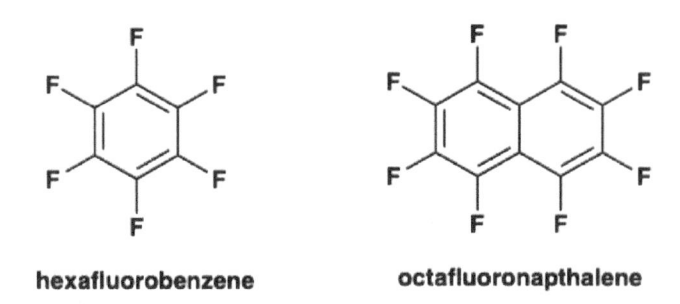

hexafluorobenzene   **octafluoronapthalene**

   a. The density of water is 1.00 g/mL, the density of dichloromethane is 1.32 g/mL. If you mix dichloromethane and water together, which layer will be on top and which layer will be on the bottom?
   b. The density of hexa-fluorobenzene is 1.61 g/mL. If you mix dichloromethane, water and hexafluorobenzene together, how many layers will there be and what will their positions be?
   c. If you add decalin to the mixture you created in (b), which layer will it dissolve in?
   d. If you add sodium benzoate to the mixture you created in (b), which layer will it dissolve in?
   e. If you add octa-fluoronaphthalene to the mixture you created in (b), which layer will it dissolve in?

4. Assume that caffeine has a solubility of 64 g/100 mL in dichloromethane, and in water it is 4 g/100 mL.
   a. What is the partition coefficient (K) for caffeine given these solubilities?
   b. Suppose we have 100 mL of water containing 5 g of caffeine and we extract it with 100 mL of dichloromethane twice. Given a partition coefficient of 21.51, how much total caffeine will be extracted in grams? (Use formula and example shown in lab manual)

5. Caffeine crystals always contain at least one molecule of water per caffeine molecule. Draw chemical structures to explain why a water molecule might be essential to producing a stable crystal of caffeine.

caffeine

6. For each molecule below, speculate whether the molecule **might** be water soluble, organic soluble, or both. Then describe with words or pictures how these molecules would interact with each solvent.

8.13 Study Guide—Extraction

1. Given a mixture of acidic, basic, and neutral organic compounds, be able to devise a separation scheme based on extraction.
2. Understand how to separate aqueous and organic phases using Pasteur pipettes.
3. Given a reaction mixture, know how to remove inorganic acids or bases via extraction.
4. Know how to determine which layer is the aqueous layer (or organic layer) during an extraction.
5. Be able to predict acid base equilibrium using pKa data.
6. Understand which potential acid/base reactions could be used to successfully separate mixtures of organic compounds.
7. Be able to recognize and understand whether or not a given mixture of compounds could be separated using extraction.
8. Understand the factors that determine acidity.

Thin Layer Chromatography

CHAPTER 9

9.1 Introduction

Thin layer chromatography (TLC) is an analytical technique that is commonly used to determine the purity of compounds or for the preliminary identification of reactions. This technique helps chemists analyze mixtures, determine the conditions to separate compounds using column chromatography, identify compounds from within mixtures, and estimate the relative amounts. At its most fundamental level, TLC is used by organic chemists to follow the progress of reactions by monitoring the disappearance of starting materials and the appearance of products. In commercial processes, TLC can be used in many applications: purity of foods from pesticide contamination, urine analysis for evidence of drug usage, pigment separation in dye processing. As the name suggests, the adsorbent is supported on an aluminum or glass backing as a thin coating on the flat surface. TLC separates compounds based on their polarity and is very similar in principle to extraction. The compound is partitioned between two phases based on its difference in solubility in the two phases. In the case of TLC, one of the phases is termed the mobile phase and the other is termed the stationary phase. The stationary phase is normally silica or alumina powder in the form of a thin layer placed on a supporting material such as aluminum or glass. The mobile phase is a mixture of or single volatile organic or non-organic solvents.

9.2 Technique of Thin Layer Chromatography

First put a small quantity of sample in a solvent in which it is soluble. Dip a small microcapillary spotter into the solution of your material. This will cause some of the solution to rise into the tube by capillary action. Carefully touch the loaded capillary spotter lightly onto the silica at a point marked on the baseline drawn (in pencil) across one end of the plate, about 1 cm from the end. This will cause some of the liquid in the capillary spotter to be drawn onto the adsorbent, forming a small spot of your material and the solvent. The amount of material that you spot on the plate is very important; it will take practice to apply the correct amount. Too much applied material will cause the plate to be overloaded and your spots will streak and be large. Too little material will cause the spots not to be visible upon inspection after elution. The most accurate results are obtained when there is just enough sample to visualize the spots after development. TLC is a very sensitive analytical procedure. A small amount of sample goes a long way.

Place the TLC plate carefully into the developing tank so that the baseline is at the bottom and the back of the plate leans against the sides of the container at a slight angle from vertical. It is important to ensure that the sides of the plates are not touching the walls of the chamber, and only the back is touching. You can use tweezers or forceps to transfer and handle the plates. The baseline where the sample is spotted must be at a level above that of the solvent. The solvent front will rise in a horizontal straight line up the plate by capillary action until it reaches about 1 cm from the top of the plate. If the solvent front is not straight, the TLC must be repeated on a new plate after checking that the adsorbent edges are not in contact with the walls of the chamber. After elution, carefully remove the plate, mark the solvent in pencil, and allow the solvent to evaporate in the hood. As the mobile phase ascends the plate, the mixture of compounds dissolves in the mobile phase to a different extent, because of differences in their attractions to the mobile and stationary phases.

During the elution process, the stationary phase adsorbs the mixture of compounds. As the mobile phase travels up over the stationary phase, the mixture will move up at different rates relative to the mobile phase. A reversible and continuous attraction between the mobile and stationary phase causes the difference in rate of movement. Compounds with less attraction for the adsorbent move rapidly with the eluant. Compounds with more attraction for the adsorbent move slowly with the eluant. The stationary phase of TLC plates is normally very polar, and therefore the more polar the compound in the mixture, the more strongly it adheres to the adsorbent and the more slowly it moves. Intermolecular forces between the eluant and the compounds determine the solubility of the compounds in the mobile phase. The more polar the eluant, the more rapidly the compounds will move. Polar compounds, which are very attracted to the solid phase, require polar mobile phases to attract them away from the adsorbent.

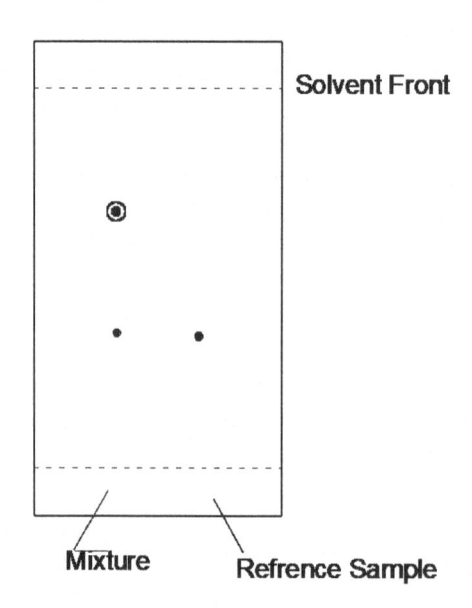

If the material is colored, you will be able to inspect the plate visually to observe the spots that have traveled up the plates. Normally this is not the case, and to inspect the TLC plate you will have to use some sort of visualization technique. The most useful technique for inspecting a TLC plate is observation of the plate under UV light or staining with iodine vapors. The great advantage of the UV light is that it is non-destructive to the TLC plate and the compounds on the plate. Analysis is quick, but one must take precaution when working with UV light. Never look directly at the UV light source; it can be damaging to the eye. Also, the wavelengths used for visualizing TLC plates can be damaging to the skin after prolonged exposure. The UV light causes most aromatic molecules, and molecules possessing extended conjugation, to give out a bright purple fluorescence against a dark background. The problem here is that not all molecules posses a conjugated double bond chromophore. Coated TLC plates with zinc sulfide are common in most organic labs. The zinc sulfide fluoresces green, except where the eluted substance is, which quenches this fluorescence, giving a dark spot. Therefore, a TLC plate should show a series of dark spots with a light green background.

Staining with iodine is another common procedure for visualizing TLC plates. To carry out this procedure, a chamber is prepared that contains sand and a few small crystals of iodine. The TLC plate after elution is placed in the chamber for a few minutes; any compounds will appear as dark brown spots on a light brown background. There are also a series of chemical reagents that react with the compounds on the TLC plate after elution. Several of these solutions are specific for certain types of organic functional groups and are very powerful techniques for visualizing TLC plates. This method has one disadvantage: the plates and the compounds on the plates are destroyed after visualization.

The ratio of solid phase to sample on the TLC plate must be high for efficient chromatographic resolution. TLC is usually an analytical technique rather than a preparative method. Several important factors determine the efficiency of a chromatographic separation. The solid phase should have a maximum rate of selectivity toward the substances being separated so that the differences in the rate of elution will be large. Silica gel is the most common adsorbent used for routine TLC of organic materials and analysis.

9.3 Solvents for Thin Layer Chromatography

The eluting solvent is also important in how it effects the separation of a mixture of compounds on a TLC plate. The mobile phase must have a good selectivity in its ability to dissolve the substances being separated. The solubility of different compounds in the eluting solvent plays the most important role in how the compounds separate and move on the plate. A more important property of the solvent is its ability to be adsorbed on the adsorbent. The mobile phase must have some magnitude of affinity on the adsorbent; it can displace the compounds being separated, thereby "pushing" them up the plate. If the mobile phase is too strongly adsorbed, it can fully displace all of the compounds, causing them to move up the plate together near the solvent front with no separation. If the solvent is weakly adsorbed, it will not move the compounds up the plate enough to allow them to separate. The ideal mobile phase is one where the affinity for the adsorbent and the compounds are of equal difference, thus causing the compounds to separate efficiently. Mixtures of solvents are most commonly used because the polarity of the mobile phase can be adjusted by changing the percentages of the miscible solvents. The more polar the solvent, the more the compound will move up the plate. As a general rule, the eluting power of solvents increases with increased polarity.

Retention Factor (R_f)

The most useful measurement that can be made from a developed TLC plate is the relation between the distance moved by the compound spot compared to the distance moved by the eluting solvent. This is the retention factor of a particular compound. It is referred to as R_f.

$$R_f = \text{(Distance moved by compound)} / \text{(Distance moved by mobile phase)}$$

Compounds that move up to the top of the plate will have an R_f value that approaches 1; whereas those that do not move very far will have R_f values that are near 0. Rf values by definition must fall between 0 and 1 and are reported to 2 decimal places. In theory, a given compound should always give the same Rf value under the given chromatographic conditions (adsorbent, eluant, temperature). However, it is virtually impossible to standardize the activity of the solid phase and the concentration of the mobile phase. Usually the variance of an R_f value is around 10 percent. R_f values are useful to anyone following a procedure, particularly if developed in conjunction with a standard material, as they indicate the likely region in which to look for the compounds on the TLC plate.

Identification of an unknown can be achieved by co-spotting the authentic material on the same plate as the unknown sample to be tested. The method is based on spotting roughly equal amounts of the unknown material onto exactly the same place on the baseline and also spotting the pure unknown and the authentic material on either side of the mixed spot. Any slight difference in R_f will cause the mixed spot to appear elongated. If the mixed spot does not show any elongation, the compounds are most likely the same. The method of spotting both materials on the same TLC plate in different lanes can lead to difficulty in identification if the compounds are the same or if the R_f is very similar.

The technique of multiple elution is a method used to separate close spots. This technique involves developing the TLC plate using a solvent system in which the highest running component has a R_f of 0.3 or lower. The plate is removed from the chamber, allowed to dry, and the process is repeated until adequate separation is observed. If a solvent system in which the spots had a greater R_f value than 0.3 was chosen, the spots of compound would end up running together rather than separating. In the repeat elutions, the solvent front begins to elute the more polar materials before it has reached the higher running material, and this becomes the major problem in the multiple elutions.

When a TLC plate is developed and shows a long streak instead of a clear round spot, that is probably caused by overloading the TLC plate. The resolution of the TLC plate and the size of the spot should decrease with concentration.

Molecular View of TLC

- The solvent is drawn up the plate by capillary action
- The adsorbed compounds are *partitioned* between the solution (mobile phase) and silica gel (stationary phase)
- Non-polar compounds interact poorly with the –OH groups on the TLC plate surface, and thus travel more quickly up the plate
- Polar compounds interact strongly with the –OH groups and travel more slowly

Three Meanings of Polar

- Solvent (mobile phase; eluant)
  - More polar solvent: ALL compounds "move" faster [**ALL R_f-values increase**]
  - Less polar solvent: **ALL** compounds "move" slower [**ALL R_f-values decrease**]

- Test compound (analyte; "spot")
  - More polar compound "moves" slower [relative R_f–values lower]
  - Less polar compound "moves" faster [relative R_f–values higher]
- Silica gel (stationary phase; the TLC plate itself)
  - **ALWAYS** polar, so . . . more polar compounds stick more, move slower
  - Less polar compounds dissolve in ANY solvent better, move faster

9.4 Prelab

Written Prelab: Record the following in your lab notebook:
- Your Name and Date
- Experiment Title
- Table of molecular structures and properties including:
  - molecular weight (MW)
  - boiling point (bp)
  - melting point (mp)
  - density (d) for liquids
- References for your property data and experiment
- A brief plan of procedure, which means "enough detail that you could perform the experiment without your laboratory manual"

compound name	structure	MW	bp	mp	d
fluorene					
fluorenone					
biphenyl					
benzophenone					
benzyl alcohol					
acetaminophen					
aspirin					
caffeine					
petroleum ether or hexanes					
diethyl ether					
ethyl acetate					
ethanol					
dichloromethane					

Electronic Prelab: Prior to the beginning of your laboratory section, login to our Chemistry 2540 Carmen page and complete the prelabs in the labeled experimental module.

9.5 Thin Layer Chromatography—Procedure

Thin layer chromatography (TLC) is a technique used to separate and/or purify compounds based on their partition coefficient between a solid stationary phase (adsorbent) and a liquid phase (eluant).

As you collect your TLC plates from different parts of the experiment they should be taped to a piece of white paper for calculations to be performed. All TLC plate results should be re-drawn in your lab notebook.

Part 1: Separation of Fluorene and Fluorenone

1. **TLC Chamber:** Fill the Coplin jar to a depth of about 0.5 cm with petroleum ether. Cap it and allow it to stand while you prepare your plate.

2. **Origin:** Obtaina TLC plate from your TA. Use a pencil to lightly draw a line across the plate 1 cm from the bottom. Lightly mark the plate with three evenly spaced spots along the origin and label as 1, 2, and 3.

    The plates should be handled by the edges to avoid contamination with oils and amino acids on the surface of your hands.

3. **Spotting:** Using glass capillary spotters, place a small spot of fluorene on lane #1, a small spot of 50:50 fluorene and fluorenone on lane #2, and a small spot of fluorenone on lane #3.

    The solutions of these samples will be provided in small test tubes by your TA. It is important to make the spots as small as possible (1–2 mm in diameter).

4. **Development:** Place the TLC plate into the developing chamber and allow the eluant to move up the plate to a level about 0.5 cm from the top. Remove the plate from the chamber and using a pencil, immediately mark the position of the solvent front. Allow the plates to dry and then observe them under a UV lamp. Lightly mark the observed spots with a pencil. elution with petroleum ether

5. Prepare a second TLC plate in the manner described above, then repeat the experiment using 95:5 petroleum ether-ethyl acetate as the eluant.

    Record the Rf values for both compounds on each TLC plate in your notebook along with a sketch of the visualized TLC plates.

Part 2: Visualization of Biphenyl, Benzophenone, and Benzyl Alcohol

1. **TLC Chamber:** Fill the Coplin jar to a depth of about 0.5 cm with 95:5 petroleum ether-ethyl acetate. Place the cap on the jar while you prepare your plate for analysis.

2. **Origin:** Obtain a TLC plate from your TA. Use a pencil to lightly draw a line across the plate ~1 cm from the bottom. Lightly mark the plate with three evenly spaced spots along the origin and label as 1, 2, and 3.

3. **Spotting:** Using glass capillary spotters, place a small spot of Solution A on Lane #1, Solution B on Lane #2, and Solution C on Lane #3.

    The solutions of these samples will be provided in small test tubes by your TA.

    Remember, it is important to make the spots as small as possible and be careful not to overload the plates. The applied spots should be about 1–2 mm in diameter.

4. **Development:** Develop the TLC plate by placing it into the developing chamber and capping the Coplin jar to allow the eluant to travel up the plate. Remove the plate from the chamber when the eluant has reached about 0.5 cm from the top. Immediately mark the solvent front.

5. **Visualization:** Allow the plates to dry before visualizing the plates. First, inspect the plate under UV light and mark the spots with a pencil. Second, stain the plate with phosphomolybdic acid (PMA). Dip the plate in the bottle containing the PMA stain. Develop the plate by heating it on a hot plate covered with aluminum foil at the marked location in the room.

6. **Identify:** Based on your knowledge regarding these parathion of compounds via TLC analysis, determine the identity of each solution. (biphenyl, benzophenone, benzyl alcohol)

   Record the Rf values for both compounds in your notebook along with a sketch of the visualized TLC plate.

Part 3: Separation of Analgesic Drugs (Pain-Killers)

In this experiment you will be given an unknown, which consists of about half of a commercial analgesic tablet. This may contain a single compound or a mixture of two unknowns. You will also have available a set of solutions of known compounds to use as references. They include acetaminophen (AA), aspirin (A), and caffeine (C). Your task is to determine which of the reference compounds are in your unknown analgesic. Note that your unknown may contain one or more of the reference compounds.

1. **TLC Chamber:** Fill Coplin jar to a depth of about 0.5 cm with ethyl acetate (the eluant). Then cap it and allow it to stand while you prepare your plate for analysis.

2. **Solution Preparation:** Prepare your unknown for spotting by mixing, adding 1 mL of a 50:50 mixture of ethanol and dichloromethane. Shake the mixture for a few minutes and allow the solid material to settle to the bottom of the vial.

3. **Spotting:** Make a TLC plate as shown below. Use a lead pencil to lightly draw a line across the plate about 1 cm from the bottom. Mark one plate with four spots. On the plate, spot acetaminophen, aspirin, caffeine and your unknown.

   Lane 1 – acetaminophen

   Lane 2 – aspirin

   Lane 3 – caffeine

   Lane 4 – unknown

4. **Development and Visualization:** Run the TLC plate to a level about 0.5 cm from the top, remove the plates from the chamber, and using a lead pencil, immediately mark the position of the solvent front. Allow the plates to dry and then observe them under a UV lamp. Lightly mark the observed spots with a lead pencil. You should also stain your plate with PMA stain to help visualize the spots that are present.

5. **Calculations:** Calculate the R_f values and use the information to determine the component(s) of your unknown. Record the R_f values for all compounds along with a sketch of the visualized TLC plate.

   Note: If the solution of unknown is too concentrated on your plate, tailing and/or overlapping of the spots may occur. If this happens, dilute the solution of the unknown with more of the solvent mixture and try again with new plates. Do not reuse a spotter unless you are sure it was used for the same solution previously. It is important that the reference solutions not be contaminated; NEVER place spotters directly into the reagent bottles.

Waste Disposal

Solvents must be discarded in the waste organic solvent can.

As you collect your TLC plates from different parts of the experiment they should be taped to a piece of white paper for calculations to be performed. All TLC plate results should be re-drawn in your lab notebook.

9.6 Post Lab Data Submission

Thin Layer Chromatography

	compound	distance to spot (mm)	distance to solvent front (mm)	R_f value	compound ID	eluant
Part A	fluorene	19	35			petroleum ether
	fluorenone	0				
	fluorene	30	30			5% ethyl acetate in petroleum ether
	fluorenone	16				

	solution	distance to spot (mm)	distance to solvent front (mm)	R_f value	compound ID	
Part B	solution A	20	32			
	solution B	5				
	solution C	31				

	compound	distance to spot (mm)	distance to solvent front (mm)	R_f value	compound ID	
Part C	caffeine	21	34			
	acetaminophen	19				
	aspirin	6				
	unknown #	6				
		6				

Login to our Chemistry 2540 Carmen page and complete any listed postlab assignments in the labeled experimental module. Postlab assignments are due as listed on the Course Schedule.

9.7 Digital Lab Report Guidelines

Login to our Chemistry 2540 Carmen page and download a copy of the appropriate *Digital Lab Report Template* for this experiment in the labeled experimental module. Follow the instructions listed in the *Digital Lab Report Template* with regard to the preparation of ChemDraw drawings, Formal Procedure section, and the answers to Concept Questions. Submit your completed Digital Lab Report as a Microsoft Word Document (.doc or .docx file only) or Adobe PDF to the Chemistry 2540 experiment assignment. Digital Lab Reports are due as listed on the Course Schedule, and late submissions will be penalized –10 pts per day late.

9.8 Practice Problems

1. Given the following TLC plate containing a mixture of naphthalene and benzoic acid, answer the following questions:

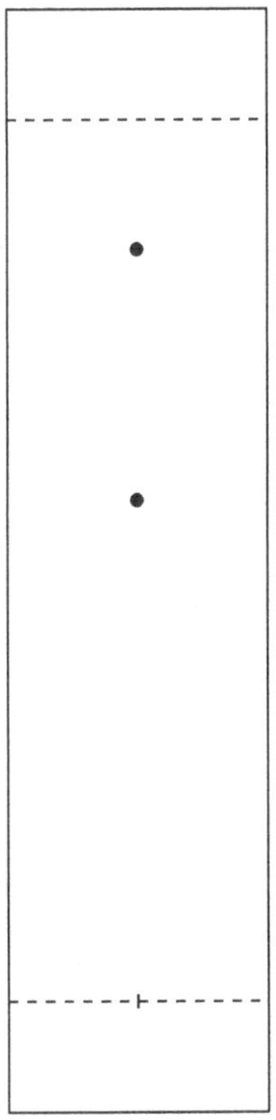

Solvent System = 1:1 Hexanes: Ethyl Acetate

a. What are the identities of the two spots on the TLC plate? Explain the logic used in identification.
b. What would happen to the Rf of the spots if you changed the solvent system to 1:2 hexanes: ethyl acetate?
c. What would happen to the Rf of the spots if you changed the solvent system to 2:1 hexanes: ethyl acetate?
d. What is the R_f of naphthalene and what is the Rf of benzoic acid?

2. The following compounds were all analyzed on the TLC plate below:

Determine which spot belongs to which compound, keeping in mind polarity and intermolecular forces determine how a compound will interact with the TLC plate.

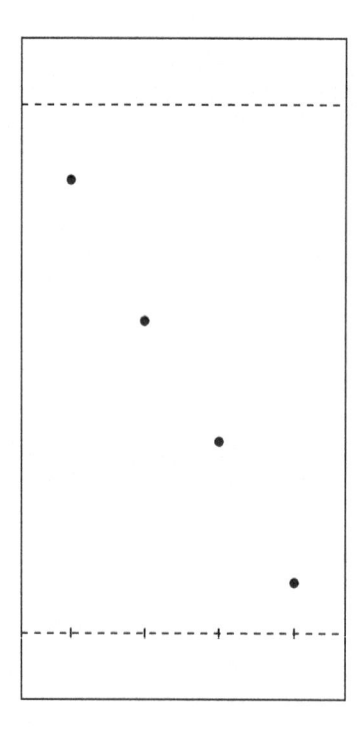

3. Polarity. Circle the more polar molecule in each pair. Explain your choice.

4. Rank (1–4) the order of Rf for the following mixtures on a TLC plate (1 = largest R_f, 4 = smallest R_f).

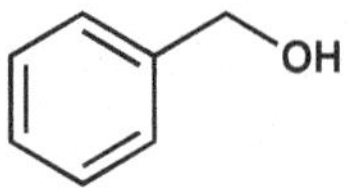

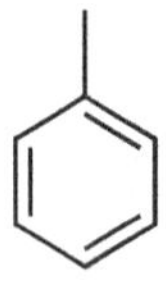

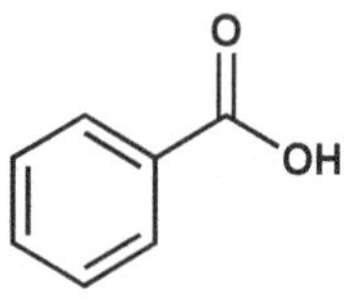

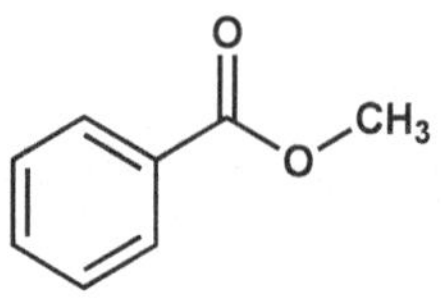

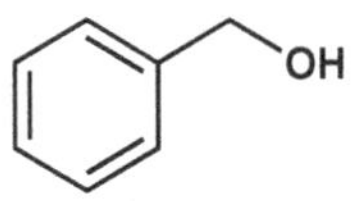

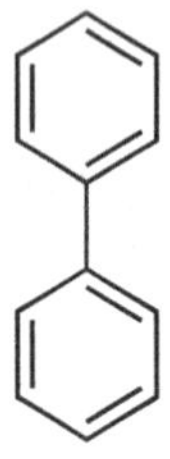

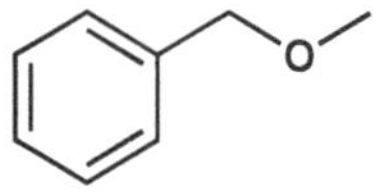

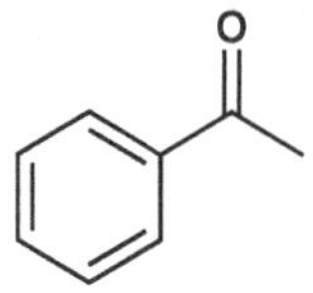

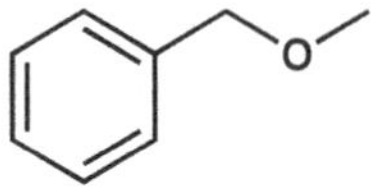

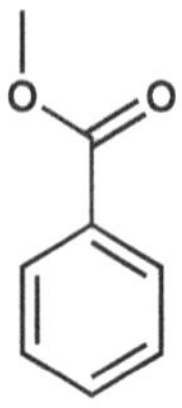

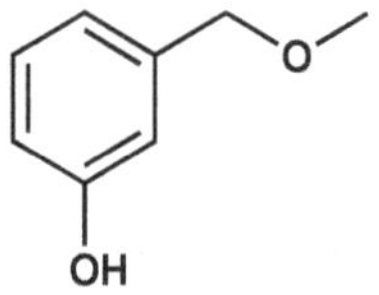

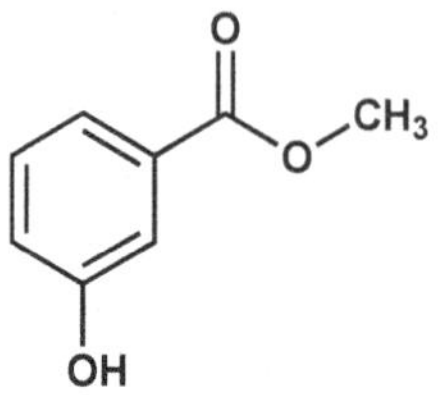

Row 1: benzyl alcohol (PhCH₂OH) | toluene (PhCH₃) | benzoic acid (PhCOOH) | methyl benzoate (PhCOOCH₃)

___   ___   ___   ___

Row 2: benzyl alcohol (PhCH₂OH) | biphenyl | benzyl methyl ether (PhCH₂OCH₃) | acetophenone (PhCOCH₃)

___   ___   ___   ___

Row 3: benzyl methyl ether (PhCH₂OCH₃) | methyl benzoate | 3-hydroxybenzyl methyl ether | methyl 3-hydroxybenzoate

___   ___   ___   ___

9.9 Study Guide—Thin Layer Chromatography

1. Understand what is meant by mobile phase, eluant, stationary phase, and R_f.
2. Given a series of organic solvents, be able to predict their relative polarities.
3. Know the characteristics that a good eluant will have for a given analysis.
4. Given a chromatogram of a mixture, be able to determine the R_f of the components of the mixture.
5. Understand the relationship between the R_f of a compound and its polarity.
6. Know how to visualize colorless materials on a chromatograph using UV light and staining techniques. Know the limitations of these methods.
7. Given a compound that has a particular R_f value with a given eluant, be able to predict what will happen to the R_f value as the eluant polarity is increased or decreased.
8. Draw a picture at the molecular level of the interactions taking place on a TLC plate with a compound.

Column Chromatography

CHAPTER 10

10.1 Introduction

Separation of Ferrocene and Fluorenone

Column Chromatography is a separation/purification technique. Column chromatography is one of the most powerful techniques in organic chemistry. The technique focuses on the distribution of organic mixtures between a solid and a mobile phase. The separation comes into effect based on the difference in how strongly the components of the mixture are adsorbed to the stationary phase and how soluble they are in the mobile phase. The differences in solubility between the phases are correlated to the compound's polarity; the more polar the functional group, the stronger the bond to alumina or silica gel. In this experiment, you will use column chromatography to separate a mixture of ferrocene and fluorenone.

Definitions:

- **Stationary Phase** — the adsorbent used in column chromatography (usually silica gel or alumina)— the stationary phase is usually a very polar material.
- **Mobile Phase** — the solvent that is used as the eluent in the column chromatography.

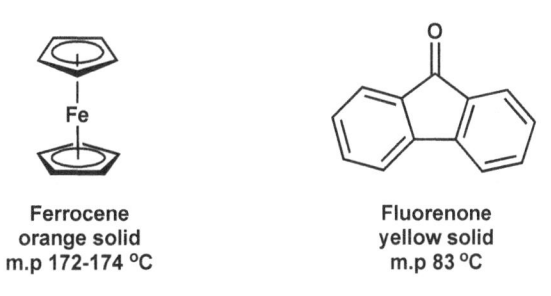

Ferrocene
orange solid
m.p 172-174 °C

Fluorenone
yellow solid
m.p 83 °C

This technique is used for preparative chromatographic separation in the research laboratory. The standard apparatus for running a column is a long glass tube that has a stopcock on one end. A small piece of cotton or glass wool should be pushed firmly into the tapered end of the column. The cotton must not be inserted so tightly that solvent is unable to flow through the column. After inserting the cotton a small amount of sand is placed on top of the cotton to prevent the adsorbent from passing through the cotton. The simplest collection system is a series of test tubes arranged in racks which can be placed under the columns in series and labeled.

The overall steps involved in column chromatography are PACK, LOAD, AND ELUTE:

- ◆ Depositing an adsorbent or stationary phase, in this case alumina, into a column. This process is often referred to as "packing a column."
- ◆ Loading your sample onto the top of the column.
- ◆ Passing a solvent or solvent mixture through the column.
- ◆ Collecting the eluants from the bottom of the column in small volumes.
- ◆ Checking each fraction for the presence of the desired compound.
- ◆ Pooling of fractions that contain only one compound and then evaporating them.

Choosing the Solvent System

Before running the chromatography column, the best solvent for proper separation is determined using TLC analysis. In theory, the difference in R_f between two spots needs to be greater than 0.3 to achieve a complete separation with one solvent system. For separation where the difference in Rf is less than 0.3, multiple solvent systems are used to create a gradient with increasing polarity.

Loading the Sample

After packing the column, you will need to load your sample onto the top of the column in as tight a band as possible. Typically, the mobile phase is drained to the level of the stationary phase, then a solution of the sample (dissolved in a minimum volume of mobile phase or less polar solvent) is carefully transferred to the top of the stationary phase without disturbing it. However, for this experiment, the sample will be transferred to the top of the mobile phase as a solid. Rinse the sample vial with a small amount of elution solvent and add it to your column carefully, using a long tipped pipette. Open the column stopcock, allowing the solvent and your sample solution to drain down to the surface of the sand, and then close the stopcock. To prevent any disturbance of the sample, add a small portion of sand to the top of the column at this point.

Eluting the Column

The column is developed by allowing the mobile phase to drain through the column at a reasonable rate. Fractions should be collected in test tubes in intervals. Be sure to label your test tubes with numbers to keep track of the fractions. The fractions should be monitored by TLC to determine the purity and effectiveness of the separation. All of the fractions containing homogeneous material (fractions containing a single spot by TLC with the same Rf) can be combined, and the solvent can be removed by evaporation. The parameters that affect separation include the type of adsorbent, the polarity of the mobile phase, the size of the column relative to the amount of material to be purified, and the rate of elution.

10.2 Prelab

Written Prelab: Record the following in your lab notebook:

- Your Name and Date
- Experiment Title
- Table of molecular structures and properties including:
  - molecular weight (MW)
  - boiling point (bp)
  - melting point (mp)
  - density (d) for liquids
- References for your property data and experiment
- A brief plan of procedure, which means "enough detail that you could perform the experiment without your laboratory manual"

compound name	structure	MW	bp	mp	d
ferrocene					
fluorenone					
petroleum ether					
diethyl ether					

Electronic Prelab: Prior to the beginning of your laboratory section, login to our Chemistry 2540 Carmen page and complete the prelabs in the labeled experimental module.

10.3 Column Chromatography—Procedure

Column Preparation

1. To a loaded buret with cotton and sand, carefully add ~20 mL of petroleum ether.
2. Using a weigh paper funnel, slowly pour the entire vial of pre-weighed alumina into the buret.

    Be sure to open the buret's stopcock slightly when you start to add the alumina. This will prevent air bubbles from being trapped inside the stationary phase.

3. After adding all the alumina, drain the petroleum ether until it is level with the top of the stationary phase.

    Draining the solvent below the top of the alumina will cause cracks in the stationary phase.

Column Loading

4. Obtain a vial containing a 50:50 mixture (by weight) of ferrocene-fluorenone. Weigh the vial full with the cap. Then, using a micro-spatula, scrape a majority of the solid off of the side-walls of the vial (it will look powdered and be free-flowing).
5. With a weigh paper funnel, pour the solid into the column onto the stationary phase. To determine the quantity transferred, weigh the vial with the cap (You do not need to get all the solid out of the vial.)
6. Using a long-tipped disposable pipette, carefully rinse the side-walls of the buret with ~1 mL of petroleum ether.

    This technique prevents disruption of the top layer of the stationary phase. Open the stopcock and drain the liquid until it is level with the top of the stationary phase.

7. Add a thin layer of protective sand to cover the top of the column. The sand acts to protect the alumina from being disturbed by solvent addition.

Column Elution

8. Fill the buret with petroleum ether and begin eluting the column. First, collect the eluting liquid in a small beaker. Once you see an orange colored band ~2 mL from the bottom of the buret, begin to collect the eluting liquid in medium sized test tubes.

    During elution, if you observe crystals forming on the outside of the buret tip, rinse these crystals into the test tube with small amounts of petroleum ether to maximize your recovery. Remember to keep adding petroleum ether to the buret until all the orange fraction has eluted out of the column. When this occurs, you will observe clear liquid draining from the buret.

9. Once the orange ferrocene has fully eluted, change the solvent to 1:1 petroleum ether – diethyl ether and elute the column. Continue to collect liquid into medium sized test tubes until all the yellow fluorenone has eluted from the column.

    You will observe clear liquid draining from the buret when this occurs.

Fractional Analysis

10. Check the fractions (solution in test tubes) individually by TLC analysis.

    Because both compounds are colored, it should be obvious which fractions contain ferrocene and which contain fluorenone. However, before combining any of the fractions, check them by TLC. Use 95:5 petroleum ether-diethyl ether as the eluent. You should be able to fit 4-6 spots on the given TLC plate. You should examine each TLC plate with a UV lamp. Make sure to circle the spots on the TLC plates under the UV lamp, and determine which test tube contains the same compound.

11. Combine the test tubes containing the same pure compound into separate 50 mL round bottom flasks, and carefully evaporate the solvent using the Buchi Rotovap.

12. Once the petroleum ether – diethyl ether solvent has evaporated, use a small amount of DCM to transfer the solid to separate, pre-weighed vials with cap. Attach the vials to the rotovap and evaporate the DCM, resulting in two vials: one containing dry ferrocene and the other containing dry fluorenone.

13. Determine the mass of pure ferrocene and pure fluorenone by reweighing the vials.

    Calculate a percent recovery for each (based on your total starting quantity)

    Mass of purified ferrocene / Mass of initial mixture 100% = percent recovery of ferrocene

    Mass of purified fluorenone / Mass of initial mixture 100% = percent recovery of fluorenone

    Mass of mixed fraction / Mass of initial mixture 100% = percent recovery of mixed fraction

10.4 Postlab Data Submission

Prepare this table of Postlab Data in your *Laboratory Notebook* after your completed experimental narrative, and fill in the appropriate data in the correct box:

		Column Chromatography			
sample	distance to spot (mm)	distance to solvent front (mm)	R$_f$ value	Experimental mass	% recovery
ferrocene/fluorenone mixture					
pure ferrocene	30	36			
pure fluorenone	11	36			
mixed fractions					

Login to our Chemistry 2540 Carmen page and complete any listed postlab assignments in the labeled experimental module. Postlab assignments are due as listed on the Course Schedule.

10.5 Digital Lab Report Guidelines

Login to our Chemistry 2540 Carmen page and download a copy of the appropriate *Digital Lab Report Template* for this experiment in the labeled experimental module. Follow the instructions listed in the *Digital Lab Report Template* with regard to the preparation of ChemDraw drawings, Formal Procedure section, and the answers to Concept Questions. Submit your completed Digital Lab Report as a Microsoft Word Document (.doc or .docx file only) or Adobe PDF to the Chemistry 2540 experiment assignment. Digital Lab Reports are due as listed on the Course Schedule, and late submissions will be penalized −10 pts per day late.

10.6 Practice Problems: Column Chromatography

1. **Column Chromatography.** The separation of the following mixture of compounds has been assigned to you. Rank the following molecules based on their expected order of elution from a chromatography column using a mixture of 95:5 petroleum ether diethyl ether as a mobile phase.

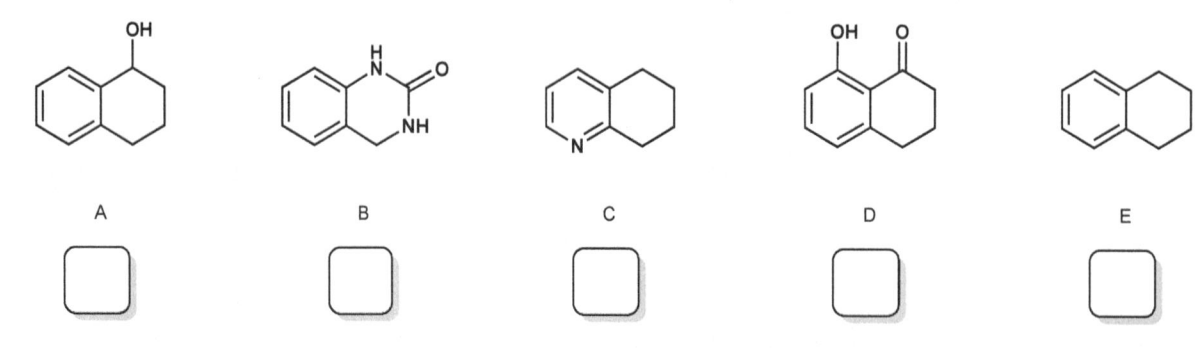

A   B   C   D   E

2. **Thin-Layer Chromatography.** You take TLC's of your fifteen test tube fractions from the above separation using 95:5 diethyl ether-petroleum ether as your TLC mobile phase and this is what you see:

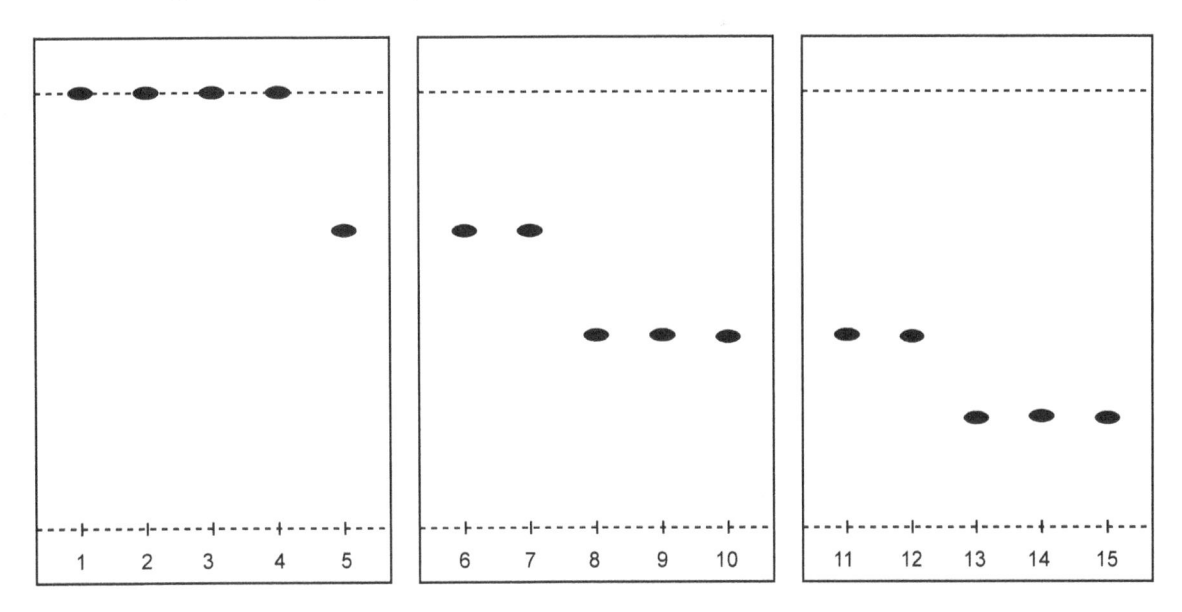

You are puzzled only 4 compounds appear to be present. Where is the 5th compound? Briefly describe your strategy to find it.

3. **Alternatives.** The above TLC plate must be viewed under a UV light since the compounds are colorless (to humans, that is). An alternative to use of UV light is to stain the TLC plate with a solution of $KMnO_4$. If this treatment stains the entire plate purple except where there are molecules that contain hydrogen-bond donors (which appear light yellow after staining), which of the compounds A–E above would you expect to appear light yellow on a TLC plate after staining with $KMnO_4$?

4. **Concept Question.** Which of the following compounds would be visible under UV light?

10.7 Study Guide—Column Chromatography

1. Understand the principles behind column chromatography.
2. Be able to describe the dry-pack method for preparing a column.
3. Know the meaning of mobile phase, stationary phase, and eluant.
4. Given to compounds, be able to predict which would pass through a given stationary phase more quickly using a given eluant.
5. Be able to describe several methods of analyzing chromatography fractions for their contents.
6. Given a series of solvents, rank them according to their polarity.
7. Be able to draw a picture on a molecular level for the types of interactions that are taking place in column chromatography.

Simple and Fractional Distillation

CHAPTER 11

Distillation is a physical method of separating mixtures based on differences on their volatilities in a boiling liquid mixture.

Distillation—Separation of a Mixture of Liquids

Distillation is one of the oldest and still most common methods for the purification of organic liquids. Distillation is a physical process used to separate chemicals from the mixture by the differences in their boiling point (how easily they vaporize).

11.1 Distillation of a Liquid

When heated, the temperature of the liquid increases until it reaches a temperature called the boiling point. With additional heating, the liquid vaporizes to the gas phase. The boiling point of a substance is a physical property. The vapor pressure of a liquid increases with temperature, and the point at which the vapor pressure equals the pressure above the liquid is defined as the boiling point. Pure liquids have well-defined, sharp boiling points. The process of distillation is to heat a substance until it vaporizes, cool the vapors, and collect the condensed liquid in a separate location. The successful application of distillation techniques depends on several factors. These include the difference in vapor pressure of the compounds present, the volume of the sample to be distilled, and the distillation apparatus. The primary principle of distillation relies on the fact that the vapor above a liquid mixture is richer in the more volatile component in the liquid, the composition being controlled by Raoult's law: The vapor pressure of an ideal solution is dependent on the vapor pressure of each chemical component and the mole fraction of the component present in the solution. The total vapor pressure (p) of a two component mixture is defined as:

$$p = p_a x_a + p_b x_b$$
p_i = vapor pressure of the pure compound
x_i = mole fraction of the component

The heating of a liquid and condensation of the resulting vapor is the basis for the purification method defined as distillation. Organic liquids that contain very small amounts of impurities are easily purified by simple distillation. A typical simple micro-distillation apparatus consists of a conical vial containing the material to be distilled (pot), a Hickman still adapter, a water jacket condenser, and an adapter to hold a thermometer. The distillation flask on the microscale setup is usually a 5-mL conical vial filled to ~2/3–3/4 of total capacity. To promote even heating, a magnetic spinvane is used to stir the liquid while it is heating on a heater/stirrer plate. This stirring of the mixture prevents any bumping (sudden violent boiling).

132 CHAPTER 11 ❖ Simple and Fractional Distillation

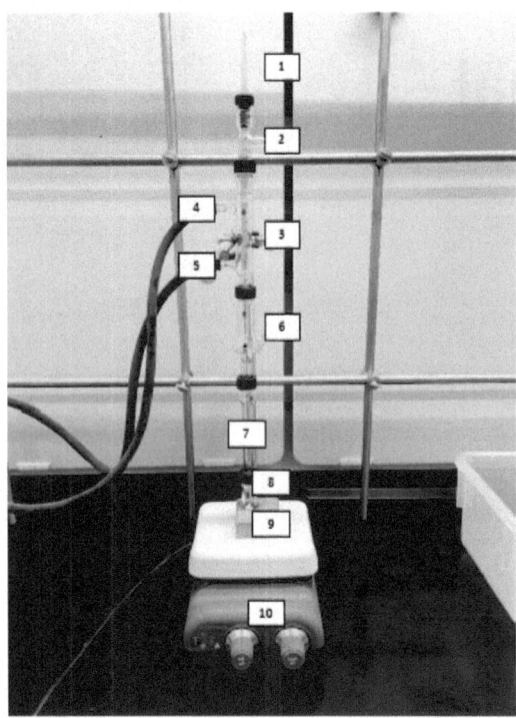

Microscale Distillation Apparatus (Fractional Distillation)
1 – Thermometer
2 – Microscale Thermometer Adapter
3 – Microscale Water Condenser
4 – Water Condenser Outlet
5 – Water Condenser Inlet
6 – Hickman Still
7 – Air Condenser
8 – Conical Vial
9 – Aluminum Block
10 – Hotplate

The conical vial connects to a Hickman still head adapter with a ground glass joint. The ground glass joints must be lined up and screwed together tightly with a black O-ring and a screw cap. If an O-ring and screw cap are not used, the vapor will escape the distillation apparatus. The condenser cools the vapor, causing it return to the liquid state, and it directs the condensing liquids into the Hickman still-head receiving flask. The most common type of condenser is the water-jacketed type in which the water supply is connected to the bottom port of the condenser with rubber tubing, and a piece of rubber tubing drains out of the top joint of the condenser and down the drain. The water always flows into the lower hose connection and out of the upper hose connection. Before turning on the water, check the hose connections to ensure that they are secure and will not come off. You can secure the rubber hose by wrapping a small piece of copper wire around the joint where the hose and glass are connected. The water flow needs to be slow and constant.

The amount of heat to apply is determined by the rate of distillation; the best procedure is to heat slowly. The liquid should gently bubble and vaporize. As vapor rises from the liquid, it moves up the apparatus, raising the temperature of the apparatus. The vapor will fill the distillation flask and most of the distillation head. The thermometer bulb should be surrounded and covered in vapors. If vapor creeps past the thermometer bulb without contacting it, the measured boiling point will be low. The vapor condenses in the condenser and then drips down into the collection bulb in the Hickman still head. If the rate of distillation is too rapid, the measured boiling point is likely to be inaccurate and the purity of the liquid will be compromised.

11.2 Distillation of Mixtures

The plot produced by plotting the boiling points of ethanol-butanol mixtures versus their compositions is shown below. Note that the curve represents the boiling point for any mixture of butanol and ethanol. The x axis represents the mole fraction of butanol in the mixture. The mole fraction of ethanol can be determined by the formula (1- mole fraction butanol). For example, if you have a 0.2 mole fraction of butanol, you have a 0.8 mole fraction of ethanol. Remember also that the boiling point of the mixture remains in between the boiling points of the pure compounds. To determine the boiling point of the mixture, you must first find the corresponding mole fraction of interest and then read the temperature on the y axis that corresponds to that mixture composition on the curve. For example, a 0.4 mole fraction of butanol: 0.6 mole fraction of ethanol. The boiling point of that mixture is 88 °C.

As the mixture starts to boil, vapors form and are isolated and analyzed for composition. The principle behind distillation suggests that the vapor phase will be enriched in the lower boiling point liquid. The boiling points of the mixtures versus the vapor compositions of the mixtures are plotted in Figure 11.2. The curve represents the composition of the vapor above a boiling mixture. For example, a mixture that is 0.5 butanol and boils at 88 °C and the composition of the vapor above the liquid is 0.82 mole fraction in ethanol.

If we plot both the liquid composition and the vapor composition versus temperature on the same set of coordinates, the result is called a boiling point composition diagram for ethanol/butanol mixtures. The lower curve is the composition of the liquid versus boiling point (bp) and the upper curve is the composition of the vapor versus boiling point. A diagram of this nature helps to visualize and explain what occurs during distillation of a mixture. For example, if you have a 0.5 mole fraction in ethanol and the mixture begins to boil at 91 °C, the composition of the vapor is 0.82 mole fraction in ethanol. Condensing the liquids of the vapors affords a liquid which is enriched in the higher boiling compound. As the distillation progresses, the boiling mixture becomes more enriched in butanol and the boiling point increases. The amount of butanol in the vapor will also start to increase as the distillation proceeds, and toward the end of the distillation, the vapor will be nearly pure butanol.

The primary message: The vapor above a liquid mixture is enriched in the more volatile component.

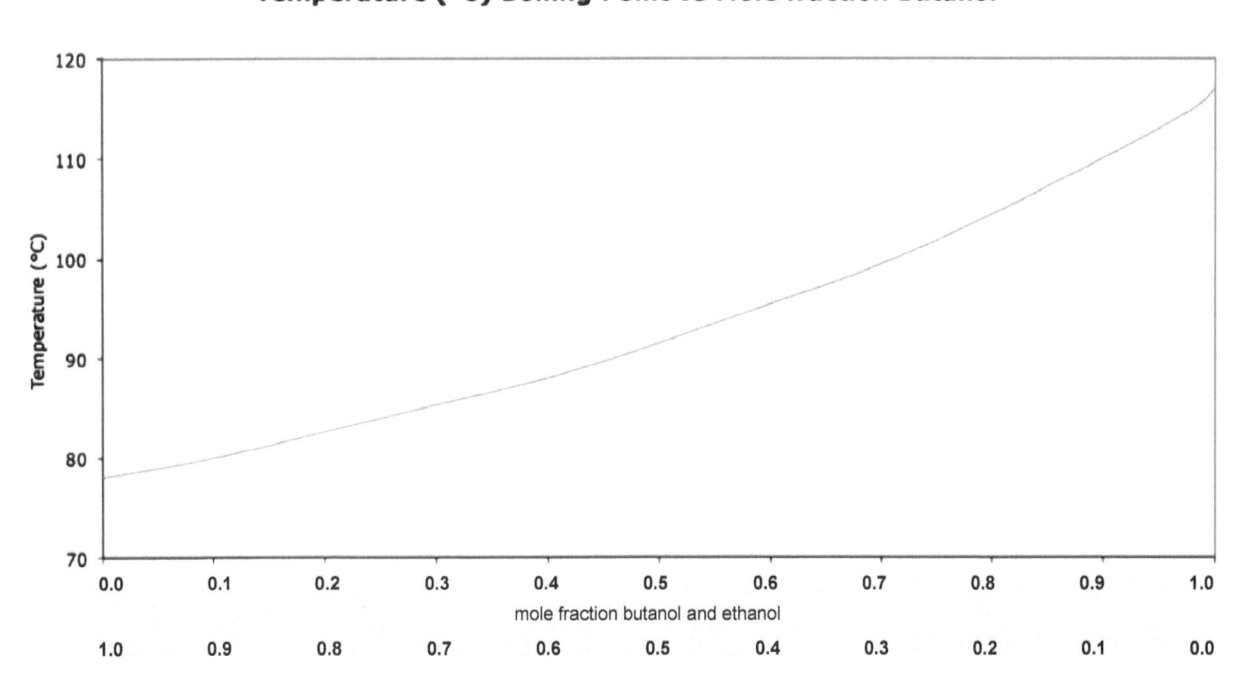

Figure 11.1 Boiling Points of Ethanol and Butanol Mixtures.

134 CHAPTER 11 ❖ Simple and Fractional Distillation

Figure 11.2 Vapor Composition of Ethanol and Butanol Mixtures Plot.

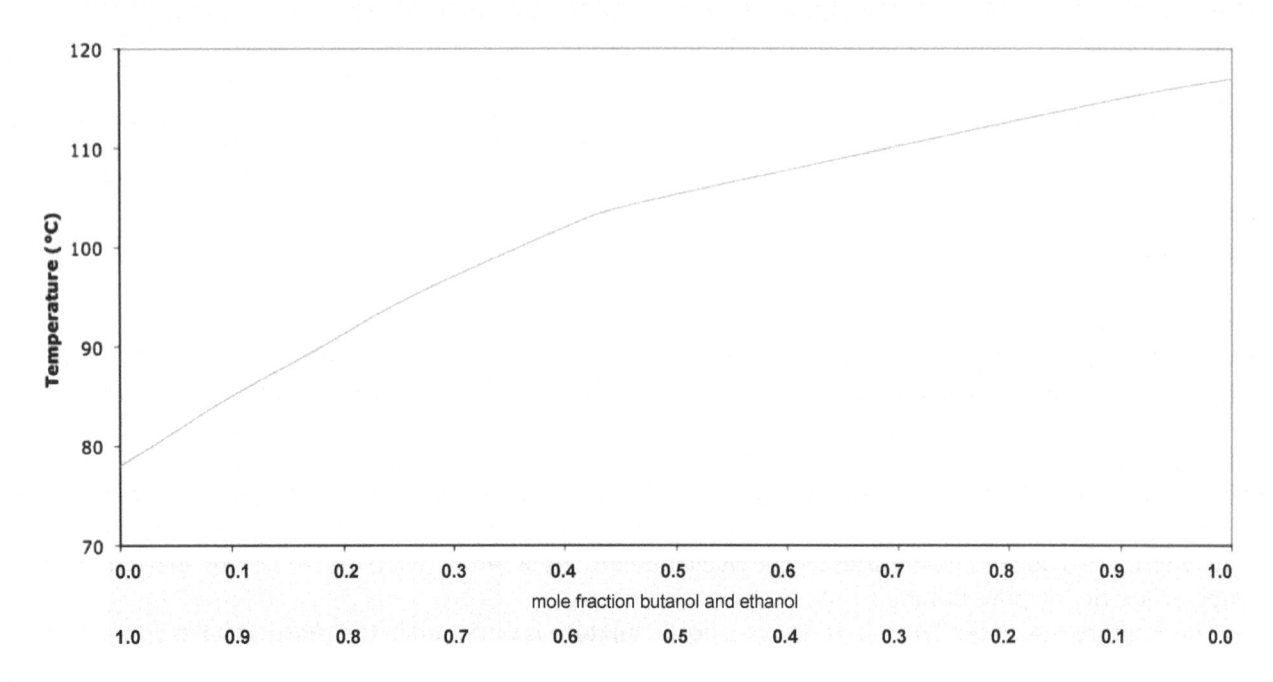

Mixture of Ethanol and Butanol
Temperature (°C) Vapor Pressure vs mole fraction butanol

Figure 11.3 Phase Composition Plot for Butanol and Ethanol Mixtures.

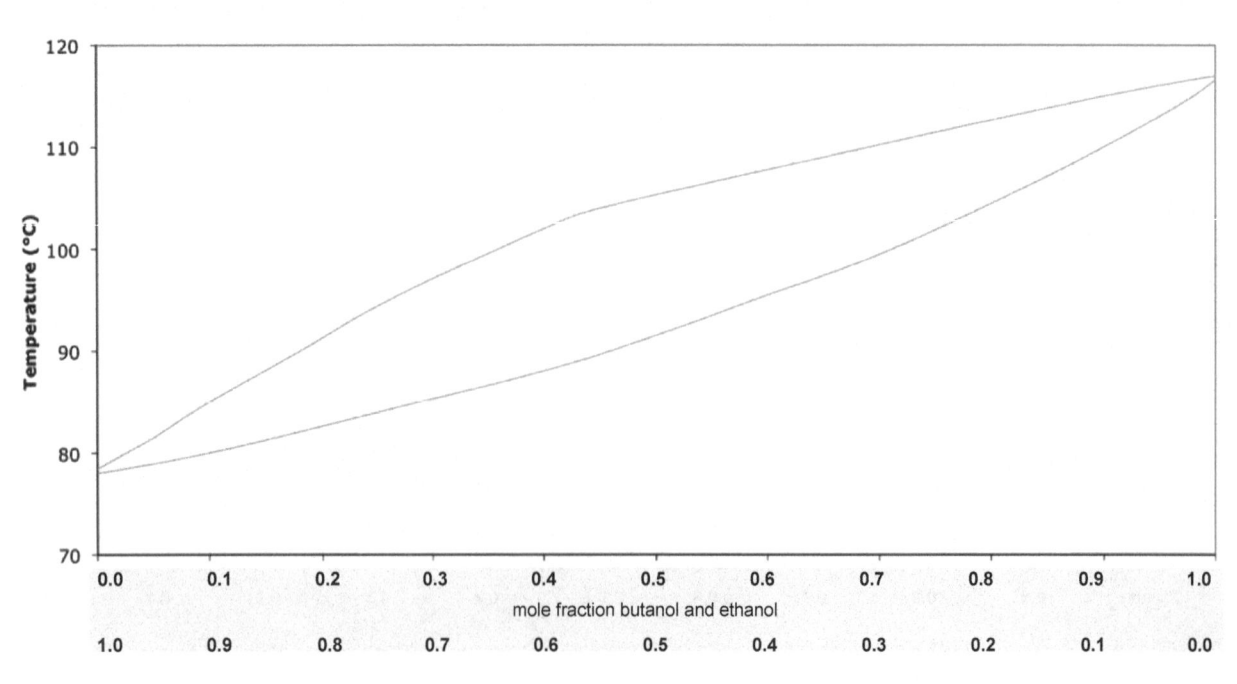

Butanol and Ethanol Mixture Boiling Point Composition Diagram
Temperature (°C) vs mole fraction butanol

11.3 Simple Distillation vs. Fractional Distillation

A simple distillation is limited because it can be used only to separate two components that have a very large difference in boiling points. It also can be used to purify a substance that has a very small amount of impurities present that have a lower boiling point. Simple distillation fails to purify materials that are severely contaminated in one distillation. The process enhances the purity of the lower-boiling-point component, but does not improve it to the desired 100 percent. With multiple simple distillations, the compound could be greatly purified, but that would require a great deal of time and effort and would be inefficient. To efficiently separate volatile liquids, a technique called fractional distillation is used. This achieves separation by allowing for a greater distance between the distillation pot and the collection vessel. This increased distance allows for an equilibrium to be set up between the liquid and vapor in the path the vapor travels before it is collected. In effect, this constant equilibrium of vapor to liquid over a long distance makes fractional distillation much more efficient, because it is essentially like carrying out multiple successive simple distillations. The apparatus used for fractional distillation is similar to the apparatus for simple distillation. The only major difference is that the distance between the distillation pot and the collection head is increased. The length of the column, and if there is material present within, is the major factor in determining the degree of separation that can be achieved.

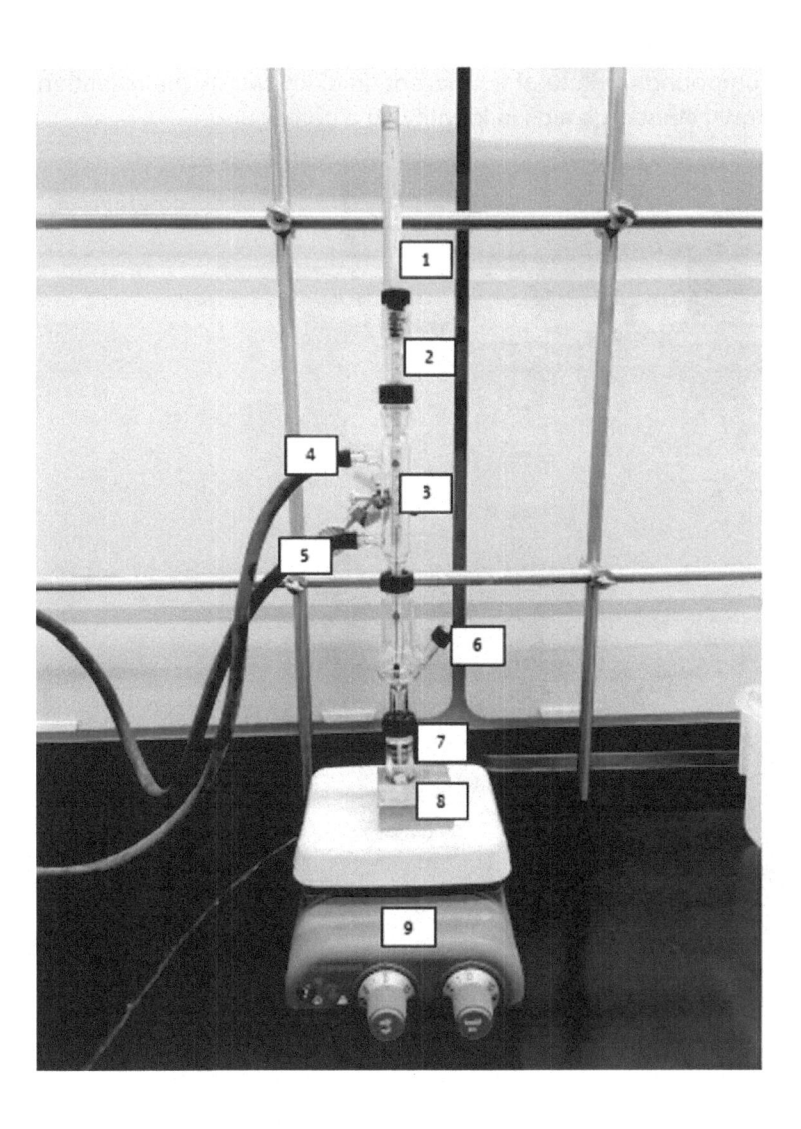

Microscale Distillation Apparatus (Simple Distillation)

1 – Thermometer
2 – Microscale Thermometer Adapter
3 – Microscale Water Condenser
4 – Water Condenser Outlet
5 – Water Condenser Inlet
6 – Hickman Still
7 – Conical Vial
8 – Aluminum Block
9 – Hotplate

136 CHAPTER 11 ❖ Simple and Fractional Distillation

The other factor that determines the degree of separation that can be achieved is the rate at which the distillation is carried out. The best separations are achieved using a slow and steady rate. A slow distillation rate maximizes the number of vaporizations and condensations that can take place in the fractionating column. Also, to maintain a constant temperature, the column can be insulated with aluminum foil, glass wool, or other materials. If the temperature of the column fluctuates widely, it becomes difficult to maintain a slow, constant distillation rate.

11.4 Gas Chromatography

Gas chromatography (GC) is a chromatographic technique used in the chemistry lab for separating and analyzing compounds in the gas phase. GC allows for the determination of purity of a substance by analyzing the relative quantities of components in a given mixture. GC also allows you to identify the compounds in a given mixture. The instrument used in gas chromatography is a gas chromatograph. A picture of the gas chromatograph we will use in lab in shown below. There are several components to a gas chromatograph, which include: a mobile phase (usually helium gas), an oven to allow all components to stay in the gas phase, a column that contains a stationary phase and a detector. The stationary phase is liquid or polymer absorbed onto a solid support inside of a piece of metal tubing called a column. When a sample is injected into the GC, it will interact with the walls inside the column. Because each compound interacts differently with the stationary phase, this causes each compound to elute at a different time, known as the retention time. The comparison of retention times to known standards aids in identifying a compound.

Gas Chromatograph

In gas chromatography, a small amount of sample (1–2 uL) is drawn up into a micro syringe. The syringe needle is placed into a hot injector port of the gas chromatograph, and the plunger of the needle is depressed to inject the sample. The injector is set to a temperature higher than the components' boiling points to vaporize them into the gas phase. The carrier gas or mobile phase flows through the injector and pushes the gaseous components into the GC column that is inside the oven. When the components are within the column, the separation of the components takes place. The molecules partition between the carrier gas and the stationary phase. After the components move through the GC column at different rates, they reach the detector. The detector sends a signal to the chart recorder which results in a peak on the chart paper. The area of the peak is proportional to the number of molecules generating the signal.

Analysis of the Gas Chromatograph

The data that can be obtained from the gas chromatograph are the retention times of the peaks and the area of the peaks. The number of peaks on the chromatograph correspond to the number of compounds in your sample. The order of the peaks in the chromatogram usually correspond to the compounds in order of lowest to highest boiling point. To determine the percentage composition, the area under each curve needs to be determined using the following formula:

$$\text{Area} = (\text{height}) \times (\text{width @ 1/2 height})$$

The height and width @ 1/2 height can be measured using a centimeter ruler. You should measure the peak heights to the nearest millimeter. Once the area of each peak is calculated, the area can be converted to the percentage composition of each individual compound. We will assume that each component of the mixture causes the same response in the detector. Therefore, the areas under the curves can be used to calculate the percent composition directly.

$$\text{Percentage Composition of Component 1} = [\text{area of Component 1} / \text{total area}] \times 100\%$$

Retention time (t_R) can be calculated by the following method by measuring from the t = 0 mark on the chromatogram to the center of the peak on the horizontal axis. This distance should be measured to the nearest millimeter. The distance measured can be converted into a time using the following equation:

$$\text{Distance to Component 1 (cm)} / [\text{Chart Paper Speed (cm)}] = \text{Retention Time}$$

The retention time should be the same value for each individual component on each of the injections. The retention time is constant for the compounds based on the parameters of the gas chromatograph. Adjusting any of the parameters of the gas chromatograph will cause a change in retention time. The main parameters for a gas chromatograph are flow rate and oven temperature. For example, increasing the carrier gas (mobile phase) flow rate will decrease the retention time because the compounds will move through the stationary phase at a faster rate. The other variable of temperature will have a similar effect. If you were to increase the oven temperature, the retention times for the components in the mixture would decrease.

138 CHAPTER 11 ❖ Simple and Fractional Distillation

An example chromatogram with all of the measurements described above is shown below:

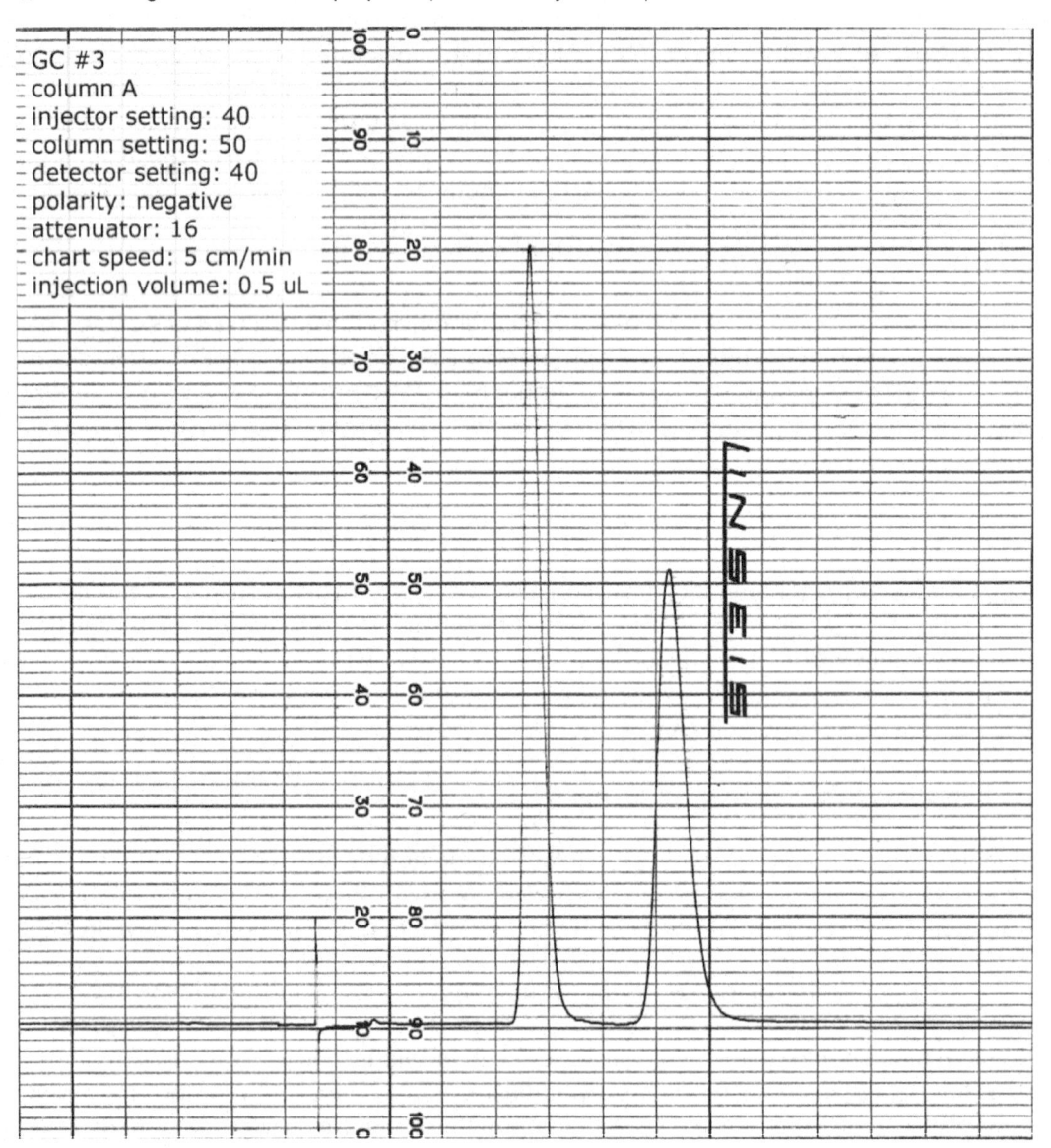

Figure 11A. Chromatogram of THF and n-propanol (1:1 mixture by volume).

```
GC #3
column A
injector setting: 40
column setting: 50
detector setting: 40
polarity: negative
attenuator: 16
chart speed: 5 cm/min
injection volume: 0.5 uL
```

CHAPTER 11 ❖ Simple and Fractional Distillation 139

Figure 11B. Chromatogram of THF and n-propanol (1:1 mixture by volume) with measurements. (Note: one grid cell is 10 mm wide and 2 mm tall).

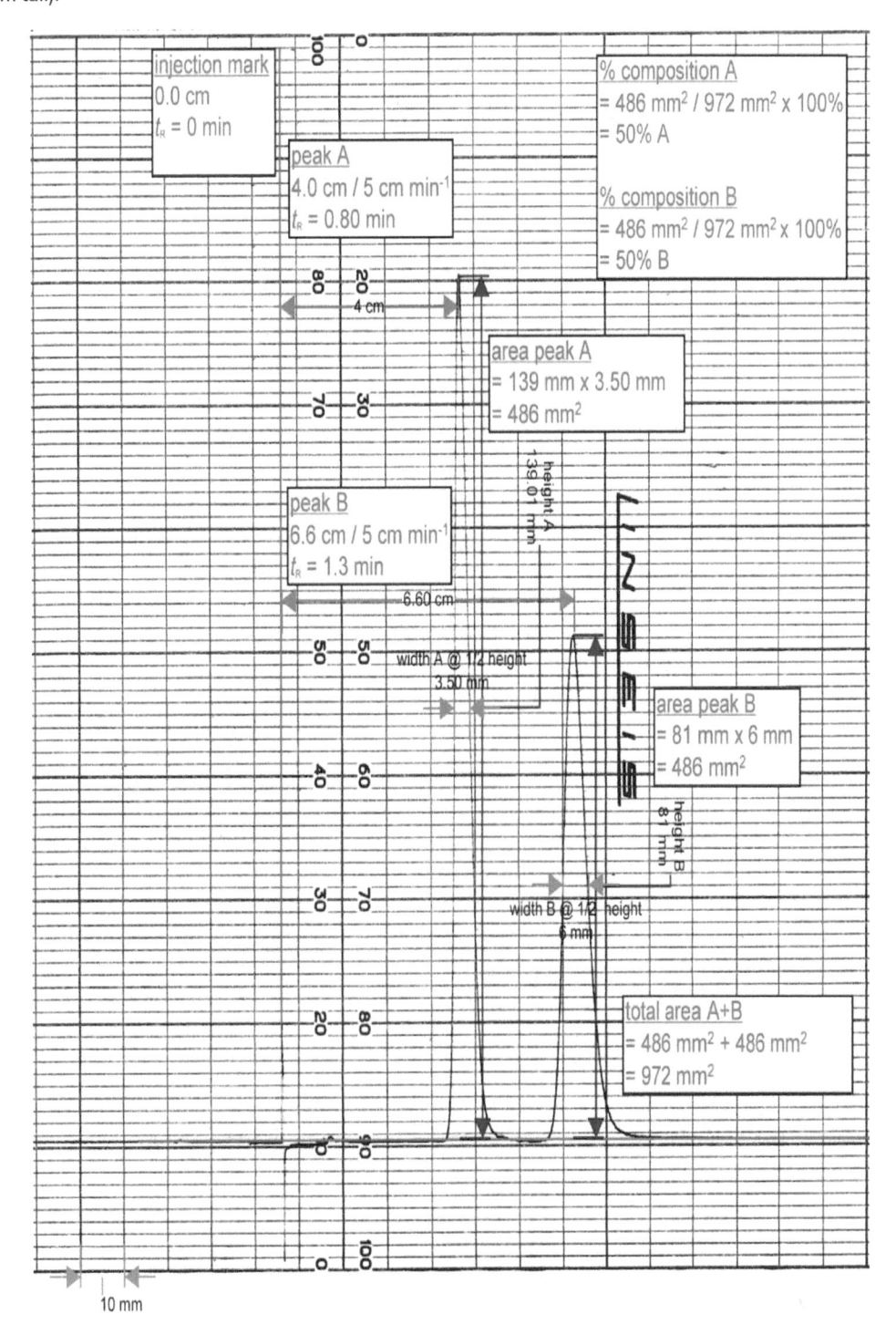

injection mark
0.0 cm
t_R = 0 min

peak A
4.0 cm / 5 cm min^{-1}
t_R = 0.80 min

% composition A
= 486 mm^2 / 972 mm^2 x 100%
= 50% A

% composition B
= 486 mm^2 / 972 mm^2 x 100%
= 50% B

4 cm

area peak A
= 139 mm x 3.50 mm
= 486 mm^2

height A
139.01 mm

peak B
6.6 cm / 5 cm min^{-1}
t_R = 1.3 min

6.60 cm

width A @ 1/2 height
3.50 mm

area peak B
= 81 mm x 6 mm
= 486 mm^2

height B
81 mm

width B @ 1/2 height
6 mm

total area A+B
= 486 mm^2 + 486 mm^2
= 972 mm^2

10 mm

Gas Chromatography Injection Instructions

To take a GC of a sample in the liquid phase, a glass syringe must be used to make the injection.

1. Condition the syringe with your sample. To do this, withdraw 5–7 uL of your sample using the syringe, then quickly shoot the sample out onto the KimWipe or paper towel lying in front of the machine. Repeat this process 2 times.
2. Properly load the sample into the syringe.
    a. Ensure that you have withdrawn the proper injection volume (typically 1 μL when using the glass syringe)
    b. There should be no air bubbles in the middle of the sample as this will lead to errors in its processing. A small air bubble at the top of the sample is OK.

    The easiest way to load the syringe is to draw up ~5 uL into the syringe barrel while the needle tip is submerged in the solution. Depress the plunger while maintaining the needle tip within the solution and then withdraw ~5 uL a second time. Repeat as needed. This will remove the air bubbles from the barrel. Once the syringe is free of air bubbles, you can depress the plunger down to the 1 uL needed for the injection.
3. Turn on the plotter to the appropriate chart speed before injecting your sample. (1 mm/sec or 1 cm/min)
4. When preparing to inject the sample, it is suggested that you use one hand to inject the sample by pressing the plunger and the other hand to steady the end of the syringe above the needle. You should not feel any resistance when inserting the needle into the injection port. If this occurs, carefully remove the needle and try inserting it again. *The needle is extremely fragile and expensive, so this cautionary measure is important.*
    a. The injection port is typically very hot, so be careful not to burn yourself when injecting the sample into the machine.
5. To inject the sample into the gas chromatograph, the needle should be perpendicular to the injection port. Insert the needle completely into the injection port so it is flush against the machine. Depress the barrel and tap the side-port that corresponds to the column that you are using. This action records a tick mark on the chromatogram. This tick mark ($t = 0$) is important for accurate R_t calculations. After tapping the side port, you can remove the syringe from the gas chromatograph.
6. After the appropriate number of peaks are recorded, you may turn off the detector and advance the paper to speed up the process. While your samples are being processed, you can condition the syringe with the next sample or pass the syringe on to the next student.

Reminders

- The screw at the top of the plunger can be loosened and tightened as necessary so that the sample can be easily loaded.
- If the recorded peaks run off the chromatogram, prepare another sample with a smaller injection volume. *The height of the peaks correspond to the injection volume.*

Figure 11C. Poor Quality Chromatogram: Contaminated syringe and low peak concentration.

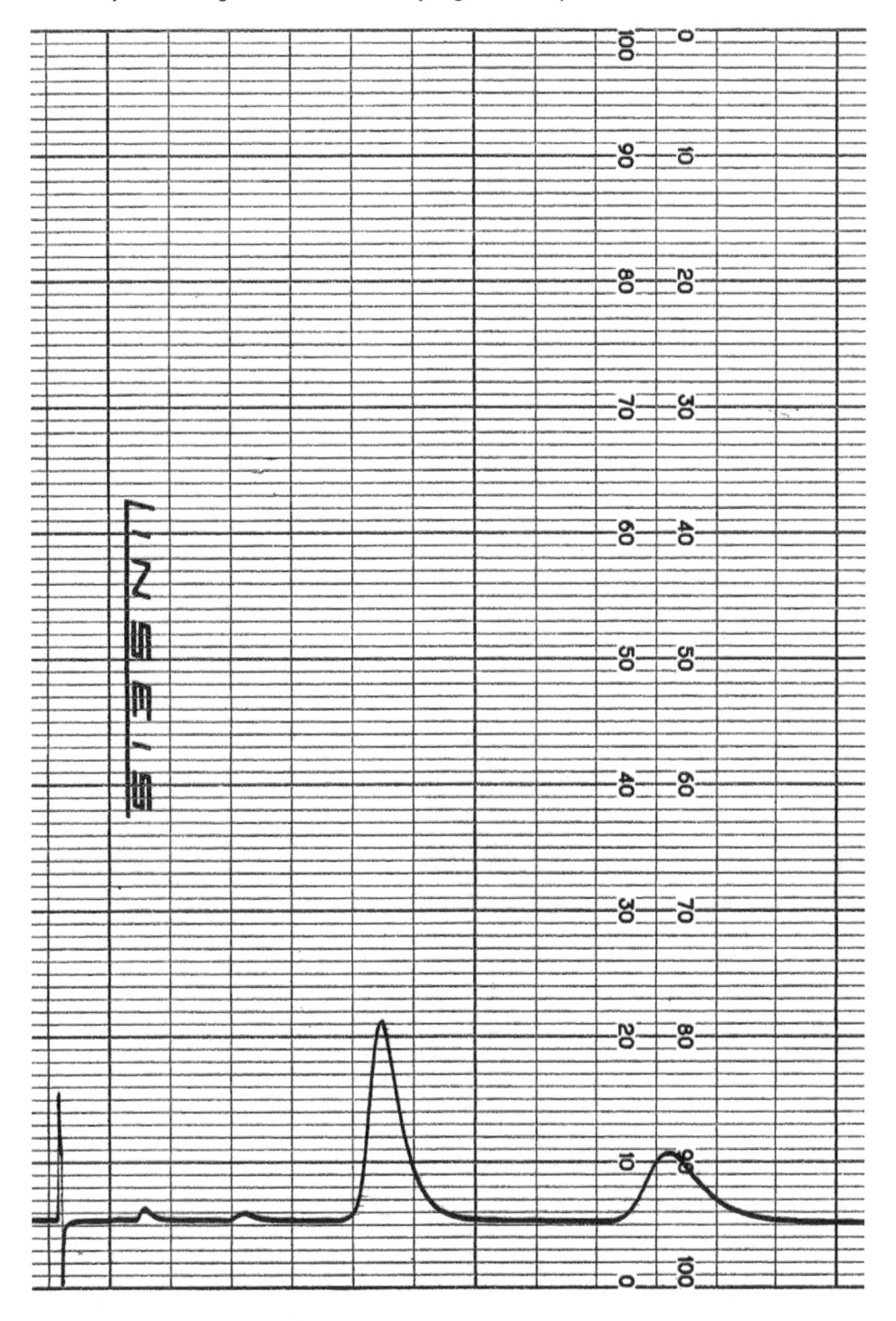

Figure 11D. Poor Quality Chromatogram: Contaminated syringe, peak shelving, and zero-baseline knob disturbance.

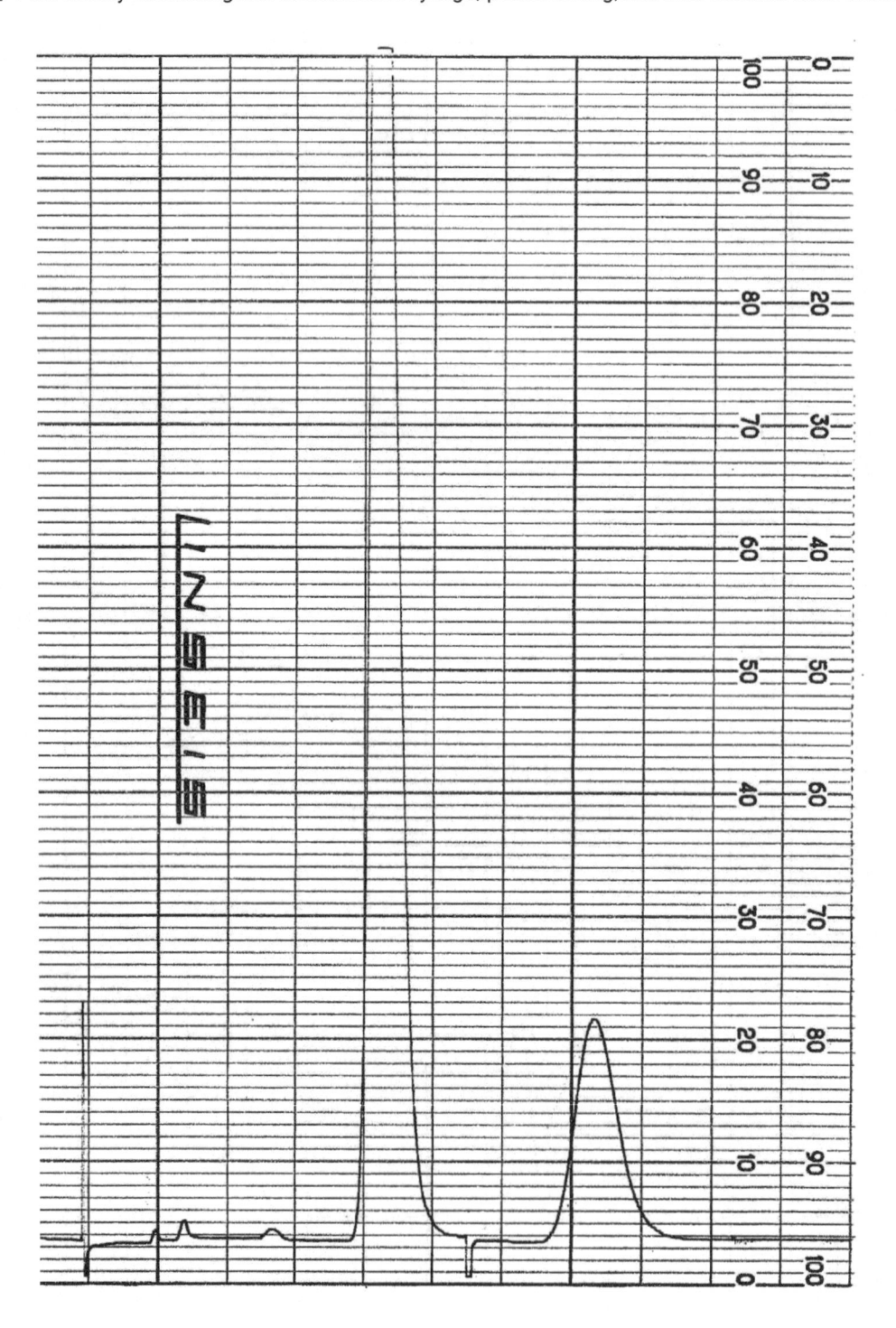

CHAPTER 11 ❖ Simple and Fractional Distillation 143

Figure 11E. Poor Quality Chromatogram: Multiple injection marker touches and double injection.

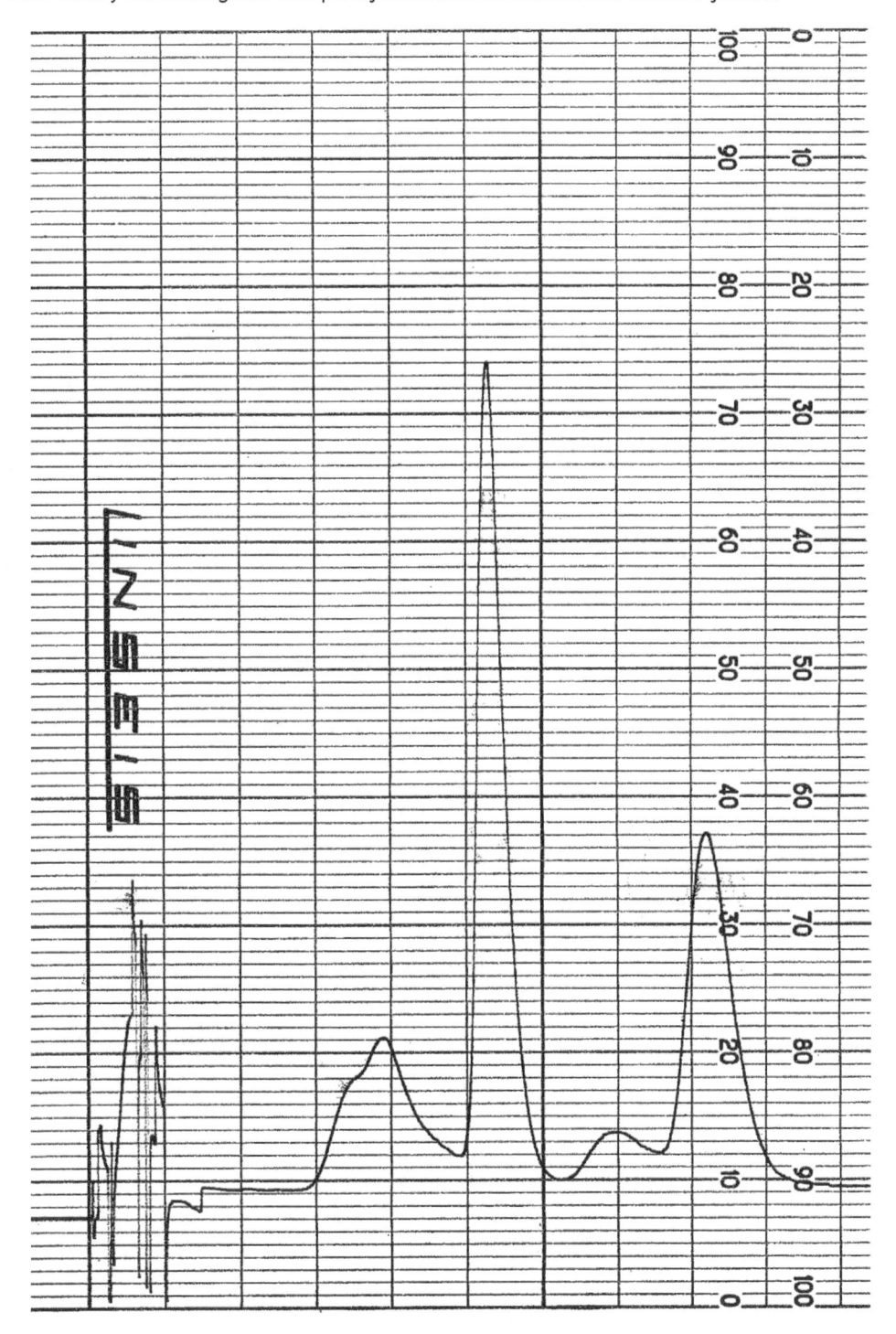

11.5 Prelab

Written Prelab: Record the following in your lab notebook:

- Your Name and Date
- Experiment Title
- Table of molecular structures and properties including:
  - molecular weight (MW)
  - boiling point (bp)
  - melting point (mp)
  - density (d) for liquids
- References for your property data and experiment
- A brief plan of procedure, which means "enough detail that you could perform the experiment without your laboratory manual"

compound name	structure	MW	bp	mp	d
pentane					
cyclohexane					
toluene					
o-xylene					
tetrahydrofuran					
1-propanol					

Electronic Prelab: Prior to the beginning of your laboratory section, login to our Chemistry 2540 Carmen page and complete the prelabs in the labeled experimental module.

11.6 Distillation and Gas Chromatography—Procedure

GOALS:

1. Separate a two-component organic mixture (1:1, tetrahydrofuran and 1-propanol) by microscale simple distillation. The quality of the separation will be determined using gas chromatography.
2. Separate a two-component organic mixture (1:1, unknown composition) using a microscale fractional distillation. The quality of the separation will be determined using gas chromatography.
3. Identify the components within your unknown mixture using retention time data. (Potential components are pentane, ethyl acetate, methylcyclohexane, and toluene.)

Based on the semester, your TA will instruct you on which portion of the experiment to do.

Part 1: Simple Distillation

In this part of the experiment, you will evaluate the separation efficiency of a simple distillation on a 1:1 (by volume) mixture of tetrahydrofuran and 1-propanol. You will analyze your simple distillation composition of distillate and pot residue by gas chromatography (GC).

Procedure:

1. **Set up and Heating:** Transfer 3 mL of the 1:1 (by volume) mixture to a 5-mL conical vial. Set up the simple distillation as shown in the picture below. Heat the mixture slowly to perform a simple distillation. The approximate initial temperature setting on your heater stirrer is 3.

    Conduct the distillation until you have collected ~1 mL of distillate and then stop. **Note the boiling range of your distillate.** *Early in the distillation, visually observe the "distillation front" (condensing vapors on the interior of the glass). If the "front" stays in one place and does not move up the distillation column for a period of 10 minutes, you should increase the setting on your hot plate to 4.*

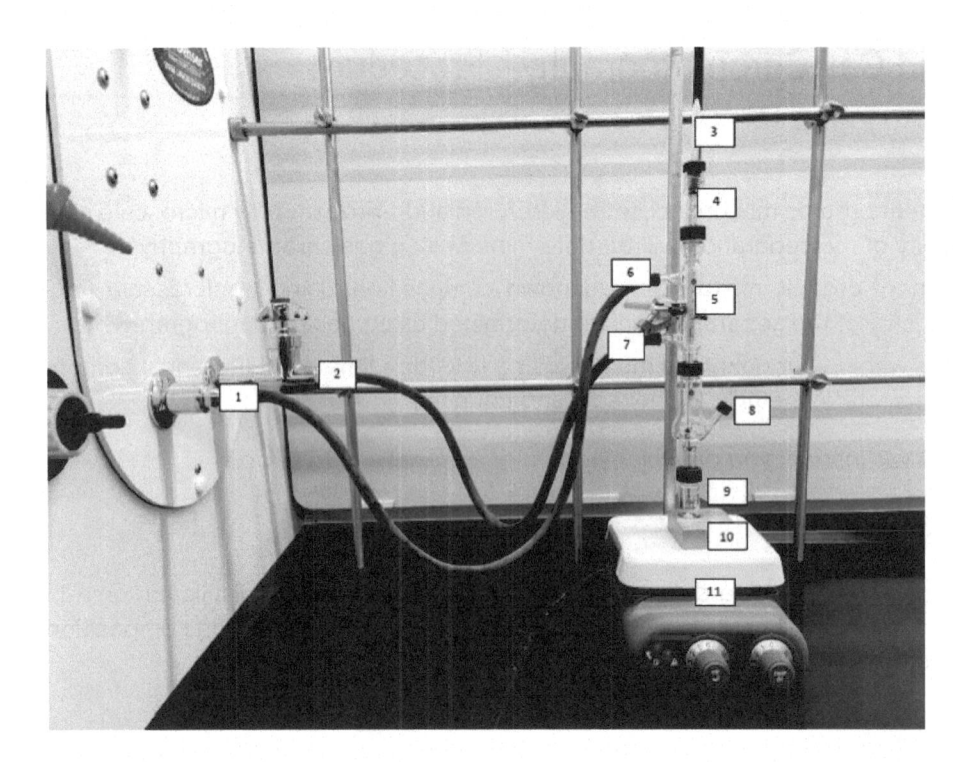

146 CHAPTER 11 ❖ Simple and Fractional Distillation

Microscale Distillation Apparatus
(Simple Distillation)
1 – Ecodenser Inlet
2 – Ecodenser Outlet
3 – Thermometer
4 – Microscale Thermometer Adapter
5 – Microscale Water Condenser
6 – Water Condenser Outlet
7 – Water Condenser Inlet
8 – Hickman Still
9 – Conical Vial
10 – Aluminum Block
11 – Hotplate

2. **Distillate and Pot Removal:** Once your distillation is complete, use a glass pipette to remove the liquid from the still reservoir. Let the apparatus cool and then remove the liquid left in the pot to a labeled vial.

   Caution: Tetrahydrofuran and 1-propanol should not be allowed to come into contact with the hot plate or the hot sand bath. Do not burn yourself. Do not touch the hot plate or aluminum block when they are hot. Allow the heater-stirrers and heating blocks to cool so that they can be handled without burning before returning them to their proper location.

3. **Gas Chromatographic Analysis (GC) of Distillate and Pot Residue:** With the assistance of your teaching assistant, run a GC of your distillate and your pot residue. THE GC SYRINGES ARE VERY DELICATE AND MUST BE HANDLED CAREFULLY. Your teaching assistant will provide assistance in making injections. Make sure to clearly label your chromatograms. You should watch the video on Carmen and read the previous section in preparation for this part of the experiment.

Part 2: Fractional Distillation

The possible unknowns for Part 2 are any two of the following compounds: pentane, ethyl acetate, methylcyclohexane, and toluene. Be sure to record the identifier of your unknown; you will need this to submit your Post-Lab.

1. **Set-up:** Transfer ~4.5 mL of the unknown mixture assigned to you into a 5-mL conical vial. Set up the fractional distillation as shown in the picture below. Heat the mixture slowly to perform a fractional distillation. The approximate initial temperature setting on your heater stirrer is 3.

   You will probably need to insulate the apparatus with aluminum foil, from the top of the conical vial to the thermometer area in the Hickman still.

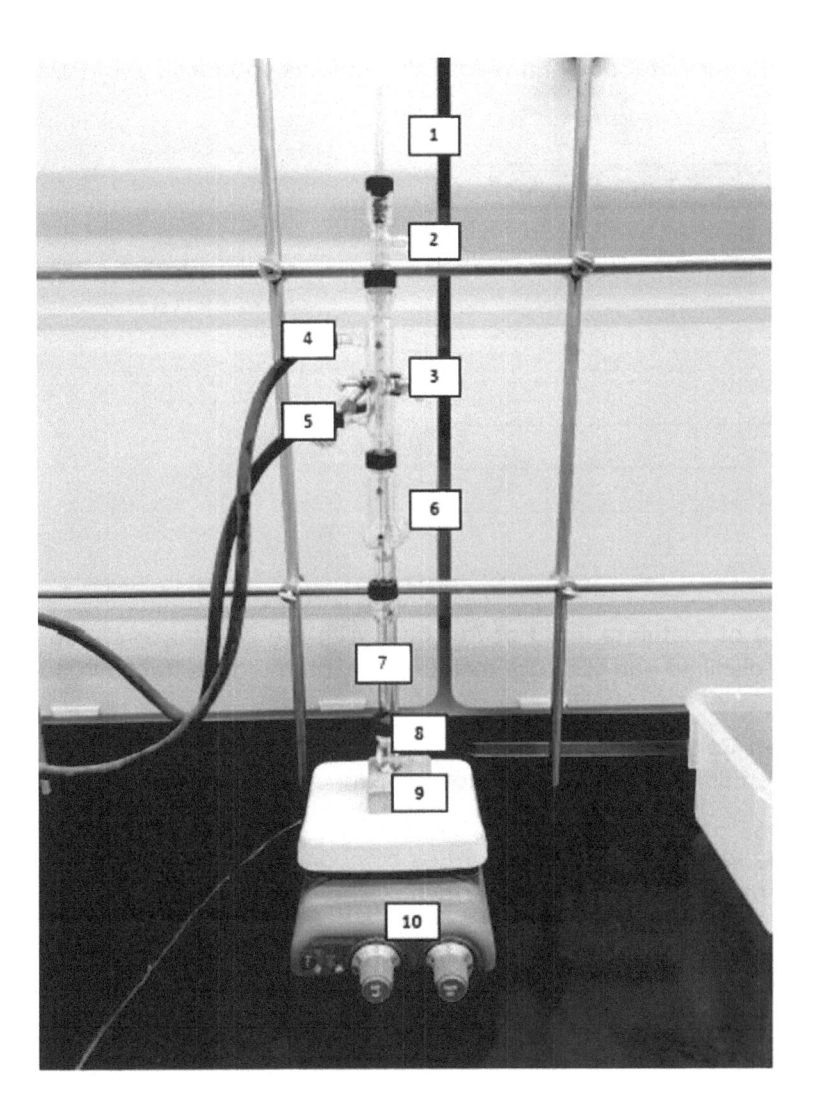

Microscale Distillation Apparatus (Fractional Distillation)

1 – Thermometer
2 – Microscale Thermometer Adapter
3 – Microscale Water Condenser
4 – Water Condenser Outlet
5 – Water Condenser Inlet
6 – Hickman Still
7 – Air Condenser
8 – Conical Vial
9 – Aluminum Block
10 – Hotplate

2. **Distillate Removal:** Once you have collected approximately 0.5 mL of distillate in the still reservoir, withdraw it via pipette into the vial labeled "initial 0.5 mL fraction" and cap the vial. Be sure to record the boiling point at which this distillate was collected.

3. **Temperature Analysis:** Continue the distillation, recording the temperature upon collection of each subsequent 0.5 mL (these subsequent fractions should be combined in your graduated cylinder and set aside). When there is only a small amount of material (~0.5 mL) left in the pot, stop the distillation. Let the apparatus cool and then remove the liquid left in the pot to a vial labeled pot residue.

Make sure you are monitoring and recording the temperature in your notebook at 0.5-mL intervals.

Construct a Distillation Table like this in your notebook and record this data as you distill your Part 2 Unknown Mixture

mL collected	T (°C) at collection
0.5	
1.0	
1.5	
2.0	
2.5	
3.0	
3.5	
4.0	

4. **Gas Chromatographic Analysis (GC) of Distillate and Pot Residue:** With the assistance of your teaching assistant, run a GC of your distillate and your pot residue. The intermediate fractions do not need to be analyzed by GC.
5. **Determine Identification of Unknown Components:** You will need to compare the retention times of your two unknowns to the retention times of the four unknown mixture GC completed by your teaching assistant.

    Based on the information you know about how GC separates components and order of elution, you should be able to determine the identity of your two unknowns. **The boiling points recorded should not be used to identify the unknowns.**

Waste Disposal

When you have completed the experiment, ALL of your fractions should be disposed of in the organic waste beaker.

11.7 Postlab Data Submission

Login to our Chemistry 2540 Carmen page and complete any listed postlab assignments in the labeled experimental module. Postlab assignments are due as listed on the Course Schedule.

11.8 Digital Lab Report Guidelines

Login to our Chemistry 2540 Carmen page and download a copy of the appropriate *Digital Lab Report Template* for this experiment in the labeled experimental module. Follow the instructions listed in the *Digital Lab Report Template* with regard to the preparation of ChemDraw drawings, Formal Procedure section, and the answers to Concept Questions. Submit your completed Digital Lab Report as a Microsoft Word Document (.doc or .docx file only) or Adobe PDF to the Chemistry 2540 experiment assignment. Digital Lab Reports are due as listed on the Course Schedule, and late submissions will be penalized −10 pts per day late.

11.9 Practice Problems

1. **Gas Chromatography.** Answer the following questions about retention times of the following compounds given: naphthalene (boiling point = 218°C), phenol (boiling point = 181.7°C), and toluene (boiling point = 110.6°C).

   a. List the order of elution for the above compounds from the GC?

   b. What will happen to the retention time if the flow rate is increased?

   c. What will happen to the retention time if the temperature of the column is increased?

   d. You calculate the following peak areas from your GC chromatogram what are the percentages of each compound?

   e. Calculate the retention times for the following components from the following information. Component A = 7.6 cm, Component B = 10.4 cm, Component C = 12.9 cm. Chart speed = 1.5 cm/min.

   f. You have access to the following information and supplies in the lab: An unknown sample, a mixture of 4 known compounds (one of the components corresponds to your unknown), and a list of four compounds in the mixture and their boiling points. A GC with plotter attached that will only allow you to make ONE injection and obtain ONE chromatogram. How could you determine the unknown sample identity?

CHAPTER 11 ❖ Simple and Fractional Distillation

2. Which compound of each set has the highest and lowest boiling point? Describe the factors that mitigate these values.

A   CH₄   CH₃CH₃   CH₃CH₂CH₃   CH₃CH₂CH₂CH₃

B   CH₃Cl   CH₂Cl₂   CHCl₃   CCl₄

C (n-heptane)   (2,3-dimethylbutane)   (2,2,3-trimethylbutane)

D (diethyl ether)   (propanol)   (acetic acid, H₃C-COOH)   (acetic anhydride, H₃C-CO-O-CO-CH₃... acetone H₃C-CO-CH₃)

E (hydroquinone, 1,4-dihydroxybenzene)   (4-methoxyphenol with OCH₃ para)   (4-methoxyphenol)   (phenol)   (anisole)

F (toluene)   (o-phenylenediamine)   (phenol)   (thiophenol)   (phenylphosphine)

3. Examine the chromatogram shown below and answer the following questions.

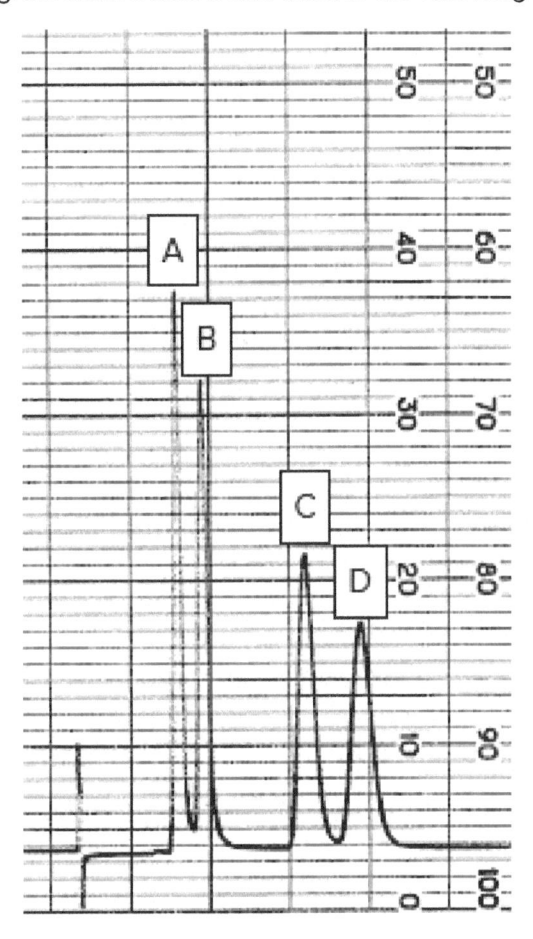

a. Which compound has the longest retention time?
b. Which compound has a higher boiling point: B or C?
c. Which compound would elute from the GC second?
d. Assume the structures below are present in the chromatogram. Assign A-D.

e. Assume the structures below are present in the chromatogram. Assign A-D.

11.10 Study Guide

Distillation

1. Know what is meant by a boiling point, pot, condenser, fractionating column, and fraction.
2. Given a phase diagram, be able to predict the composition of vapors above a liquid that boils at a given temperature, and be able to predict the boiling point of the liquid that results from condensation of that vapor.
3. Understand the glassware that is involved in the assembly of a simple and fractional distillation apparatus.
4. Draw a picture at the molecular level of a compound when it is boiling.

Gas Chromatography

1. Understand what is meant by the mobile phase (carrier gas) and the stationary phase.
2. Understand what is meant by retention time and know how to calculate it.
3. Understand the effects that column temperature, carrier gas flow rate, and boiling points of sample components have on retention times.
4. Given a GC trace, be able to determine the relative amounts of components; be able to determine the retention time of components.
5. Draw a picture at the molecular level for a compound interacting with the GC column.

Synthesis of Aspirin

CHAPTER 12

12.1 Introduction

Anhydrides are generated from carboxylic acids using either high temperature or a suitable dehydrating agent. Anhydrides are unstable, and anhydrides will quickly recombine with any available water to regenerate a carboxylic acid.

Anhydrides react readily with nucleophiles to form substitution products. Nucleophilic substitution reactions of anhydrides are similar to other nucleophilic acyl substitution reactions of carboxylic acid derivatives. Specifically, nucleophilic attachment occurs at one carbonyl group, while the second carbonyl group becomes part of the leaving group.

CHAPTER 12 ❖ Synthesis of Aspirin

Anhydrides combine with a range of nucleophiles to create a variety of acyl substitution products but always result in a carboxylic acid by-product.

benzoic anhydride + (an amine) → n-butylbenzamide (an amide) + benzoic acid

formic anhydride + (an alcohol) → benzyl formate (an ester) + formic acid

propionic anhydride + (a thiol) → S-phenyl propanethioate (a thioester) + propionic acid

12.2 Prelab

Written Prelab: Record the following in your lab notebook:

- Your Name and Date
- Experiment Title
- The reaction equation for the experiment you will be performing
- The completed stoichiometry table show below
- A Plan of Procedure
- References for your property data and experiment

Electronic Prelab: Prior to the beginning of your laboratory section, login to our Chemistry 2540 Carmen page and complete the prelabs in the labeled experimental module.

Reagent	MW	g	mmol	equivalents	d	mL
salicylic acid	138.12	0.21	1.52	1.00		
acetic anhydride	102.09	0.5184	5.07	3.33	1.08	0.48 mL
phosphoric acid (85%)	98.00	0.0716125	0.7306	0.4806	1.685	0.05 mL
Theoretical product						
aspirin	180.16	0.2738	1.52			
acetic acid	60.05	0.09127b	1.52		1.044	0.087

12.3 Synthesis of Aspirin—Procedure

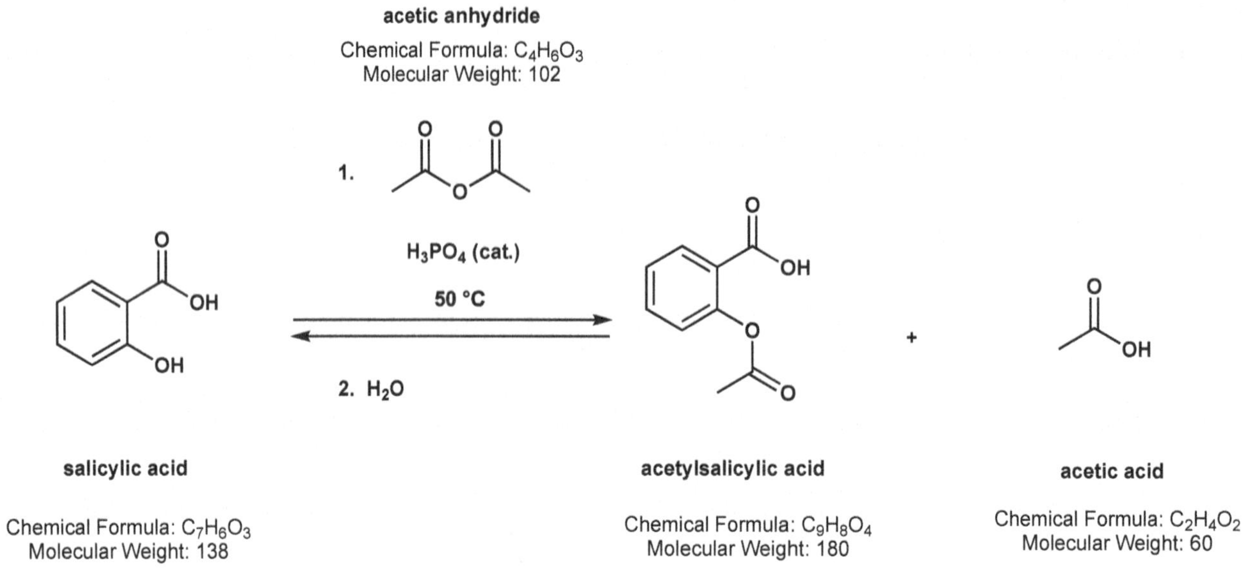

acetic anhydride
Chemical Formula: $C_4H_6O_3$
Molecular Weight: 102

salicylic acid
Chemical Formula: $C_7H_6O_3$
Molecular Weight: 138

acetylsalicylic acid
Chemical Formula: $C_9H_8O_4$
Molecular Weight: 180

acetic acid
Chemical Formula: $C_2H_4O_2$
Molecular Weight: 60

Reaction conditions: 1. H_3PO_4 (cat.), 50 °C; 2. H_2O

Procedure:

1. **Water Bath:** Prepare a 50 °C hot water bath using 80 mL of water in a 150-mL beaker on top of a hot plate

2. **Reagents:** Transfer the salicylic acid (~0.21 g) to a dry 5-mL conical vial, then add acetic anhydride (~0.48 mL) and 85% phosphoric acid (1 drop, 0.05 mL in stoichiometric calculations) from a pasteur pipette.

3. **Reaction:** Transfer a magnetic spinvane to the vial and attach an air condenser. Clamp the reaction assembly so that the vial is partially submerged in the water bath. Stir the reaction mixture for 10 minutes after dissolution of the solids.

Aspirin Apparatus
1 – Air Condenser
2 – Small Clamp
3 – Conical Vial (Partially Submerged)
4 – Water Bath
5 – Hot Plate

4. **Post-Reaction:** After the 10 minute reaction time, allow the vial to cool to room temperature. Detach the air condenser, then remove the spinvane using clean forceps. Place the conical vial in a small beaker to cool. *During this time period, the product should begin to crystallize from the reaction mixture. If it does not crystallize, scratch the walls of the vial with a glass rod at the liquid-air interface.*
5. **Crystallization:** Cool the reaction mixture for 10 minutes in an ice-water bath to ensure complete crystallization of the product.
6. **Quench:** Add water (~3 mL) and stir with a microspatula.
7. **Product Collection**: Isolate the crystals using Hirsch funnel vacuum filtration. *You may rinse the vial to aid in the transfer of the product with small portions of ice-cold water (1 mL). When all the crystals have been transferred to the funnel, wash the crystals with several additional small portions of ice-cold water (1 mL). Allow the crystals to air-dry for several minutes.*
8. **Product Storage:** Remove the crystals from the funnel and transfer to a pre-weighed vial with cap.
9. **Characterization:** Determine the percent yield of your purified aspirin sample after drying.

0.48 mL $\frac{1.089}{mL}$ = 0.5184

158 CHAPTER 12 ❖ Synthesis of Aspirin

12.4 Postlab Data

Prepare this table *of Postlab Data* in your *Laboratory Notebook* after your completed experimental narrative, and fill in the appropriate data in the correct box:

Synthesis of Acetylsalicylic Acid			
starting materials	**experimental mass (g)**	**mmol**	
salicylic acid	0.2475	1.7919	
acetic anhydride	0.5184	5.07787	
product	**experimental mass (g)**	**mmol**	**% yield**
aspirin	0.2079	1.1539	64.399

Theoritical mass : 0.3228

Login to our Chemistry 2540 Carmen page and complete any listed postlab assignments in the labeled experimental module. Postlab assignments are due as listed on the Course Schedule.

12.5 Digital Lab Report Guidelines

Login to our Chemistry 2540 Carmen page and download a copy of the appropriate *DigitalLab Report Template* for this experiment in the labeled experimental module. Follow the instructions listed in the *Digital Lab Report Template* with regard to the preparation of ChemDraw drawings, Formal Procedure section, and the answers to Concept Questions. Submit your completed Digital Lab Report as a Microsoft Word Document (.doc or .docx file only) or Adobe PDF to the Chemistry 2540 experiment assignment. Digital Lab Reports are due as listed on the Course Schedule, and late submissions will be penalized –10 pts per day late.

12.6 Practice Problems

1. *Anhydrides.* Provide the organic products for the following reactions.

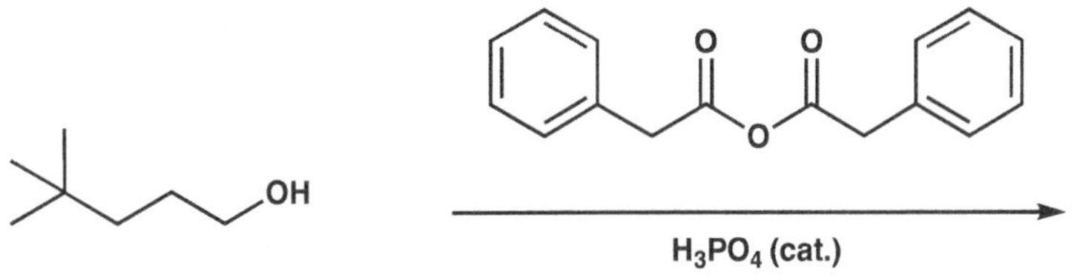

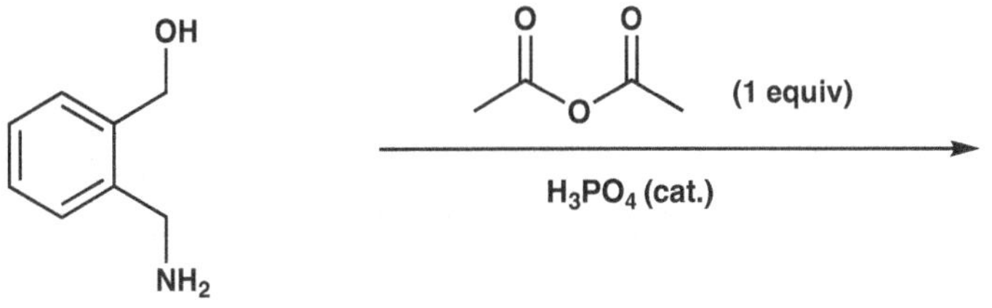

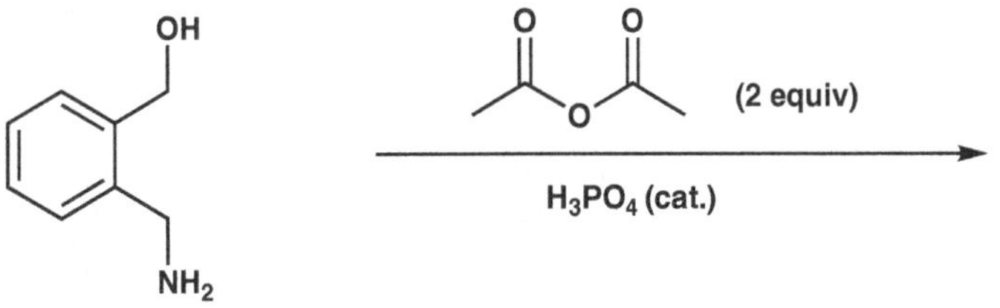

2. After the addition of water to quench the reaction, filtration is performed to isolate the final product crystals. Regarding waste, where should the filtrate be disposed of, and why?

3. What is the catalyst in this reaction and what is the general purpose of a catalyst?

4. Acetic anhydride plays two roles in this reaction, what are those two roles?

5. What is driving the equilibrium of the reaction in the forward direction?

6. *Mechanisms.* Provide the mechanisms for the following esterification reactions. Be sure to include all electron movement and intermediates. *Note the difference in the mechanism under neutral conditions. The experiment in lab was performed under acidic conditions, and that mechanism is in your course notes.

12.7 Study Guide—Preparation of Aspirin

1. Be able to explain the role that phosphoric acid plays in this reaction.
2. Be able to predict the products expected from the reaction of other alcohols and phenols with acetic anhydride.
3. Be able to discuss the crystallization process used in this reaction. What would be a good recrystallization solvent for aspirin? Why were the initially collected crystals rinsed with *cold* water?
4. Be able to suggest at least three techniques you might use to establish the identity of your product (aspirin).

Reduction of Vanillin

CHAPTER 13

13.1 Introduction

The most common and useful reagents for reducing aldehydes, ketones, and other functional groups are metal hydride reagents. The two most common metal hydride reagents are sodium borohydride (NaBH$_4$) and lithium aluminum hydride (LiAlH$_4$). These reagents contain a hydrogen-metal bond (M-H) that serves as a source of the hydride ion (H:⁻), which is a strong base and a good nucleophile. Because metal atoms uniformly have electronegativities that are lower than that of hydrogen, the pair of electrons in the M-H bond is highly polarized toward the hydrogen, giving it a significant negative charge. However, the reactivity of neutral molecules (such as borane) and negatively charged ions (borohydride and aluminum hydride) is significantly different, and the reactivity and electron-richness of a hydride is substantially increased in the structures with an overall excess of electron density. Borane is considered an electrophilic reagent because of the electron deficiency and lack of an octet at the boron atom (often described as an empty p-orbital); although not used as a source of reactive hydrides, borane is useful in other types of chemical transformations (such as the hydroboration of alkenes). The formal negative charge on the Lewis structures of NaBH$_4$ and LiAlH$_4$ is often a source of confusion when predicting the reactivity of these molecules, so it is better to imagine the partial charges (δ+/δ−) that can be assigned using differences in electronegativity.

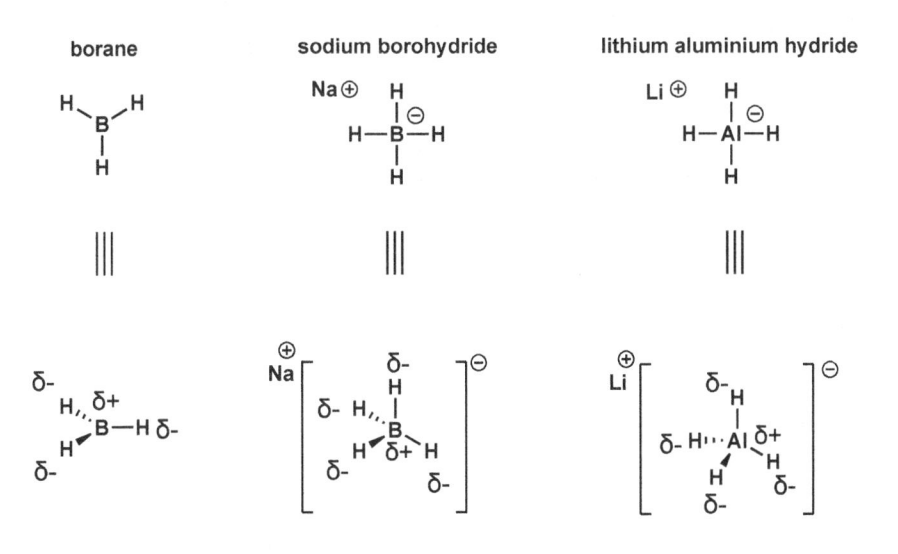

Selected Pauling Electronegativity Values	
C	2.55
H	2.20
B	2.04
Si	1.90
Al	1.61
Na	0.93
Li	0.91
K	0.82

164 CHAPTER 13 ❖ Reduction of Vanillin

Electronegativity differences also predict that the partial charge on hydrogen would be greater in LiAlH$_4$ than in NaBH$_4$ (Al-H is more polar than B-H) and experiments confirm that LiAlH$_4$ is the more reactive of the two compounds. However, this is not the only factor that explains the difference in reactivity: because the lithium counterion is smaller and more charge-dense than sodium, there is a stronger ionic interaction between this lithium and the oxygen of the carbonyl that is being reduced, and this interaction increases the rate of hydride transfer. Support for this can be observed in the reactions of lithium borohydride (LiBH$_4$), which is more similar in reactivity to LiAlH$_4$ than NaBH$_4$. Interestingly, the reagents sodium hydride (NaH) and potassium hydride (KH) are strong bases but do not possess nucleophilic hydrides, so they are not used in reducing carbonyl compounds. When an aldehyde or ketone is reacted with NaBH$_4$ or LiAlH$_4$, in an appropriate solvent, then treated by an acidic or water workup after the reaction, an alcohol is the product. The net chemical transformation is the addition of one molecule of H$_2$ across the carbonyl pi bond.

NaBH$_4$ selectively reduces aldehydes and ketones in the presence of most other functional groups. Reduction with NaBH$_4$ is usually carried out in methanol as the solvent. LiAlH$_4$ also reduces aldehydes and ketones and many other functional groups (e.g. epoxides, amides, esters, acid chlorides). These reactions are usually performed in ethereal solvents because LiAlH$_4$ quickly deprotonate alcohols to create alkoxides and hydrogen gas. A comparison of solvent choices for these molecules is compiled here:

	H$_3$O$^+$	H$_2$O	HO$^-$	MeOH	EtOH	i-PrOH	Et$_2$O	THF	DME
NaBH$_4$	REACTS	REACTS	good solubility	IDEAL solubility (slow rxn)	good solubility	some solubility	insoluble	insoluble	insoluble
LiAlH$_4$	REACTS	REACTS	REACTS	REACTS	REACTS	REACTS	good solubility	good solubility	good solubility

The phenol functional group in vanillin is acidic enough to react with sodium borohydride. Although this reaction could be conducted in methanol, one equivalent of hydride would be wasted in a fast deprotonation step. The use of basic water as the solvent for this reaction is uniquely suited to vanillin for several reasons: a) the sodium hydroxide of the solvent deprotonates vanillin before NaBH4 is added, which prevents a valuable molecule of hydride from being used as a base, b) because of the charge, the vanillin anion is more soluble in water than vanillin itself, and c) although NaBH$_4$ reacts with neutral and acidic water, it is stable in the presence of aqueous base.

An additional advantage of using basic water as the solvent is that after the reduction reaction when the solution is neutralized, the uncharged vanillyl alcohol product has a low solubility in water, so it precipitates out and can be isolated by filtration. However, the amount of acid used to neutralize the reaction is of critical importance, and excess acid will keep the vanillyl alcohol protonated to a greater extent, which increases its water solubility (it is a cation), slowing down or inhibiting the precipitation/crystallization of crude vanillin out of water.

166 CHAPTER 13 ❖ Reduction of Vanillin

One clue about the complex mechanism of carbonyl reduction by borohydride can be found in the mineral sassolite, which is a form of crystalline boric acid (B(OH)$_3$). In a two-dimensional layer of the crystal structure, one can observe a repeating pattern of (B(OH)$_3$) with a trigonal planar boron surrounded by three HO groups that participate in strong hydrogen bonding with adjacent molecules. Although the B-O bond is quite strong and contributes to the stability of the mineral, it would still seem that the boron should be lacking stability because does not have an octet; however, three-dimensional structure reveals that above and below the boron of each layer of the crystal is an oxygen atom from a B(OH)$_3$ molecule on another

one layer of the of B(OH)₃ crystal structure in 2D

two layers of the B(OH)₃ crystal structure 3D

layer. In this way, the empty orbital on boron is stabilized by electrons from these oxygen atoms in other layers (which satisfies the octet rule) but a negative formal charge on boron is technically avoided because these oxygen atoms in different layers are too far away to be considered covalent bonds. Analysis of this crystal reveals both boron's conflicting stability requirements (negative charge with an octet vs. neutral with an empty orbital) and its affinity for forming bonds with oxygen. Borohydride is reactive towards carbonyls because of the overall negative charge of the molecule and the large partial negative of the H atoms. However, once borohydride transfers a hydride, it becomes borane (BH_3) which neither has reactive hydrides (no formal charge) nor an octet at boron. One way boron is observed to stabilize this lack of an octet is to form a covalent bond with any available oxygen atoms in solution, and in this mechanism, boron could react with any alkoxide or hydroxide in an equilibrium reaction to satisfy its octet. However, once the borohydride is negatively charged, another one of its hydride atoms can be transferred, and the process continues until boron is bonded to only oxygen atoms. Addition of acid allows the B-O bonds to readily dissociate and favor the product alcohol in the equilibrium.

168 CHAPTER 13 ❖ Reduction of Vanillin

Mechanism of Borohydride Addition

Mechanism of Hydrolysis

13.2 Prelab

Written Prelab: Record the following in your lab notebook:

- Your Name and Date
- Experiment Title
- The reaction equation for the experiment you will be performing
- The completed stoichiometry table show below
- A Plan of Procedure
- References for your property data and experiment

reagent	MW	g	mmol	equivalents	d	mL
vanillin						
sodium borohydride						
sodium hydroxide (1M)						
Theoretical product						
vanillyl alcohol						

Electronic Prelab: Prior to the beginning of your laboratory section, login to our Chemistry 2540 Carmen page and complete the prelabs in the labeled experimental module.

13.3 Reduction of Vanillin Procedure

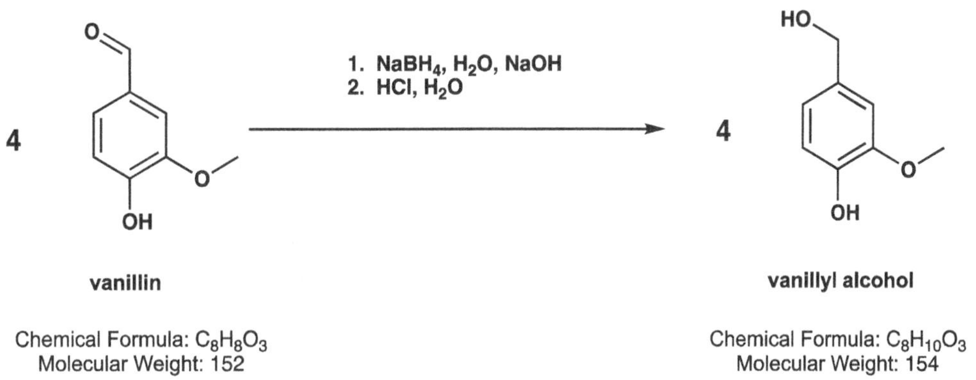

vanillin

Chemical Formula: $C_8H_8O_3$
Molecular Weight: 152

vanillyl alcohol

Chemical Formula: $C_8H_{10}O_3$
Molecular Weight: 154

Reagents: 1. $NaBH_4$, H_2O, NaOH; 2. HCl, H_2O

1. **Solution Preparation**: Determine the mass of vanillin provided in the sample vial by difference and transfer to a 125-mL Erlenmeyer flask. Add 22 mL of 1 M NaOH and cool the flask in an ice-water bath.
2. **Reducing Agent**: Weigh out ~0.4 g of $NaBH_4$ and add it to the chilled solution of vanillin with good swirling. Leave the flask in the ice bath throughout the addition.
3. **Reaction Period**: Remove the flask from the ice bath and allow it to stand at room temperature for 20 minutes. Periodically mix the solution by gently swirling the flask. *As the flask comes to room temperature, the solution appearance will change from cloudy to clear and be in yellow in color.*
4. **Work Up**: Cool the reaction mixture in an ice bath, and slowly add ~10 mL of 3 M HCl in small portions to the chilled reaction mixture with vigorous and consistent swirling in between additions. (Total addition time = ~5 min.) Add acid until the solution is weakly acidic when tested with pH paper. Allow the flask to warm to room temperature while you continue to swirl. *Too much acid and too little swirling will slow crystal formation.*
5. **Crude Product Isolation**: Once crystal formation is complete at room temperature, cool the solution in the ice bath for an additional 10 minutes. Collect the product by vacuum filtration, with a Buchner funnel, washing with three portions of cold water (~1 mL). Leave the vacuum on for 5-10 minutes to air dry the product. The product should be as dry as possible. After drying the product, obtain a crude weight.

6. **Macroscale Recrystallization**: In a small Erlenmeyer flask, heat ~15-20 mL of ethyl acetate on a hot plate with a boiling stick. Once the ethyl acetate is boiling, add the liquid in small portions to the Erlenmeyer flask containing your crude product until all of the solid dissolves.

   You should place both Erlenmeyer flasks on the top of the hot plate so that they stay warm and secure while adding solvent. Be careful not to add too much solvent. It is best to err on the side of too little solvent rather than too much. You should stir the material with your microspatula to aid in the dissolution.

7. **Slow Cooling**: Once the entire compound is dissolved, remove the Erlenmeyer flask from the heat and place it on your bench top to cool SLOWLY to room temperature.

   Once the solution achieves room temperature, crystallization should begin. If crystallization does not begin, scratch the inside of the container with a glass rod at the liquid-air interface. Once crystallization has started, it is best not to disturb the container, so as to promote large crystal formation.

8. *Ice Bath*: Once crystal formation is evident, it can be cooled in an ice bath. Cooling in an ice bath will maximize the amount of pure compound that comes out of solution.

9. **Vacuum** Filtration: After 10 minutes, remove the solvent and isolate the crystals by vacuum filtration equipped with a filter funnel.

   Before filtering the crystals, be sure to secure the filter paper by turning on the vacuum and wetting the filter paper with a small portion of cold ethyl acetate. To aid in the transfer of the crystals, you can wash them from the Erlenmeyer flask to the filter funnel using cold ethyl acetate.

10. **Drying**: Allow your vanillyl alcohol to fully dry, transfer to a pre-weighed vial with cap labeled with your hood number, and determine the weight and percent yield of your purified product.

13.4 Postlab Data Submission

Prepare this table of *Postlab Data* in your *Laboratory Notebook* after your completed experimental narrative, and fill in the appropriate data in the correct box:

Synthesis of 4-(Hydroxymethyl)-2-methoxyphenol			
starting materials	**experimental mass (g)**	**mmol**	
vanillin			
sodium borohydride			
product	**experimental mass (g)**	**mmol**	**% yield**
vanillyl alcohol			

Login to our Chemistry 2540 Carmen page and complete any listed postlab assignments in the labeled experimental module.

Postlab assignments are due as listed on the Course Schedule.

13.5 Digital Lab Report Guidelines

Login to our Chemistry 2540 Carmen page and download a copy of the appropriate *Digital Lab Report Template* for this experiment in the labeled experimental module. Follow the instructions listed in the *Digital Lab Report Template* with regard to the preparation of ChemDraw drawings, Formal Procedure section, and the answers to Concept Questions. Submit your completed Digital Lab Report as a Microsoft Word Document (.doc or .docx file only) or Adobe PDF to the Chemistry 2540 experiment assignment. Digital Lab Reports are due as listed on the Course Schedule, and late submissions will be penalized –10 pts per day late.

13.6 Practice Problems

1. *Predict the Product.* Provide the most stable organic products for the following reactions.

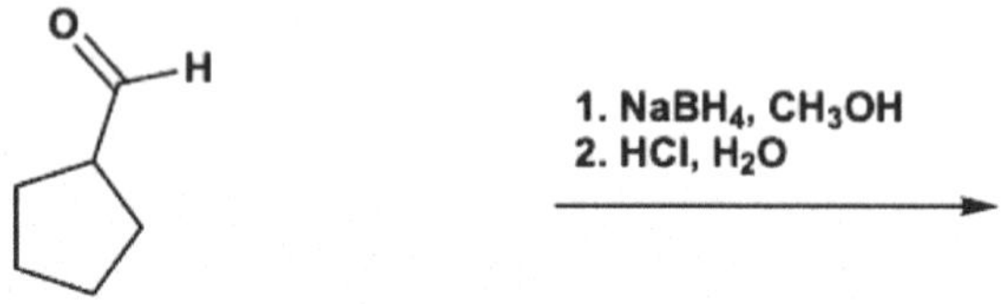

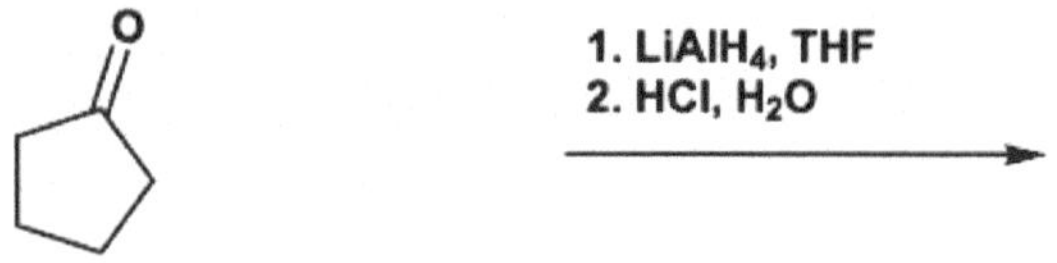

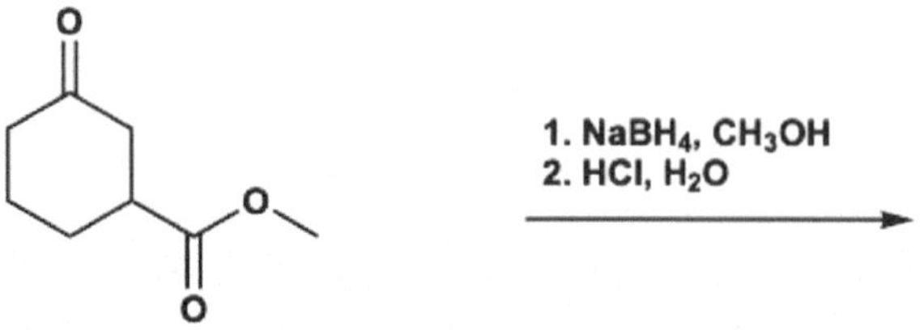

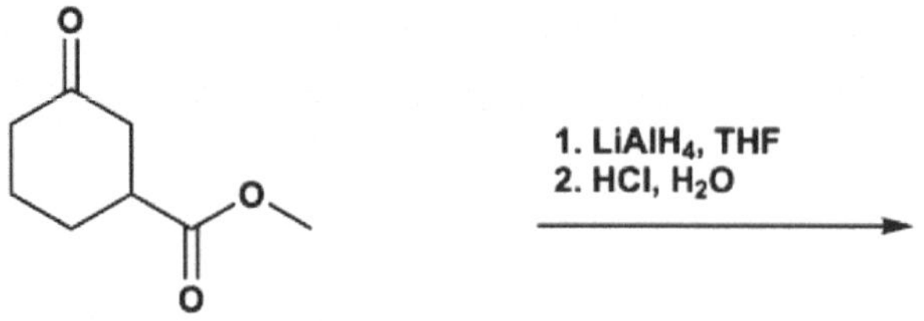

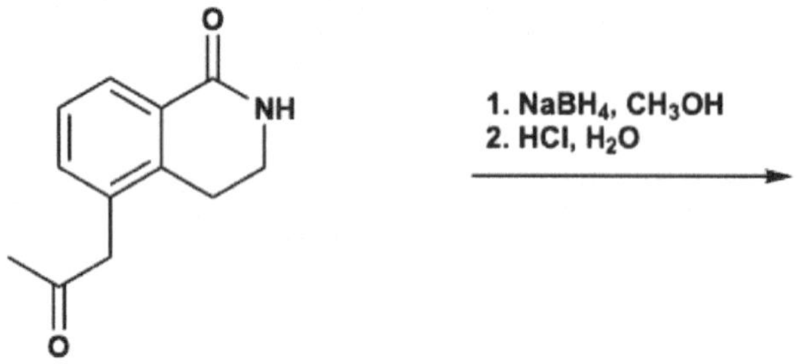

2,6-dimethylheptan-4-one → 1. NaBH₄, CH₃OH; 2. HCl, H₂O

cyclopentanecarbaldehyde → 1. NaBH₄, CH₃OH; 2. HCl, H₂O

cyclopentanone → 1. LiAlH₄, THF; 2. HCl, H₂O

methyl 3-oxocyclohexane-1-carboxylate → 1. NaBH₄, CH₃OH; 2. HCl, H₂O

methyl 3-oxocyclohexane-1-carboxylate → 1. LiAlH₄, THF; 2. HCl, H₂O

5-(2-oxopropyl)-3,4-dihydroisoquinolin-1(2H)-one → 1. NaBH₄, CH₃OH; 2. HCl, H₂O

CHAPTER 13 ❖ Reduction of Vanillin 175

[Structure: 2-(2-oxocyclohexyl)acetaldehyde] → 1. NaBH₄ (0.25 Equiv.), CH₃OH
2. HCl, H₂O

[Structure: acetophenone] → 1. NaBD₄, CH₃OD
2. DCl, D₂O

[Structure: methyl 3-acetyl-5-(2-oxoethyl)benzoate] → 1. LiAlH₄, THF
2. HCl, H₂O

2. Spilling NaBH₄ can be dangerous. What steps should be taken if NaBH₄ happens to be spilled?

3. What is the purpose of the hydrochloric acid addition to the reaction, and why is it important to obtain a slightly acid (pH 4-5) solution overall?

4. Why is it important to keep this reaction cool?

5. NaBH₄ and LiAlH₄ differ in their abilities to reduce certain functional groups. Which functional groups can each reducing agent reduce? Explain this difference in reactivity.

CHAPTER 13 ❖ Reduction of Vanillin

Provide the complete mechanism that shows the formation of the products for the following reaction. You must include all of the arrows, intermediates, and formal charges.

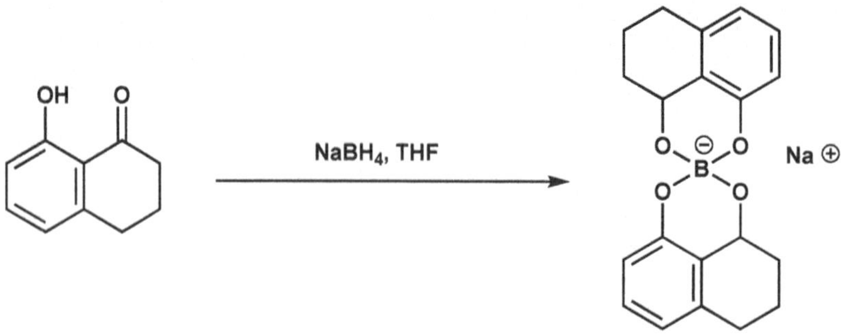

13.7 Study Guide—Synthesis of Vanillyl Alcohol

1. Be able to write the mechanism of the reaction.
2. Understand the purpose of adding HCl at the end of the reaction.
3. Be able to predict the product of the reaction of NaBH$_4$ with a given aldehyde or ketone.
4. Know why NaBH$_4$ was used in this reaction instead of LiAlH$_4$

Grignard Reaction— Synthesis of Triphenylmethanol

CHAPTER 14

14.1 Introduction

The Grignard reaction, named after the French chemist, François Auguste Victor Grignard, is an organometallic reaction in which an alkyl- or aryl- magnesium halide acts as a nucleophile and bonds with an electrophile to yield a new carbon-carbon bond. The most common examples of Grignard reactions are those in which the organomagnesium compound attacks a carbonyl electrophile to generate alcohols. These organometallic compounds have come to be known as Grignard reagents in tribute to their discoverer and always include a carbon atom bonded to a magnesium halide complex. Due to large differences in electronegativity, the carbon atom in these reagents bears a partial negative charge and the more electropositive metal is positively polarized.

$$\overset{\partial^-}{H_3C}-\overset{\partial^+}{MgBr}$$

methyl magnesium bromide

Grignard reagents are typically prepared by reaction of an alkyl halide with magnesium metal in an aprotic solvent such as diethyl ether, tetrahydrofuran, or dimethoxyethane. The Lewis basic oxygen lone pairs provided by these ethereal solvents complex tightly to the metal center and provide stability to the reactive carbon–metal bond as well as a surprising amount of organic solubility. However, careful attention must be paid to the purity of both reagents and solvents as well as the cleanliness of equipment used for these reactions, since Grignard reagents are unstable in the presence of protic solvents. The same inherent reactivity of the anion-like carbon atom of a Grignard reagent that affords the powerful nucleophilic behavior demands that it also behave as a strong base and participate in rapid proton abstraction from water (or another proton donor) to form a new and decidedly unreactive hydrocarbon C–H bond. In order to successfully prepare a Grignard reagent, great attention must be paid to avoid accidental exposure of the reaction to any source of acidic protons, especially ambient water vapor and condensate.

$$R-X \; + \; Mg° \xrightarrow{\text{Et}_2\text{O}} R-MgX$$

The electron pair in the C–Mg bond easily abstracts a proton from water (or other protic solvent like alcohols, amines, etc.), and the equilibrium for this reaction lies far to the right because of water's extremely high relative acidity compared to the resulting alkane product. Furthermore, the reaction with water is so fast that all of the Grignard reagent will decompose, or quench, before any significant C–C bond formation reaction can take place. All of these factors require that the Grignard reaction be carried out using dry glassware and under an inert environment.

$$H_3C-MgBr + H_2O \rightleftharpoons CH_4 + HOMgBr$$

$pK_a = 15.7 \qquad pK_a = 50$

Reaction of Grignard reagents with aldehydes and ketones afford alcohol products that reflect the carbon connectivity present in the starting materials. Reaction of Grignard reagents with acyl halides is sensitive to the Grignard reagent present. Interestingly, a 1:1 ratio of carbonyl to Grignard reagent provides ketone products, and two (or more) equivalents of Grignard reagent will provide tertiary alcohols in which two equivalents of the Grignard have been incorporated. It should be noted that the reaction between strong alkylating agents and acyl halides is quite exothermic, and a low temperature bath is essential to provide pure products (and avoid thermal decomposition).

Reaction of Grignard reagents with formaldehyde provides a route to primary alcohols, and reaction with solid carbon dioxide (dry ice) gives carboxylic acids after treatment with aqueous acid. Lastly, the strained nature of epoxides allows reaction with Grignard reagents via the S_N2 pathway as well.

CHAPTER 14 ❖ Grignard Reaction—Synthesis of Triphenylmethanol 179

formaldehyde → 1. R'–MgBr, Et₂O; 2. HCl / H₂O → **1° alcohol** [add 1 C to R']

carbon dioxide → 1. R'–MgBr, Et₂O; 2. HCl / H₂O → **carboxylic acid** [add 1 C to R']

epoxide → 1. R'–MgBr, Et₂O; 2. HCl / H₂O → **alcohol** [add 2 C to R']

The reaction follows the general mechanism for nucleophilic addition (nucleophilic attack followed by protonation).

Mechanism

14.2 Sensitivity and Limitations of the Grignard Reaction

Due to their significant carbanionic character, Grignard reagents react quickly with water (or other protic molecules) to form new C-H bonds, which reduces the concentration of Grignard available for the desired bond forming reaction and leads to poor product yields. For this reason, care is taken to avoid contamination of laboratory equipment with water, alcohols, and carboxylic acids, and calcium chloride drying tubes are employed to protect them from atmospheric moisture.

180 CHAPTER 14 ❖ Grignard Reaction—Synthesis of Triphenylmethanol

Protic hydrogens, such as those in the O-H bonds of alcohols, phenols, or carboxylic acids, the N-H bonds of amines and amides, and the S-H bonds of sulfides, will react with Mg0 to create hydrogen gas (H_2) faster than the insertion of Mg into a C-Br bond; therefore, compounds with protic functional groups cannot be used to form Grignard reagents.

Exposure of a Grignard reagent to other carbonyl compounds (such as acetone, commonly used to clean laboratory glassware) will result in C-C bond formation to give alcohol side products different than the target structure. For this reason, acetone must not be used to clean glassware prior to conducting a Grignard reaction; however, use of acetone to clean up at the end of the lab period is permitted.

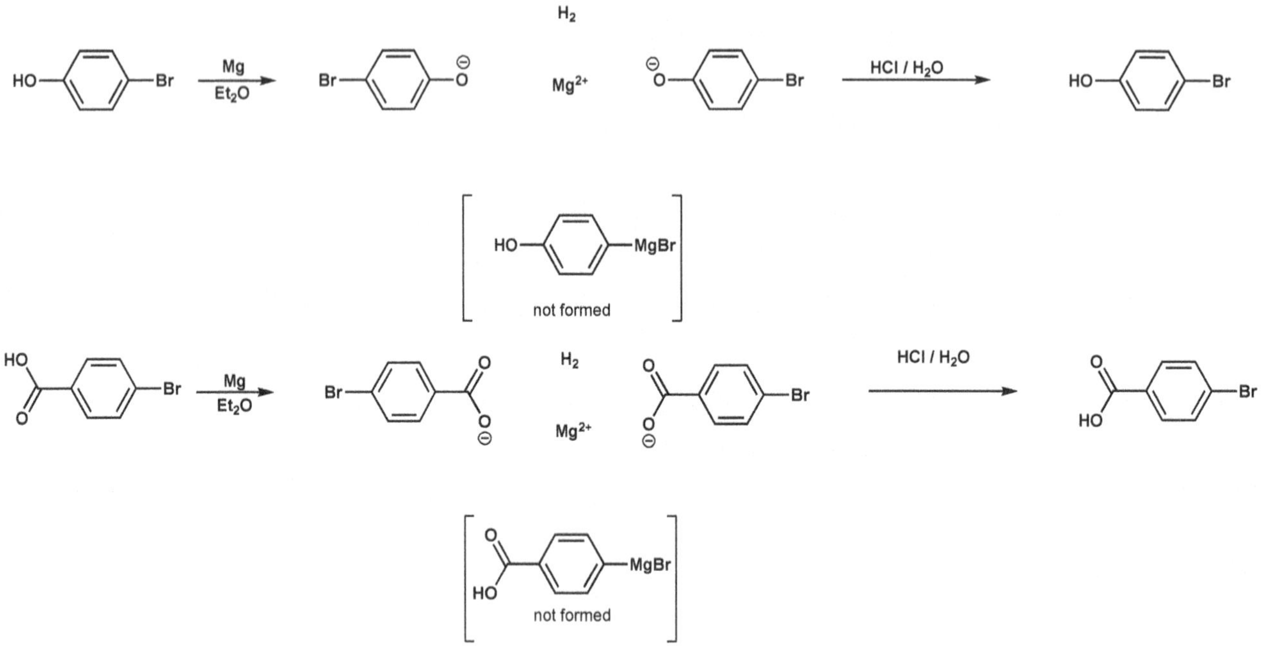

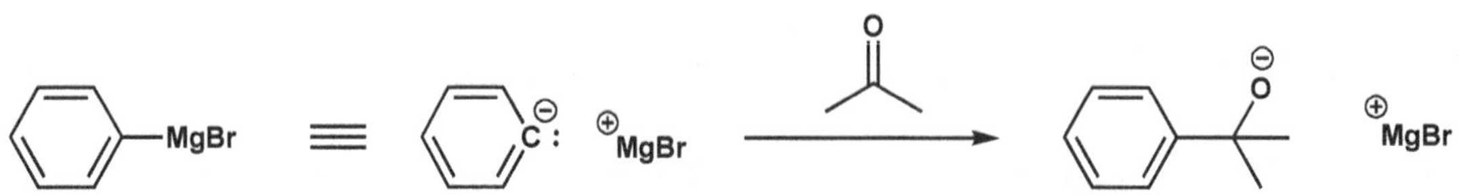

Synthetic researchers are constantly investigating new types of C-C bond forming reactions, and these efforts have uncovered metals and conditions that provide organometallic compounds that overcome some of the limitations of the Grignard reaction. One of these reports uses zinc metal and lithium chloride to give organozinc compounds that contains a ketone functional group. With the same starting material, attempts to form a Grignard reagent would lead to polymerization and decomposition of the reagent; however, the organozinc compound reacts much slower with ketones than aldehydes, allowing the formation of the product shown below in high yield (Reference: Metzger, A.; Schade, M. A.; Knochel, P.; Org. Lett., **2008**, 10 (6), 1107–1110).

CHAPTER 14 ❖ Grignard Reaction—Synthesis of Triphenylmethanol   181

The use of Grignard reagents as nucleophiles is difficult in situations where acidic beta-hydrogens can be eliminated to form unsaturated products. Furthermore, the formation of alkyl Grignard reagents can be complicated because of the competitive substitution and elimination reactions that are possible with the haloalkane starting material before the Grignard reagent can be fully formed. For these reasons, the reaction of Grignard reagents with haloalkanes is not a general method for the formation of C-C bonds.

14.3 Prelab

Written Prelab: Record the following in your lab notebook:

- Your Name and Date
- Experiment Title
- The reaction equation for the experiment you will be performing
- The completed stoichiometry table show below
- A Plan of Procedure
- References for your property data and experiment

reagent	MW	g	mmol	equivalents	d	mL
bromobenzene						
magnesium						
benzophenone						
diethyl ether						
Theoretical product						
triphenylmethanol						

Electronic Prelab: Prior to the beginning of your laboratory section, login to our Chemistry 2540 Carmen page and complete the prelab quiz in the labeled experimental module. Prelab assignments are due as listed on the Course Schedule.

14.4 Synthesis of Triphenylmethanol—Grignard Reaction—Procedure

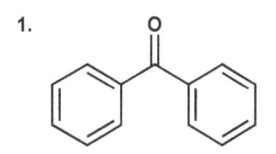

1. benzophenone
Chemical Formula: C$_{13}$H$_{10}$O
Molecular Weight: 182.07

bromobenzene
Chemical Formula: C$_6$H$_5$Br
Molecular Weight: 157.01

phenylmagnesium bromide
Chemical Formula: C$_6$H$_5$BrMg
Molecular Weight: 181.32

2. HCl / H$_2$O

triphenylmethanol
Chemical Formula: C$_{19}$H$_{16}$O
Molecular Weight: 260.34

Part 1

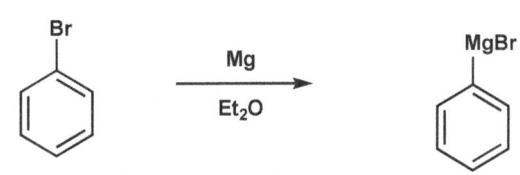

bromobenzene
Chemical Formula: C$_6$H$_5$Br
Molecular Weight: 157.01

phenylmagnesium bromide
Chemical Formula: C$_6$H$_5$BrMg
Molecular Weight: 181.32

184 CHAPTER 14 ❖ Grignard Reaction—Synthesis of Triphenylmethanol

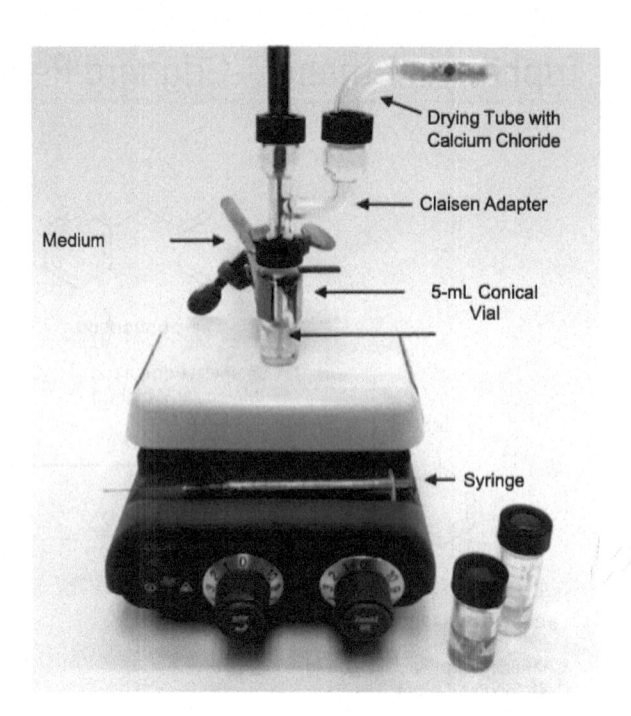

[Figure: Apparatus setup showing a heater-stirrer with a 5-mL conical vial held by a medium clamp, fitted with a Claisen adapter, a drying tube with calcium chloride, and a syringe. Two small vials sit to the right.]

Labels: Drying Tube with Calcium Chloride; Claisen Adapter; Medium; 5-mL Conical Vial; Syringe

1. Place a spinvane and 0.05 g of magnesium turnings into an oven-dried 5-mL conical vial.
2. Attach the Claisen adapter to the conical vial. On the curved joint, attach a drying tube filled with calcium chloride. Place a Teflon-rubber septum and screw cap on the straight portion of the adapter. Clamp the apparatus so that it sits centered on a heater-stirrer (no stirring at first and NO HEATING).
3. Measure 4 mL of anhydrous diethyl ether in a second 5-mL conical vial and cap it. *You should use this diethyl ether to make the solutions needed throughout this experiment.*
4. Weigh a 3-mL conical vial and dispense 0.35 mL of bromobenzene into the vial. Reweigh the vial to determine the weight of the bromobenzene and record this in your lab notebook.
5. Add 1.0 mL of diethyl ether to the vial containing the bromobenzene. Using your syringe, add 0.40 mL of this solution to the reaction apparatus through the Teflon septum.

    At this point of the reaction you should observe the evolution of bubbles and/or the solution should become cloudy or pale yellow indicating the reaction has started. If the reaction does not start, remove the rubber septum from the apparatus and insert a microspatula and twist it so as to crush the magnesium against the glass surface. This should break some magnesium pieces and start the reaction.

6. Add the remaining solution of bromobenzene from the syringe slowly over a period of 5 min. Rinse the initial vial containing bromobenzene with 0.5 mL of diethyl ether and transfer to the reaction vessel (this assists in achieving quantitative transfer of the bromobenzene). The reaction mixture should stir for an additional 15 min.

Part 2. Reaction of the Grignard Reagent with Benzophenone

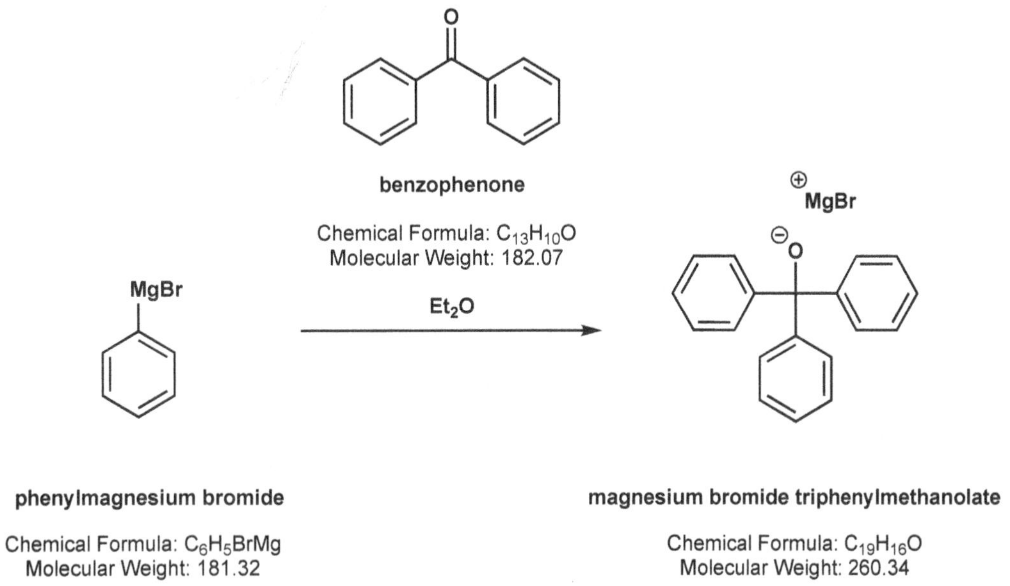

benzophenone

Chemical Formula: $C_{13}H_{10}O$
Molecular Weight: 182.07

phenylmagnesium bromide

Chemical Formula: C_6H_5BrMg
Molecular Weight: 181.32

Et$_2$O

magnesium bromide triphenylmethanolate

Chemical Formula: $C_{19}H_{16}O$
Molecular Weight: 260.34

1. Determine the mass of benzophenone provided in the sample vial by difference and transfer to a 3-mL conical vial. Dissolve the sample in 0.50 mL of diethyl ether.

2. Transfer the benzophenone solution into your syringe and add it to the reaction mixture in one portion. Rinse the vial that contained the benzophenone solution with about 0.3 mL of diethyl ether and add it to the reaction mixture (this assists in achieving quantitative transfer).

3. Once the addition has been completed, the mixture should stir for 10 min.

    In most cases, the reaction mixture will turn pinkish-red and gradually will solidify as the adduct is formed.

    When stirring is no longer effective, remove the syringe and septum and stir the mixture with a spatula.

Part 3. Hydrolysis of the Alkoxide

$$\text{magnesium bromide triphenylmethanolate} \xrightarrow{\text{HCl / H}_2\text{O}} \text{triphenylmethanol}$$

magnesium bromide triphenylmethanolate
Chemical Formula: $C_{19}H_{15}BrMgO$
Molecular Weight: 363.54

triphenylmethanol
Chemical Formula: $C_{19}H_{16}O$
Molecular Weight: 260.34

1. Slowly add 1.5 mL of 6M hydrochloric acid to the reaction mixture.

   After addition of the acid, two phases should be evident: the upper diethyl ether layer will contain triphenylmethanol and the lower aqueous hydrochloric acid layer will contain the inorganic compounds. Use a spatula to break up the solid during the addition of the hydrochloric acid. You might need to cap the vial and shake it vigorously to aid in dissolution of the solid. You should add enough diethyl ether to maintain a 3-mL volume in the upper organic phase. Make sure that you have two distinct phases before you separate the layers. There should be no solid remaining when you separate the layers.

Part 4. Work-Up, Purification and Thin Layer Chromatography

Except for the conical vial containing the crude product mixture, rinse all other conical vials with clean diethyl ether and use them as needed for the extraction step.

1. Remove the magnetic spinvane with forceps and rinse it with a little ether. Draw off the lower aqueous layer with a Pasteur pipette and place it in a separate conical vial. *Save the ether layer in the original vial because it contains the triphenylmethanol.*
2. Re-extract the aqueous phase with 0.5 mL of diethyl ether. Remove the lower aqueous layer and store it temporarily in a test tube.
3. Combine the remaining ether phase with the original ether extract. Transfer the combined ether layers to a dry 5-mL conical vial with a Pasteur pipette. Dry the ether solution with anhydrous sodium sulfate.
4. Weigh a small Erlenmeyer flask. Remove the dried diethyl ether solution from the drying agent with a Pasteur pipette and transfer it to the pre-weighed flask. Rinse the drying agent with more diethyl ether and add this rinse to the diethyl ether in the Erlenmeyer.

This is a good stopping point for the first lab period.

   Give the Erlenmeyer containing your triphenylmethanol in diethyl ether to your TA for storage. The diethyl ether will evaporate over the course of the week, leaving your crude triphenylmethanol.

5. Weigh the Erlenmeyer flask and determine the weight of your crude product. Save a small amount of this crude material to perform the TLC analysis at the end of the experiment.
6. Trituration: Add petroleum ether (~2 mL) to the flask containing the crude solid product, heat the mixture slightly (1 min) with stirring, and then cool it to room temperature.

7. **Second Crude Isolation:** Collect the triphenylmethanol by vacuum filtration on a Hirsch funnel. Rinse it with small portions of petroleum ether. Save the petroleum ether triturant as well as a small amount of the triturated solid for TLC analysis.

8. **Recrystallization:** In a small Erlenmeyer flask, heat ~15–20 mL of isopropyl alcohol on a hot plate (be sure to include a boiling stick to prevent bumping). Once isopropyl alcohol is boiling, add the liquid in small portions to the Erlenmeyer tube containing your crude product until all of the solid dissolves.

   You should place both Erlenmeyer flasks on top of the heater stirrer so that they stay warm and secure while adding solvent. Be careful not to add too much solvent. It is best to err on the side of too little solvent rather than too much. You should stir the material with your microspatula to aid in the dissolution.

9. Once all of the compound is dissolved in the isopropyl alcohol, remove the Erlenmeyer flask from the hot plate and place it in your bench top to cool SLOWLY to room temperature. Once the solution achieves room temperature, crystallization should begin.

   If crystallization does not begin, scratch the inside of the container with a glass rod at the liquid-air interface. Once crystallization has started, it is best not to disturb the container, so as to promote large crystal formation.

10. Once the flask has cooled to room temperature and crystal formation is evident, it can be cooled in an ice bath. *Cooling in an ice bath will maximize the amount of pure compound that comes out of solution.*

11. Once crystallization is complete, remove the solvent by vacuum filtration with a Hirsh funnel.

12. Allow your product to air dry, then determine the weight of the purified product.

13. Obtain one TLC plate and a glass capillary spotter. You should have three solids: crude triphenylmethanol; triphenylmethanol after trituration; and triphenylmethanol after recrystallization. To each, add a small amount of diethyl ether to dissolve the solid.

14. Run the TLC plate with 7:1 petroleum ether–diethyl ether as the eluant using the diagram below as a reference for spotting.

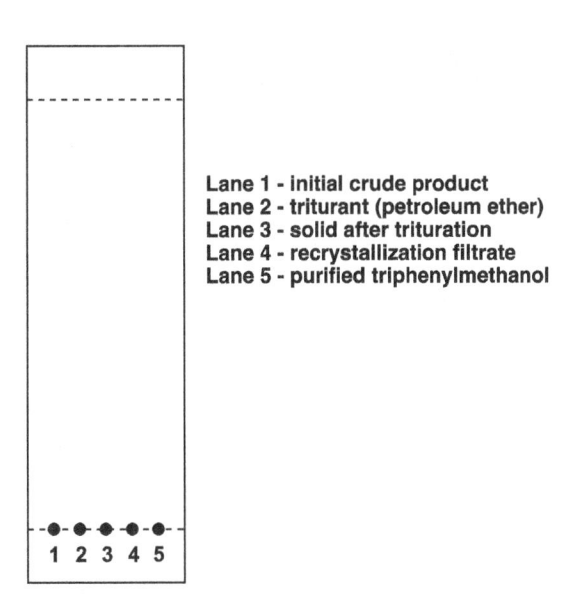

Lane 1 - initial crude product
Lane 2 - triturant (petroleum ether)
Lane 3 - solid after trituration
Lane 4 - recrystallization filtrate
Lane 5 - purified triphenylmethanol

Be sure to record the appearance of your TLC plate, as well as the Rf values of all spots, in your laboratory notebook.

14.5 Postlab Data Submission

Prepare this table of *Postlab Data* in your *Laboratory Notebook* after your completed experimental narrative, and fill in the appropriate data in the correct box:

Synthesis of Triphenylmethanol			
starting materials	**experimental mass (g)**	**mmol**	
bromobenzene			
benzophenone			
product	**experimental mass (g)**	**mmol**	**% yield**
triphenylmethanol			

Login to our Chemistry 2540 Carmen page and complete any listed postlab assignments in the labeled experimental module.

Postlab assignments are due as listed on the Course Schedule.

14.6 Digital Lab Report Guidelines

Login to our Chemistry 2540 Carmen page and download a copy of the appropriate *DigitalLab Report Template* for this experiment in the labeled experimental module. Follow the instructions listed in the *Digital Lab Report Template* with regard to the preparation of ChemDraw drawings, Formal Procedure section, and the answers to Concept Questions. Submit your completed Digital Lab Report as a Microsoft Word Document (.doc or .docx file only) or Adobe PDF to the Chemistry 2540 experiment assignment. Digital Lab Reports are due as listed on the Course Schedule, and late submissions will be penalized −10 pts per day late.

14.7 Practice Problems

1. **Predict the Product.** Predict the major organic product for each of the following Grignard reactions. Assume excess Grignard in present for each reaction.

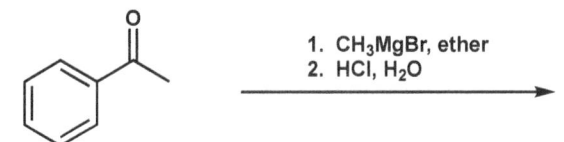

    Ph-C(=O)-CH₃ → 1. CH₃MgBr, ether 2. HCl, H₂O

    3-methylcyclohexanone → 1. CH₃CH₂MgBr, THF 2. HCl, H₂O

    propylene oxide (epoxide) → 1. CH₃MgBr, ether 2. HCl, H₂O

    cyclohexanone → 1. (CH₃)₂C=CH-CH₂MgBr, ether 2. HCl, H₂O

    PhCH₂CHO → 1. 4-methoxyphenyl-MgBr, ether 2. HCl, H₂O

    PhMgBr → 1. CO₂ 2. HCl, H₂O

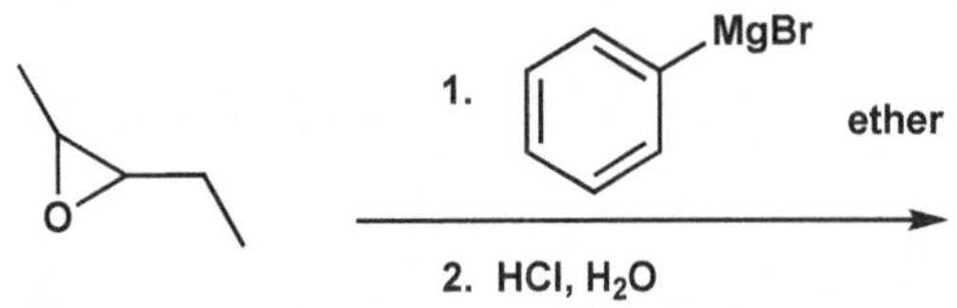

CHAPTER 14 ❖ Grignard Reaction—Synthesis of Triphenylmethanol

2,3-epoxypentane (2-methyl-3-ethyloxirane) + PhMgBr, ether; then HCl, H₂O

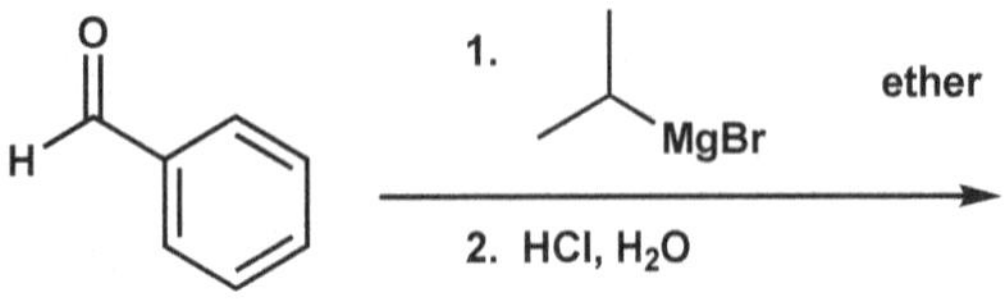

benzaldehyde + isopropylMgBr, ether; then HCl, H₂O

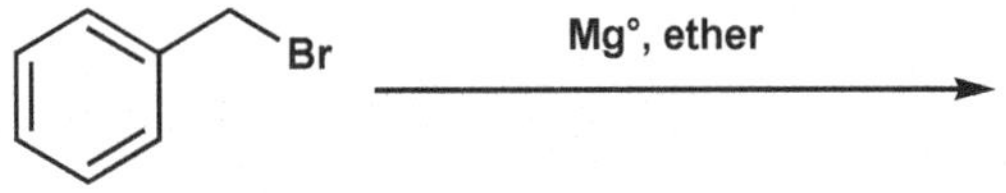

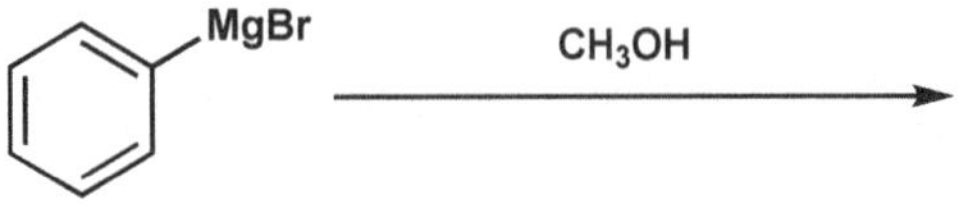

benzyl bromide + Mg°, ether

PhMgBr + CH₃OH

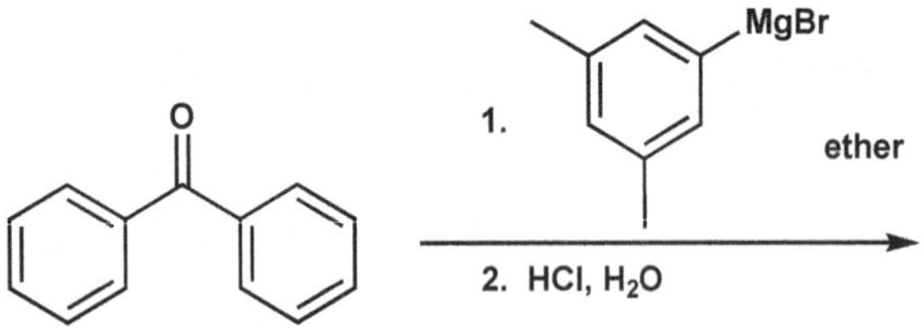

benzophenone + 3,5-dimethylphenylMgBr, ether; then HCl, H₂O

2. **Synthesis.** Provide the necessary reagents (Grignard and an electrophile) to synthesize the following molecules.

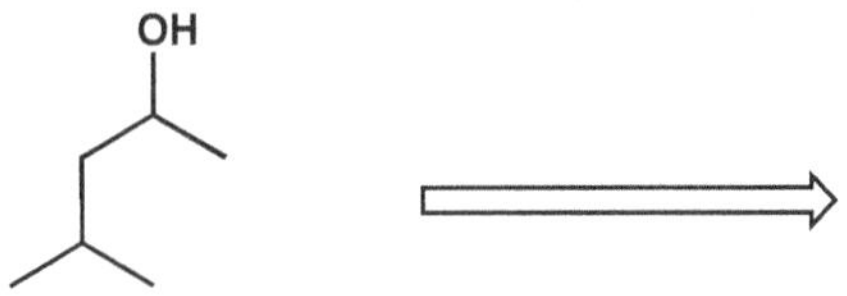

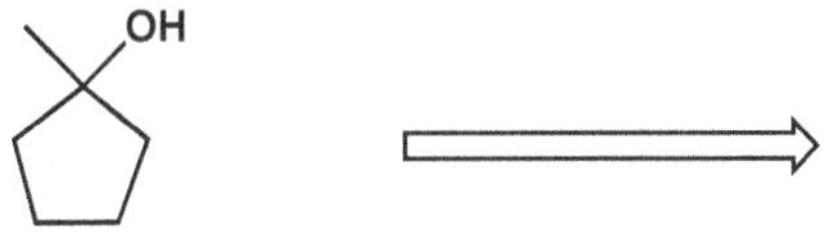

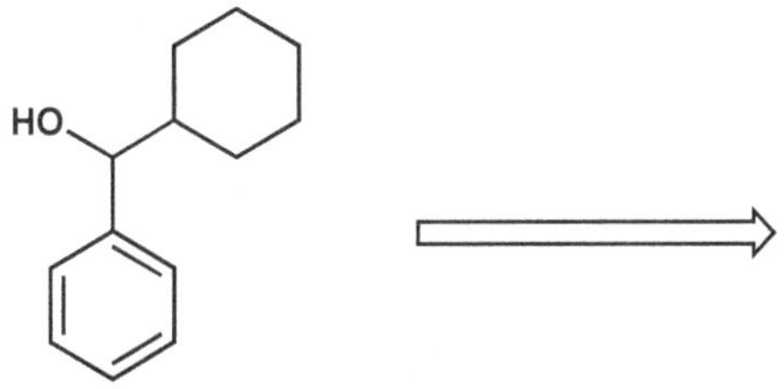

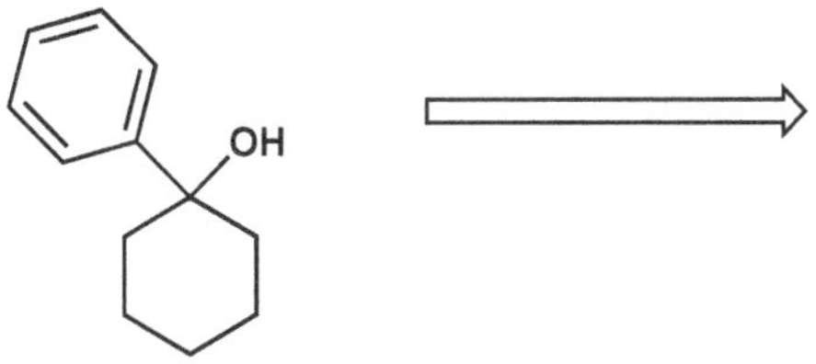

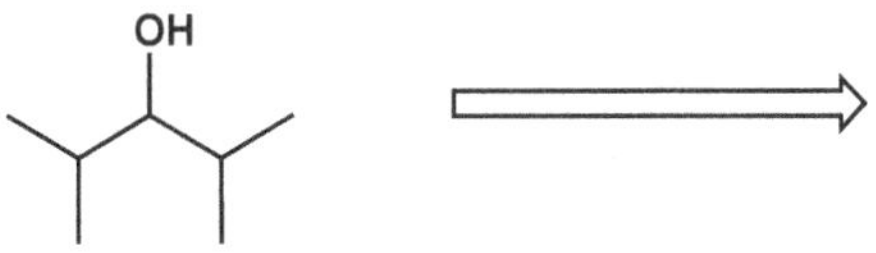

For each target alcohol, a disconnection at a C–C bond adjacent to the C–OH gives a Grignard reagent + a carbonyl electrophile:

(a) 4-methylpentan-2-ol

$$\text{(CH}_3\text{)}_2\text{CHCH}_2\text{MgBr} + \text{CH}_3\text{CHO} \;\longrightarrow\; \text{(CH}_3\text{)}_2\text{CHCH}_2\text{CH(OH)CH}_3$$

(or CH$_3$MgBr + (CH$_3$)$_2$CHCH$_2$CHO)

(b) 1-methylcyclopentan-1-ol

$$\text{CH}_3\text{MgBr} + \text{cyclopentanone} \;\longrightarrow\; \text{1-methylcyclopentanol}$$

(c) cyclohexyl(phenyl)methanol

$$\text{PhMgBr} + \text{cyclohexanecarboxaldehyde} \;\longrightarrow\; \text{Ph–CH(OH)–C}_6\text{H}_{11}$$

(or C$_6$H$_{11}$MgBr + PhCHO)

(d) 1-phenylcyclohexan-1-ol

$$\text{PhMgBr} + \text{cyclohexanone} \;\longrightarrow\; \text{1-phenylcyclohexanol}$$

(e) 2,4-dimethylpentan-3-ol

$$\text{(CH}_3\text{)}_2\text{CHMgBr} + \text{(CH}_3\text{)}_2\text{CHCHO} \;\longrightarrow\; \text{(CH}_3\text{)}_2\text{CHCH(OH)CH(CH}_3\text{)}_2$$

(f) hexan-2-ol

$$\text{CH}_3\text{CH}_2\text{CH}_2\text{CH}_2\text{MgBr} + \text{CH}_3\text{CHO} \;\longrightarrow\; \text{CH}_3\text{CH}_2\text{CH}_2\text{CH}_2\text{CH(OH)CH}_3$$

(or CH$_3$MgBr + pentanal)

All reactions: (1) Grignard in dry Et$_2$O or THF; (2) H$_3$O$^+$ workup.

14.8 Study Guide—Synthesis of Triphenylmethanol

1. Be able to describe why water inhibits formation of a Grignard reagent from an alkyl halide and magnesium.
2. Be able to describe several ways for coaxing Grignard formation to begin.
3. Know the purpose of the acidic workup that was used in this experiment. Be able to provide equations for the reactions that occur during the workup.
4. Be able to describe how Grignard reagents can be used to prepare alcohols other than triphenylmethanol.
5. Be able to interpret the TLC results you obtained in this experiment and explain their significance.
6. Be able to predict the product of other Grignard reagents reacting with electrophiles (aldehydes, ketones).

Diels-Alder Reactions

CHAPTER 15

15.1 Introduction

Pericyclic reactions are concerted processes that occur through a cyclic transition state in which more than one bond is formed or broken simultaneously within the ring. The most classic example of this type of reaction is the Diels-Alder cycloaddition reaction, which remains one of the most unique and synthetically useful reactions in synthetic chemistry.

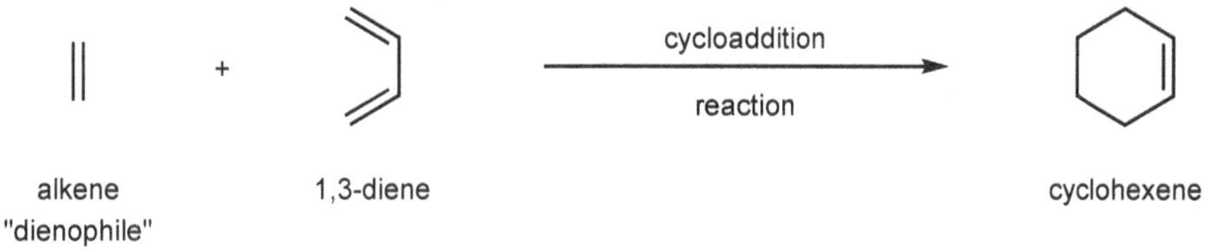

alkene "dienophile" + 1,3-diene → (cycloaddition reaction) cyclohexene

In the Diels-Alder reaction, a 1,3-diene reacts with a dienophile to form a six-membered ring adduct. Two new σ-bonds and a new π-bond are formed at the expense of three π-bonds in the starting materials. Three curved arrows are needed to show the movement of electron pairs, where the three π-bonds break and two σ-bonds and one π-bond forms. The Diels Alder reaction is exothermic by 40 kcal/mol because the energy of the two σ-bonds is worth about 20 kcal/mol more than each of the two π-bonds.

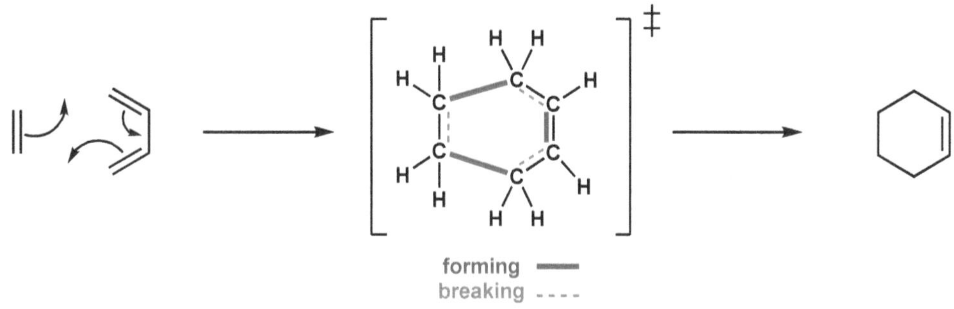

forming ——
breaking ----

The usefulness of the Diels-Alder reaction in synthesis arises from its versatility and from its remarkable stereoselectivity. In the majority of examples, all six atoms involved in forming the new ring are carbon atoms, but ring closure can also take place at atoms other than carbon, giving rise to heterocyclic compounds. Although the reaction could give rise to a number of isomeric products, one isomer is very often formed exclusively or at least in predominant amount.

The stereospecificity of the Diels-Alder reactions is very high and the stereochemistry of the dienophile is retained in the product. A *cis* dienophile will form a cis-substituted cyclohexene and a trans dienophile will form a *trans*-substituted cyclohexene.

The stereochemistry of the diene is also retained in the reaction. In the following examples, the differences in configuration resulting from the reaction of an *E,E*-diene or *E,Z*-diene are demonstrated. Both products below contain new stereocenters, but whether the *meso* product is formed, or a mixture of enantiomers is produced, is determined by the reacting diene. Since both products are synthesized from achiral starting materials, the enantiomeric products are formed as a racemic mixture via two equal-energy, but mirror image transition states.

A normal Diels-Alder reaction involves an electron-rich diene and an electron deficient dienophile, and in such cases the main interaction is that between the highest occupied molecular orbital (HOMO) of the diene and the lowest unoccupied molecular orbital (LUMO) of the dienophile. The smaller the energy difference between these frontier orbitals, the better the orbital interaction and faster the reaction.

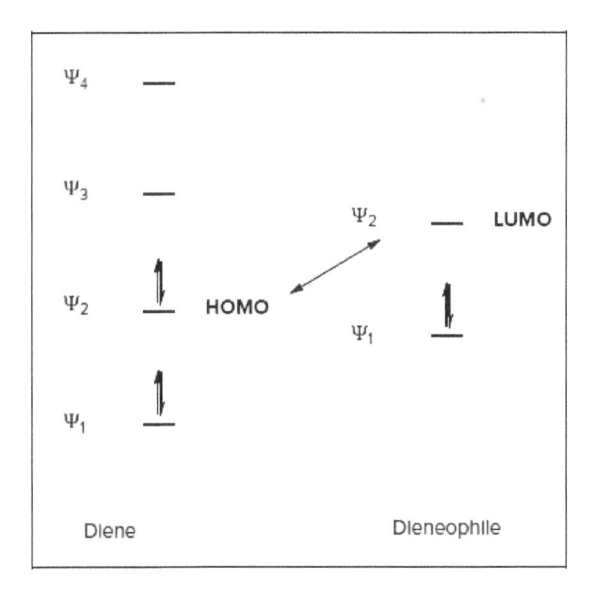

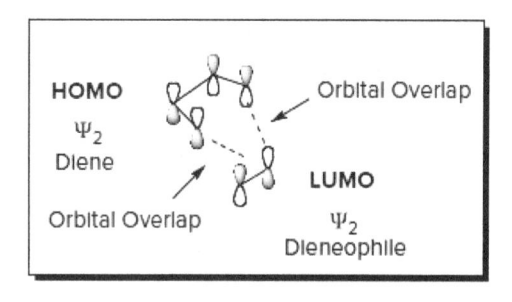

Common Features of Diels-Alder Reactions:
1. Most Diels-Alder reactions are initiated by heating.
2. The most common ring structure formed is a six membered ring.
3. Most Diels-Alder reactions are believed to be concerted. (Bonds are broken and formed in a single step.)

15.2 Prelab

Written Prelab: Record the following in your lab notebook:

- Your Name and Date
- Experiment Title
- The reaction equation for the experiment you will be performing
- The completed stoichiometry table show below
- A Plan of Procedure
- References for your property data and experiment

reagent	MW	g	mmol	equivalents	d	mL
E,E-1,4-diphenyl-1,3-butadiene						
maleic anhydride						
Theoretical product						
4,7-diphenyl-tetrahydroisobenzofuran-1,3-dione						

Electronic Prelab: Prior to the beginning of your laboratory section, login to our Chemistry 2540 Carmen page and complete the prelabs in the labeled experimental module.

15.3 Procedure—Synthesis of 4,7-diphenyl-tetrahydroisobenzofuran-1,3-dione

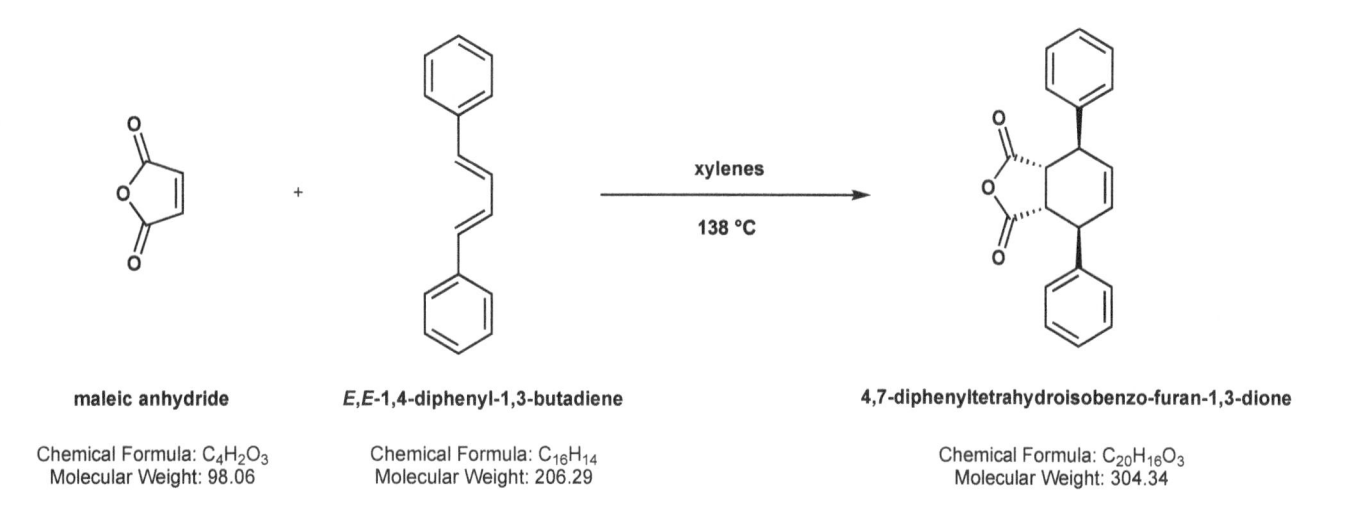

maleic anhydride
Chemical Formula: $C_4H_2O_3$
Molecular Weight: 98.06

E,E-1,4-diphenyl-1,3-butadiene
Chemical Formula: $C_{16}H_{14}$
Molecular Weight: 206.29

xylenes
138 °C

4,7-diphenyltetrahydroisobenzo-furan-1,3-dione
Chemical Formula: $C_{20}H_{16}O_3$
Molecular Weight: 304.34

Procedure

1. **Reaction:** In a pre-weighed 5-mL conical vial, add 0.100 g 1,4-diphenyl-1,3-butadiene and 0.05 g maleic anhydride, 2 mL xylenes, and a spinvane.

2. **Reaction:** Attach a water-cooled condenser equipped with a drying tube containing calcium chloride and heat the reaction at reflux for 1 hour. *During this time, the solids should dissolve to form a homogeneous mixture.*

3. **Cooling:** Allow the reaction vessel to cool to room temperature. After crystal formation is evident, cool the conical vial in an ice bath for 10 minutes. *If crystals do not appear, induce crystallization by scratching at the air-liquid interface or using a seed crystal.*

4. **Isolation:** Isolate the crystals by vacuum filtration, washing with several 1 mL portions of hexanes.

5. Transfer your product to a labeled vial, and determine the weight of your final product.

15.4 Postlab Data Submission

Prepare this table of *Postlab Data* in your *Laboratory Notebook* after your completed experimental narrative, and fill in the appropriate data in the correct box:

Synthesis of 4,7-Diphenyltetrahydroisobenzofuran-1,3-dione					
starting materials	experimental mass (g)	mmol			
E,E-1,4-diphenyl-1,3-butadiene				
maleic anhydride				
product	experimental mass (g)	mmol	theoretical mass (g)	% yield
4,7-diphenyltetrahydroisobenzofuran-1,3-dione				

Login to our Chemistry 2540 Carmen page and complete any listed postlab assignments in the labeled experimental module.

Postlab assignments are due as listed on the Course Schedule.

15.5 Digital Lab Report Guidelines

Login to our Chemistry 2540 Carmen page and download a copy of the appropriate *DigitalLab Report Template* for this experiment in the labeled experimental module. Follow the instructions listed in the *Digital Lab Report Template* with regard to the preparation of ChemDraw drawings, Formal Procedure section, and the answers to Concept Questions. Submit your completed Digital Lab Report as a Microsoft Word Document (.doc or .docx file only) or Adobe PDF to the Chemistry 2540 experiment assignment. Digital Lab Reports are due as listed on the Course Schedule, and late submissions will be penalized –10 pts per day late.

15.6 Diels-Alder Practice Problems

1. **Synthesis.** Provide the necessary reagents to synthesize the following molecules.

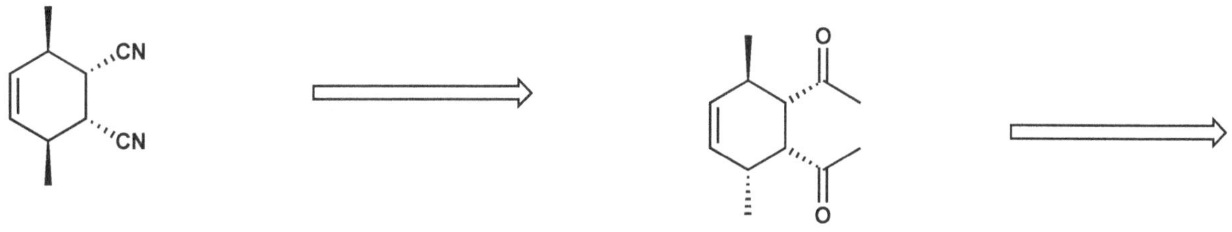

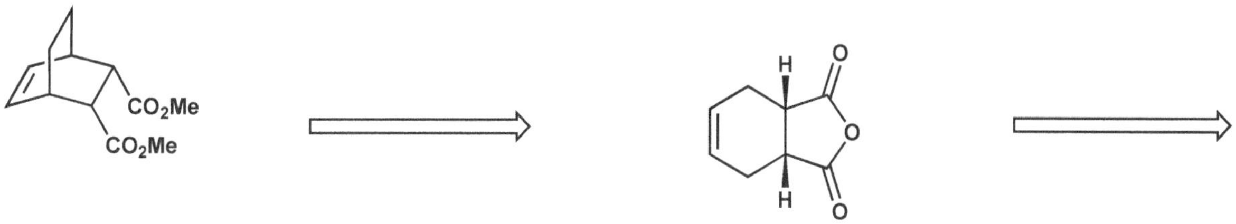

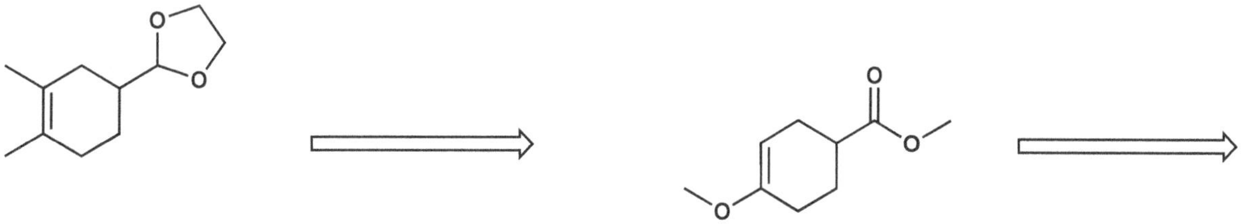

2. Provide the complete mechanism that shows the formation of the products for the following reaction.

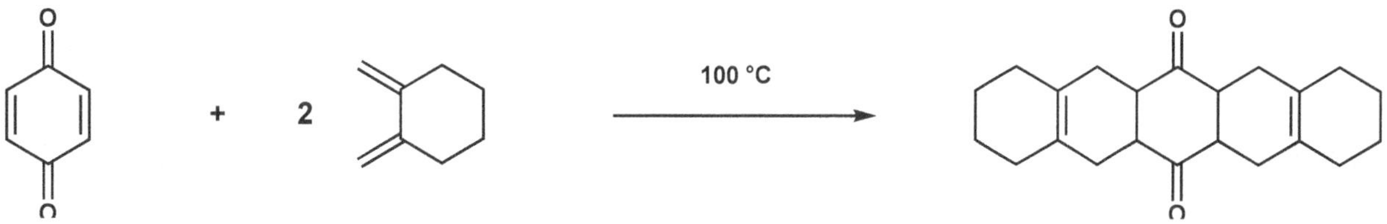

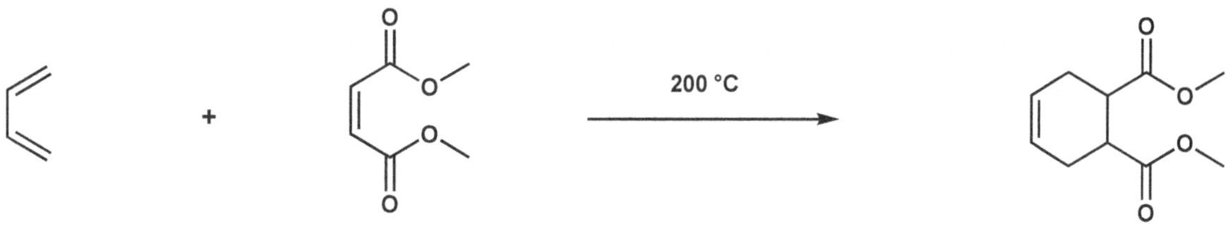

3. Predict the products for the following reactions

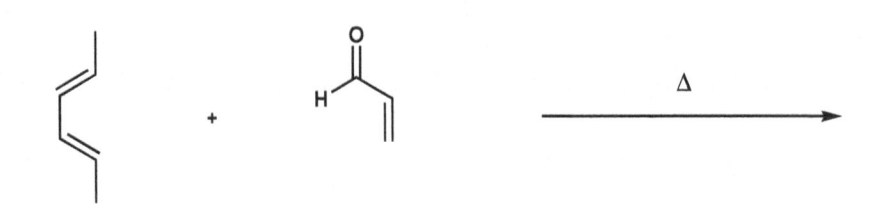

15.7 Study Guide—Diels Alder Reactions

1. Be able to predict the product of a Diels Alder reaction with predictions of preferred regio-chemistry and stereochemistry.
2. Be able to explain the mechanism for a Diels Alder reaction.
3. Be able to explain the orbital overlap in a Diels Alder reaction and be able to predict favorable reactions based on molecular orbital theory.

The Organic Chemist's Periodic Table

APPENDIX 1

The Organic Chemist's Periodic Table

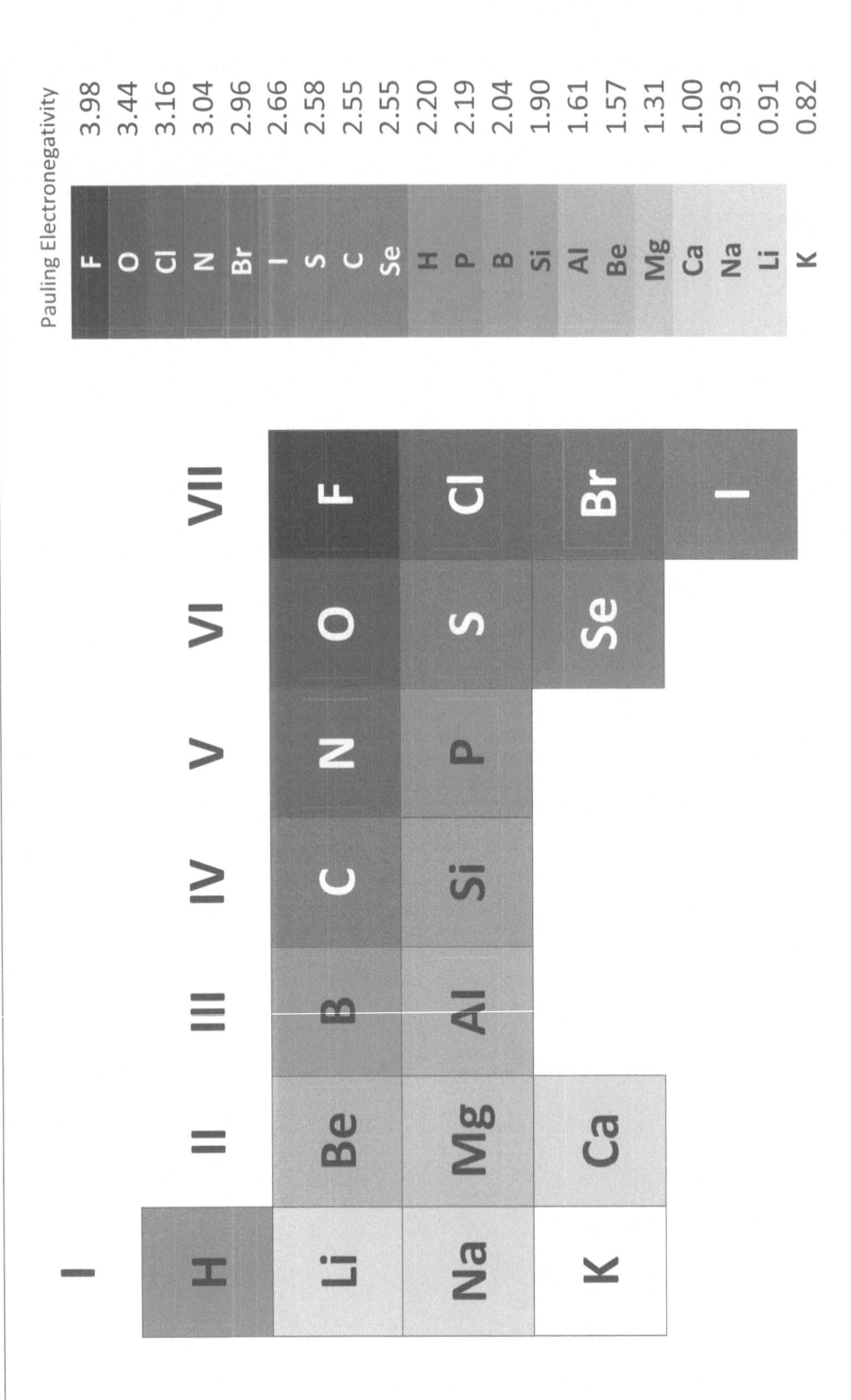

I	II	III	IV	V	VI	VII
H						
Li	Be	B	C	N	O	F
Na	Mg	Al	Si	P	S	Cl
K	Ca				Se	Br
						I

Pauling Electronegativity	
F	3.98
O	3.44
Cl	3.16
N	3.04
Br	2.96
I	2.66
S	2.58
C	2.55
Se	2.55
H	2.20
P	2.19
B	2.04
Si	1.90
Al	1.61
Be	1.57
Mg	1.31
Ca	1.00
Na	0.93
Li	0.91
K	0.82

Created by Dr. Noel M. Paul, with most sincere apologies to the other elements © 2009

A Collection of pK$_a$ + K$_a$ Tables

APPENDIX 2

acid name	acid formula	base formula	base name	K_a	pK_a
perchloric acid	$HClO_4$	ClO_4^-	perchlorate	1×10^{10}	-10
hydroiodic acid	HI	I^-	iodide	3.2×10^9	-10
hydrobromic acid	HBr	Br^-	bromide	1×10^9	-9
hydrochloric acid	HCl	Cl^-	chloride	1.3×10^8	-8
sulfuric acid	H_2SO_4	HSO_4^-	bisulfate	1.0×10^3	-3
hydronium ion	H_3O^+	H_2O	water	5.0×10^1	-1
nitric acid	HNO_3	NO_3^-	nitrate	2.4×10^1	-2
oxalic acid	$HO_2C_2O_2H$	$HO_2C_2O_2^-$	hydrogen oxalate	5.4×10^{-2}	1
sulfurous acid	H_2SO_3	HSO_3^-	bisulfite	1.3×10^{-2}	2
bisulfate	HSO_4^-	SO_4^{2-}	sulfate	1.0×10^{-2}	2
phosphoric acid	H_3PO_4	$H_3PO_4^-$	dihydrogen phosphate	7.1×10^{-3}	2
nitrous acid	HNO_2	NO_2^-	nitrite	7.2×10^{-4}	3
hydrofluoric acid	HF	F^-	fluoride	6.6×10^{-4}	3
formic acid	HCO_2H	HCO_2^-	formate	1.8×10^{-4}	4
hydrogen selenide	H_3Se	HSe^-	hydroselenide	1.3×10^{-4}	4
benzoic acid	C_6H_5COOH	$C_6H_5COO^-$	benzoate	6.3×10^{-5}	4
hydrogen oxalate	$HO_2C_2O^{2-}$	$O_2C_2O_2^{2-}$	oxalate	5.4×10^{-5}	4
hydrazoic acid	HN_3	N_3^-	azide	2.5×10^{-5}	5
acetic acid	CH_3COOH	CH_3COO^-	acetate	1.8×10^{-5}	5
carbonic acid	H_2CO_3	HCO_3^-	bicarbonate	4.4×10^{-7}	6
hydrogen sulfide	H_2S	HS^-	hydrosulfide	1.1×10^{-7}	7
dihydrogen phosphate	$H_2PO_4^-$	HPO_4^{2-}	hydrogen phosphate	6.3×10^{-8}	7
bisulfite	HSO_3^-	SO_3^{2-}	sulfite	6.2×10^{-8}	7
hypochlorous acid	$HClO$	ClO^-	hypochlorite	2.9×10^{-8}	8
hydrocyanic acid	HCN	^-CN	cyanide	6.2×10^{-10}	9
ammonium	NH_4^+	NH_3	ammonia	5.8×10^{-10}	9
boric acid	H_3BO_3	$H_2BO_3^-$	dihydrogen borate	5.8×10^{-10}	9
bicarbonate	HCO_3^-	CO_3^{2-}	carbonate	4.7×10^{-11}	10
hydrogen phosphate	HPO_4^{2-}	PO_4^{3-}	phosphate	4.2×10^{-13}	12
dihydrogen borate	$H_2BO_3^-$	HBO_3^{2-}	hydrogen borate	1.8×10^{-13}	13
hydrosulfide	HS^-	S^{2-}	sulfide	1.3×10^{-13}	13
hydrogen borate	HBO_3^{2-}	BO_3^{3-}	borate	1.6×10^{-14}	14
water	H_2O	HO^-	hydroxide	1.8×10^{-16}	16
methanol	CH_3OH	CH_3O^-	methoxide	3.2×10^{-16}	16
hydrogen	H_2	H^-	hydride	1×10^{-36}	36
ammonia	NH_3	NH_2^-	azanide/amide	1×10^{-38}	38
methane	CH_4	$^-CH_3$	methide	1×10^{-48}	48

The Lucky Seven

	inorganic acids	carboxylic acids	alcohols	alkynes	amines	alkenes	alkanes
pK_a	–5	5	15	25	35	45	55
	strongest acids: unstable H–A bond dissociates easily						**weakest acids:** stable H–A bond dissociates poorly
	←——————————— increasing acid strength = decreasing stability of H–A bond ———————————						
H–A	H–X	R–C(=O)–O–H	R–Ö–H	R–C≡C–H	R₂N–H (R,H)	R₂C=CR–H	R₃C–H
	↓	↓	↓	↓	↓	↓	↓
A:⁻	X:⁻	R–C(=O)–O:⁻	R–Ö:⁻	R–C≡C:⁻	R₂N:⁻	R₂C=CR:⁻	R₃C:⁻
	weakest bases: stable (unreactive) A:⁻						**strongest bases:** unstable (reactive) A:⁻
	——————————— increasing base strength = decreasing stability of A:⁻ ———————————→						
	stability due to:	stability due to:	stability due to:	stability due to:	stability due to:	stability due to:	(in)stability due to:
	elemental effect (size; A = Cl, Br, I) or resonance effects (A = sulfate, nitrate)	elemental effects (EN; A = O) and resonance effects	elemental effects (EN; A = O)	hybridization effects (sp; 50% s character)	elemental effects (EN; A = N)	hybridization effects (sp2; 33% s character)	elemental effects (EN; A = C) small orbitals (size) hybridization effects (sp3; 25% s character) concentrated charge localized to one atom (no resonance possible)

APPENDIX 2 ❖ A Collection of pK_a + K_a Tables **205**

Created by Dr. Noel M. Paul © 2010

206 APPENDIX 2 ❖ A Collection of pK_a + K_a Tables

The Lucky Thirteen

	inorganic acids	oxonium	carboxylic acids	ammonium	1,3-dicarbonyl	alcohols	carbonyl	alkynes	diallyl dibenzyl	amines	allyl benzyl	alkenes	alkanes
pK_a	−5	0	5	10	10	15	20	25	35	35	40	45	55

increasing acid strength = decreasing stability of H–A bond →

increasing base strength = decreasing stability of A^- ←

strongest acids: unstable H–A bond dissociates easily

weakest acids: stable H–A bond dissociates poorly

weakest bases: stable (unreactive) A^-

strongest bases: unstable (reactive) A^-

stability due to:
- inorganic acids: elemental effect (size; A = Cl, Br, I) or resonance effects (A = sulfate, nitrate)
- oxonium: elemental effects (EN; A = O) and charge neutralization
- carboxylic acids: elemental effects (EN; A = O) and resonance effects
- ammonium: elemental effects (EN; A = N) and charge neutralization
- 1,3-dicarbonyl: elemental effects (EN of O) and resonance effects
- alcohols: elemental effects (EN; A = O)
- carbonyl: elemental effects (EN of O) and resonance effects
- alkynes: hybridization effects (sp; 50% s character)
- diallyl dibenzyl: resonance effects
- amines: elemental effects (EN; A = N)
- allyl benzyl: resonance effects
- alkenes: hybridization effects (sp2; 33% s character)
- alkanes: (in)stability due to: elemental effects (EN; A = C) small orbitals (size) hybridization effects (sp3; 25% s character) concentrated charge localized to one atom (no resonance possible)

Created by Dr. Noel M. Paul © 2010

pKa Chart

APPENDIX 2 ❖ A Collection of pKa + Ka Tables   207

Compound	pKa	Solvent
trifluoromethane sulfonic acid	-14*, 0.3	(H₂O, DMSO)
perchloric acid	-10*	(H₂O)
hydrobromic acid	-9.0*, 0.9	(H₂O, DMSO)
hydrochloric acid	-8.0*, 1.8	(H₂O, DMSO)
protonated carboxylic acid	-7.8*	(H₂O)
protonated aromatic ether	-6.5*	(H₂O)
protonated ketone	-6.2*	(H₂O)
protonated alkyl ether	-3.8*	(H₂O)
sulfuric acid	-3.0*, 1.99	(H₂O, DMSO)
methane sulfonic acid	-2.6*, 1.6	(H₂O, DMSO)
protonated methanol	-2.2*	(H₂O)
protonated THF	-2.05*	(H₂O)
hydronium Ion	-1.7*	(H₂O)
nitric acid	-1.3*	(H₂O, DMSO)
trifluoroacetic acid	0.25	(DMSO)
fluoroacetic acid	2.66	(H₂O)
phosphoric acid	2.12, 7.21, 12.32	(H₂O)
hydrofluoric acid	3.17, 15	(H₂O, DMSO)
formic acid	3.77	(H₂O)
benzoic acid	4.2, 11.1	(H₂O, DMSO)
protonated aniline	4.6, 3.6	(H₂O, DMSO)
protonated pyridine	5.2	(H₂O)
carbonic acid	6.4, 10.3	(H₂O, DMSO)
protonated imidazole	6.95	(H₂O)
hydrogen sulfide	7.0	(H₂O)
phthalimide	8.3	
acetylacetone	9.13	
hydrogen cyanide	9.4, 12.9	(H₂O, DMSO)
phenol	9.95, 18.0	(H₂O, DMSO)
nitromethane	10.0, 17.2	(H₂O, DMSO)
protonated N,N-diisopropylamine	11.05	
hydrogen peroxide	11.6	
dimethyl malonate	13.0, 15.7	(H₂O, DMSO)
cyclopentadiene	15.0*, 18.0	(H₂O, DMSO)
methanol	15.5, 27.9	(H₂O, DMSO)
water	15.7, 26.1	(H₂O, DMSO)
ethanol	15.9, 29.9	(H₂O, DMSO)
isopropyl alcohol	16.5, 29.3	(H₂O, DMSO)
ammonium chloride	9.24	(H₂O)
t-butanol	17.0*, 29.4	(H₂O, DMSO)
1-cyanoacetylpyrrolidine	17.2	(THF)
N,N-dimethylacetoacetamide	18.2	(DMSO)
t-butyl 2-phenylacetate	23.6	(DMSO)
ethyne	24.0*	(H₂O)
acetophenone	24.7	
acetamide	25.5	
acetone	26.5	
N,N-dimethyl-2-phenylacetamide	26.6	(DMSO)
t-butyl acetate	30.3	(DMSO)
triphenylmethane	31.5*, 30.6	(H₂O, DMSO)
aniline	30.6	(DMSO)
diphenylmethane	33.5*, 32.3	(H₂O, DMSO)
N,N-diisopropylamine	36.0	(THF)
hydrogen	36*	
ammonia	38.0*, 41.0*	(H₂O, DMSO)
toluene	41.0*, 43.0*	(H₂O, DMSO)
benzene	43.0*	(H₂O)
cyclopropane	46*	(H₂O)
methane	48.0*, 56.0*	(H₂O, DMSO)
anisole	49.0*	(H₂O)
ethene	50.0*	(H₂O)
propane	51.0*	(H₂O)
2-methylpropane	53.0*	(H₂O)

Values <0 for H₂O and DMSO, and values >14 for water and >35 for DMSO were extrapolated using various methods.
*For a comprehensive compilation of Bordwell pKa data see: http://www.chem.wisc.edu/areas/reich/pkatable/index.htm

Developed by Christoper Callam and Leah Sabato © 2010

Nucleophile vs. Base Table

APPENDIX 3

APPENDIX 3 ❖ Nucleophile vs. Base Table

Nucleophile Vs. Base

stronger B:

(CH₃)₃C⁻

CH₃CH₂CH₂CH₂⁻

C₆H₅⁻ (phenyl anion)

(iPr)₂N⁻

(CH₃)₃CO⁻

R—C≡C⁻

H₂N⁻

CH₃O⁻
HO⁻

Et₃N

Et₂NH
NH₃

E2	S_N2+E2
S_N1+E1	S_N2

worse Nu: ←————————————————————————————→ **better Nu:**

N₃⁻

CN⁻

RS⁻

Et₃P

CH₃CO₂⁻ (acetate)

R₂S

RSe⁻

R₂Se

Ph₃P

F⁻

poor LG:
- -
good LG:

Cl⁻

Br⁻

NO₃⁻

R—SO₂—O⁻ (sulfonate)

I⁻

H₂O

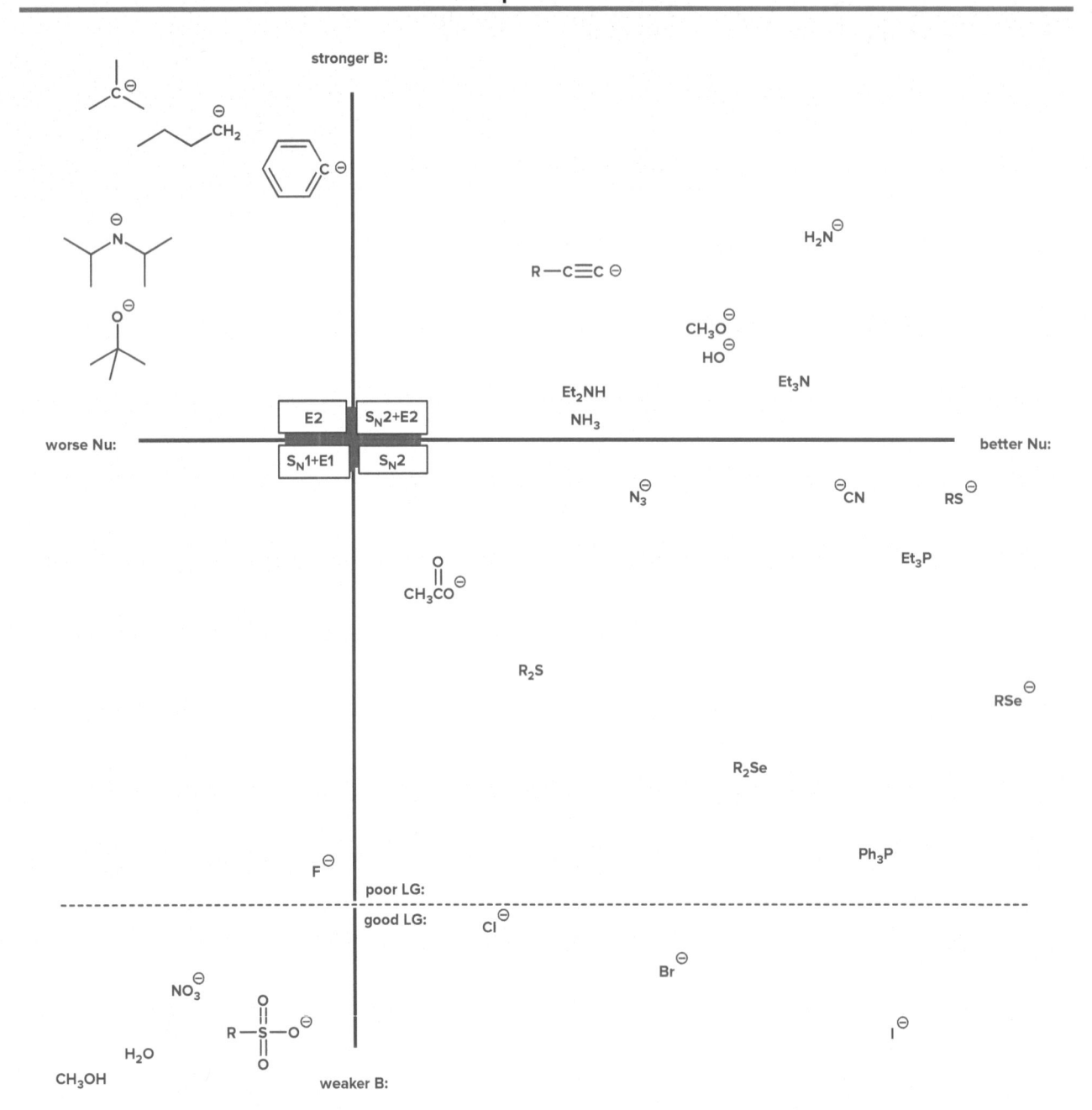

CH₃OH

weaker B:

Created by Dr. Noel M. Paul © 2010

Functional Group Directory

APPENDIX 4

Common Side-Chain Directory

APPENDIX 4 ❖ Functional Group Directory — p. 212

group name	essential Lewis structure	condensed formula abbreviation	line structure example / example common name / example IUPAC name
methyl	CH₃ with 3 H's	CH₃- / Me-	H₃C–F / methyl fluoride / fluoromethane
ethyl	-CH₂CH₃ Lewis	CH₃CH₂- / Et-	ethyl bromide / bromoethane
n-propyl	-CH₂CH₂CH₃ Lewis	CH₃(CH₂)₂- / n-Pr-	n-propyl fluoride / 1-fluoropropane
isopropyl	(CH₃)₂CH– Lewis	(CH₃)₂CH- / i-Pr-	isopropyl fluoride / 2-fluoropropane
n-butyl	-(CH₂)₃CH₃ Lewis	CH₃(CH₂)₃- / n-Bu-	n-butyl bromide / 1-bromobutane
sec-butyl	CH₃CH₂CH(CH₃)– Lewis	(CH₃)₃C- / sec-Bu-	sec-butyl iodide / 2-iodobutane
isobutyl	(CH₃)₂CHCH₂– Lewis	(CH₃)₂CHCH₂- / i-Bu-	isobutyl bromide / 1-bromo-2-methylpropane
tert-butyl	(CH₃)₃C– Lewis	(CH₃)₃C- / t-Bu-	tert-butyl bromide / 2-bromo-2-methylpropane
vinyl	CH₂=CH– Lewis	CH₂CH-	vinyl chloride / chloroethylene
phenyl	C₆H₅– Lewis	C₆H₅- / Ph-	phenyl iodide / iodobenzene
acetyl	CH₃C(=O)– Lewis	CH₃CO- / Ac-	acetyl chloride / ethanoyl chloride
benzoyl	C₆H₅C(=O)– Lewis	C₆H₅CO- or PhCO- / Bz-	benzoyl chloride / phenylmethanoyl chloride
allyl	CH₂=CHCH₂– Lewis	CH₂CHCH₂-	allyl bromide / 3-bromo-1-propene
benzyl	C₆H₅CH₂– Lewis	C₆H₅CH₂- / Bn-	benzyl chloride / (chloromethyl)benzene
propargyl	HC≡CCH₂– Lewis	HCCCH₂-	propargyl bromide / 3-bromo-1-propyne

Developed by Christopher Callam and Noel M. Paul © 2012

The Functional Group Directory (I)

compound class				
essential Lewis structure (alternate name)	**example** examplename			
alkane R—R' (alkyl group)	butane	**amine** R*—N(R)—R (amino group)	n-butylamine (NH₂)	**alcohol** R*—Ö—H (hydroxyl group)	butanol	**borane** R—B(R)—R	trimethylborane
alkene R₂C=CR₂ (olefin)	trans-2-butene	**ammonium** R*—N⁺(R)(R)—R	tetramethylammonium chloride	**ether** R*—Ö—R*	diethylether	**silane** R—Si(R)(R)—R	tetramethylsilane
alkyne R—C≡C—R (acetylene)	2-butyne	**aziridine** (N-R ring with R groups)	2-methylaziridine	**epoxide** (oxirane)	2,3-epoxypentane	**phosphine** R—P(R)—R	trimethylphosphine
aromatic hydrocarbon (arene, aryl group)	1-phenylbutane	**hydrazine** R₂N—NR₂	methylhydrazine (NH₂)	**peroxide** R—Ö—Ö—R	di-tert-butylperoxide	**thiol** R*—S̈—H (mercapto or sulfhydryl)	butanethiol (SH)
halo R*—Ẍ: (halide) (bromo, bromide)	1-bromopropane (Br)	**amide¹** R*—N⁻(R)—R (azanide)	lithium dimethylamide (Li⁺)	**alkoxide** R*—Ö:⁻	potassium ethoxide (K⁺)	**thioether** R*—S̈—R* (sulfide)	diethylthioether
		hydroxylamine R—N(R)—Ö—H	dimethylhydroxylamine (OH)	**amineoxide** R*—N⁺(R)(R)—Ö:⁻	trimethylamine N-oxide	**disulfide** R*—S̈—S̈—R*	diethyl disulfide

Developed by Christopher Callam and Leah Sabato
Expanded by Christopher Callam and Noel M. Paul © 2013

LEGEND
R = any C (except C=O) or H
R* = any C (except C=O) but never H

214 APPENDIX 4 ❖ Functional Group Directory

The Functional Group Directory (II)

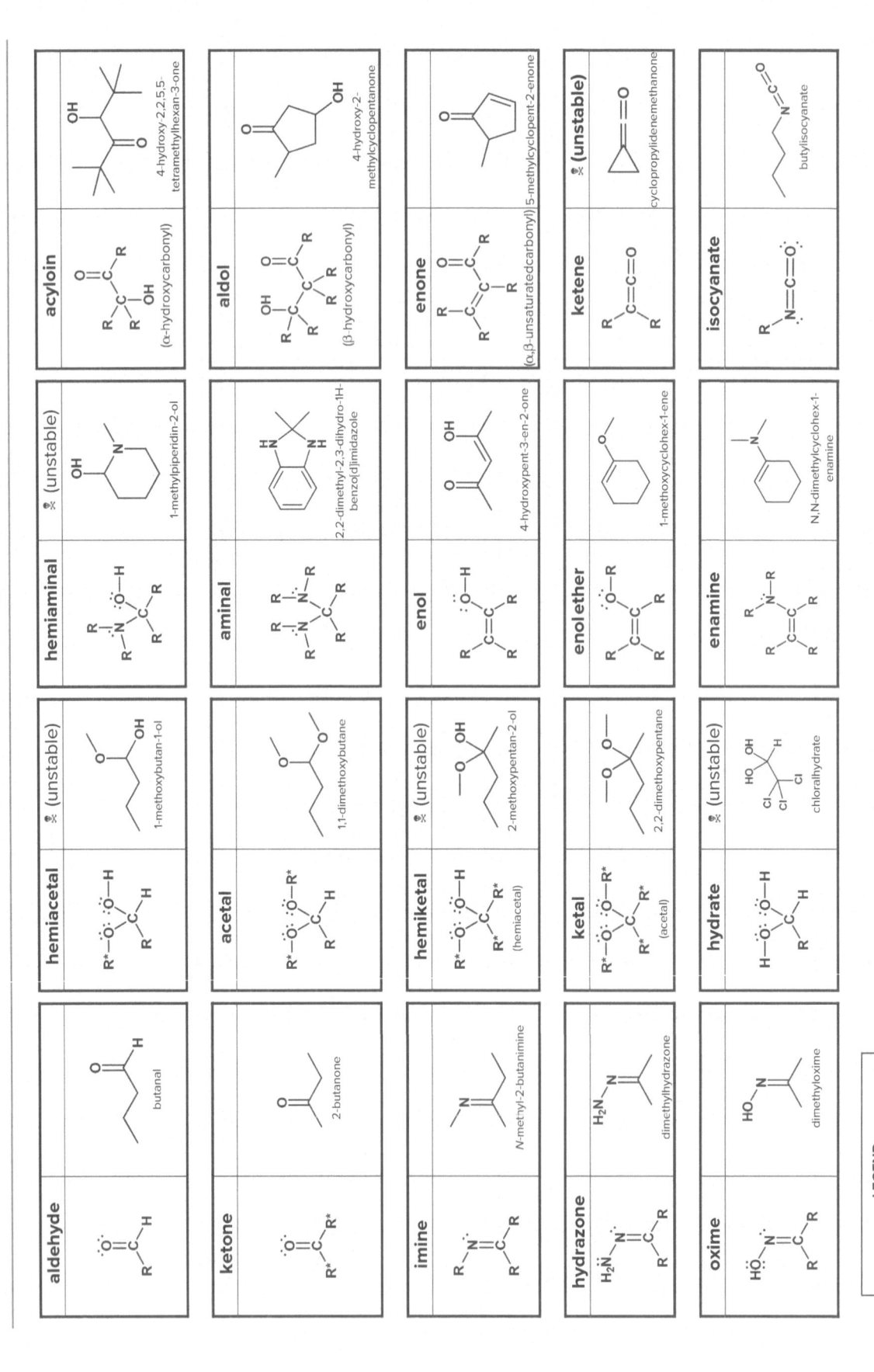

The Functional Group Directory (III)

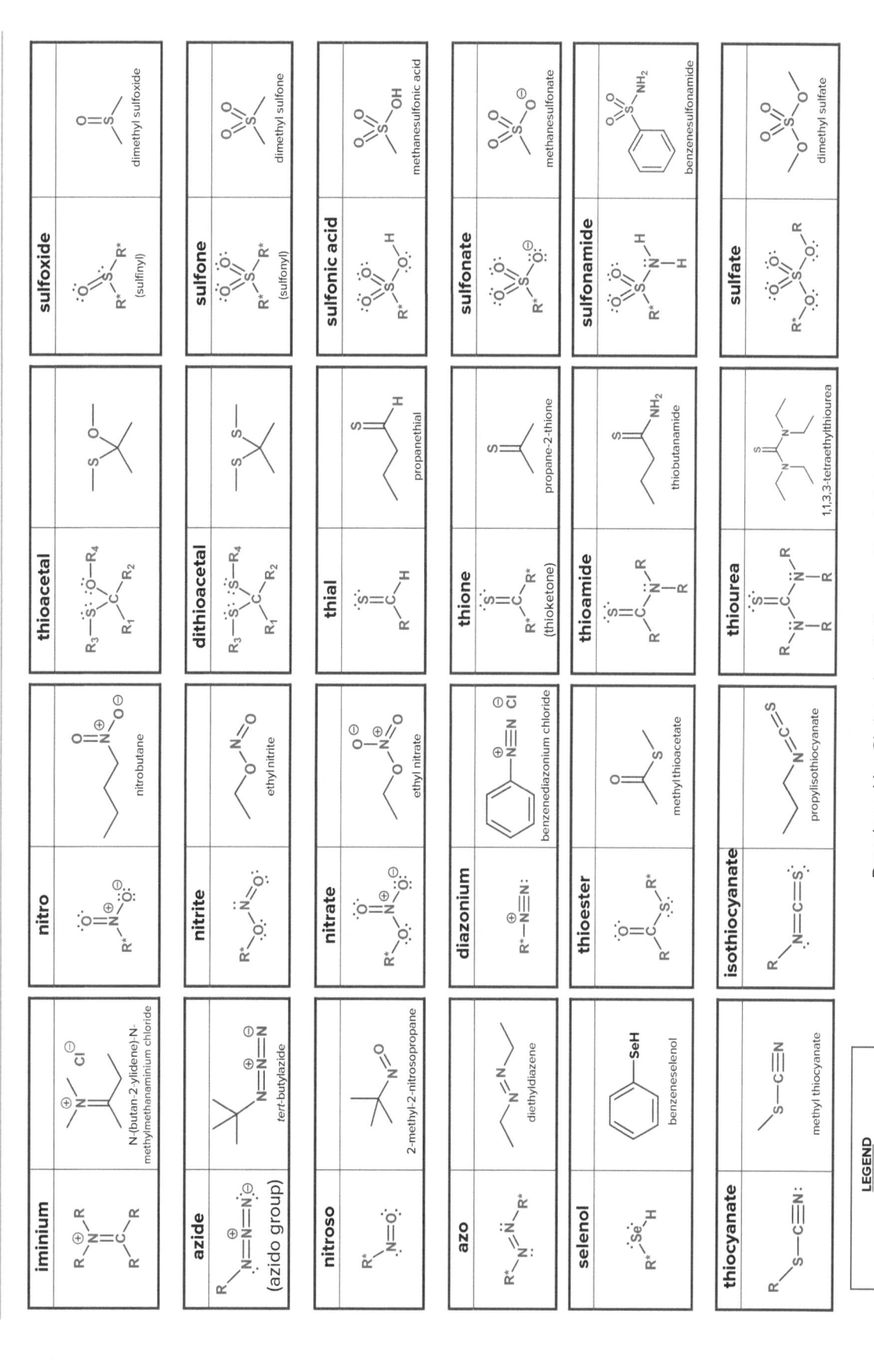

iminium	**nitro**	**thioacetal**
azide (azido group)	**nitrite**	**dithioacetal**
nitroso	**nitrate**	**thial**
azo	**diazonium**	**thione** (thioketone)
selenol	**thioester**	**thioamide**
thiocyanate	**isothiocyanate**	**thiourea**

sulfoxide (sulfinyl) — dimethyl sulfoxide
sulfone (sulfonyl) — dimethyl sulfone
sulfonic acid — methanesulfonic acid
sulfonate — methanesulfonate
sulfonamide — benzenesulfonamide
sulfate — dimethyl sulfate

Examples: N-(butan-2-ylidene)-N-methylmethanaminium chloride; tert-butylazide; 2-methyl-2-nitrosopropane; diethyldiazene; benzeneselenol; methyl thiocyanate; nitrobutane; ethyl nitrite; ethyl nitrate; benzenediazonium chloride; methylthioacetate; propylisothiocyanate; propanethial; propane-2-thione; thiobutanamide; 1,1,3,3-tetraethylthiourea.

LEGEND
R = any C (except C=O) or H
R* = any C (except C=O) but never H

Developed by Christopher Callam and Leah Sabato
Expanded by Christopher Callam and Noel M. Paul © 2013

The Functional Group Directory (IV)

carboxylic acid — butanoic acid	**acyl halide** (carboxylic acid halide, alkanoyl halide, acid halide) — butanoyl chloride	**nitrile** R*—C≡N: (cyanogroup) — butanenitrile	**orthoester** — methyl orthoacetate
carboxylic ester (ester) — ethyl butanoate	**carboxylate** — sodium butanoate	**lactone** — γ-butyrolactone	**anhydride** — acetic anhydride
carboxylic amide (carboxamide or amide) — butanamide	**amidate** (carboxamidate) — lithium N-methylacetimidate	**lactam** — δ-valerolactam	**imide** — diacetimide
amidine — 1,8-diazabicycloundec-7-ene	**peracid** — m-chloroperbenzoic acid	**carbonate** — dimethylcarbonate	**carbamate** urethane — ethyl carbamate
carbodiimide — dicyclohexylcarbodiimide	**orthocarbonate** — methyl orthocarbonate	**urea** — dimethylurea	**guanidine** — methylguanidine

Developed by Christopher Callam and Leah Sabato
Expanded by Christopher Callam and Noel M. Paul © 2013

LEGEND
R = any C (except C=O) or H
R* = any C (except C=O) but never H

Spectroscopy Reference

APPENDIX 5

5.1 – IR Spectroscopy

IR Stretching Frequency Reference Zones

Range	Bond
3250	O—H, N—H
~3200	
3000	C—H
~2700	
2250	C≡N, C≡C
~2000	
1715	C=O
~1650	
1600	C=C
~1400	
	N=O, C—C, C—O, C—N, C—X

4000 cm⁻¹ ———————————————— 600 cm⁻¹

Critical Reference Values are the center value of the FG range. Adding approximate "*Zone Lines*" can be helpful in the analysis.
(All values in units cm⁻¹)

APPENDIX 5 ❖ Spectroscopy Reference   219

Carbonyl Functional Group Stretching Frequencies

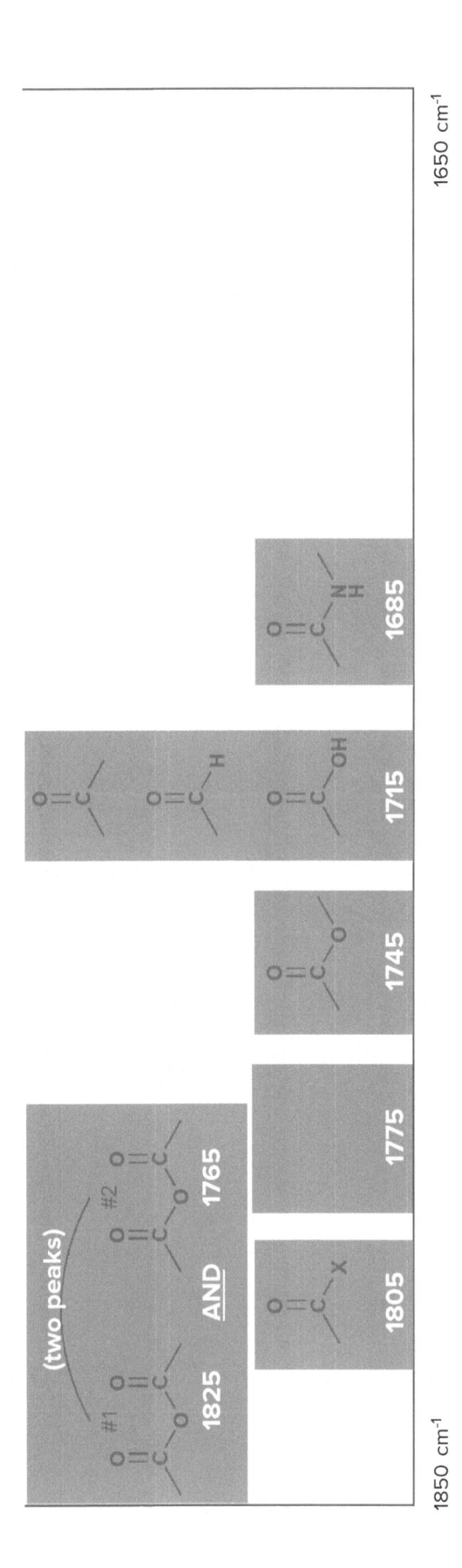

Structure	cm⁻¹
Anhydride (two peaks) #1 / #2	1825 AND 1765
Acid halide (O=C–X)	1805
Ester (O=C–O)	1745
Ketone / Aldehyde (O=C–H) / Carboxylic acid (O=C–OH)	1715
Amide (O=C–NH)	1685

1850 cm⁻¹ — 1650 cm⁻¹

Carbonyl Adjustments for Conjugation and Ring Strain

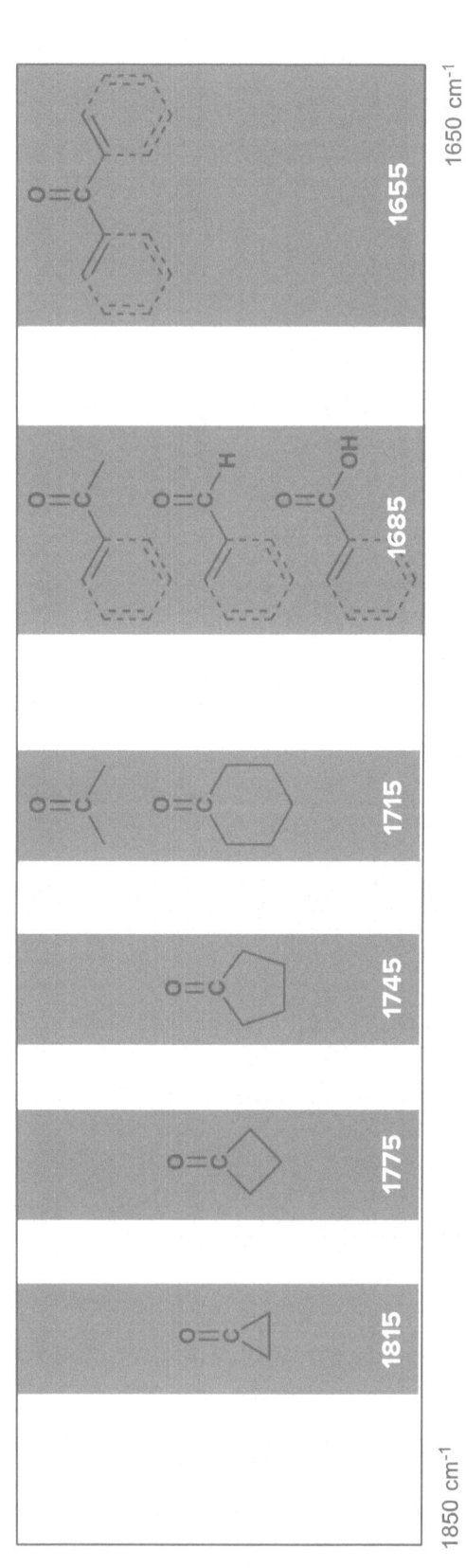

Structure	cm⁻¹
Cyclopropanone	1815
Cyclobutanone	1775
Cyclopentanone	1745
Acyclic ketone / Cyclohexanone	1715
Aryl ketone / Aryl aldehyde / Aryl carboxylic acid	1685
Conjugated enone	1655

Strain increases vibrational energy ∼+30 cm⁻¹   **Conjugation** decreases vibrational frequency ∼−30 cm⁻¹

1850 cm⁻¹ — 1650 cm⁻¹

5.2 – Mass Spectrometry

Table of Isotope Abundances with Exact Mass and Molecular Weight

^{1}H 99.98%	^{12}C 98.93%	^{14}N 99.64%	^{16}O 99.76%	^{19}F 100%
^{2}H 0.02%	^{13}C 1.07%	^{15}N 0.36%	^{18}O 0.20%	
H 1.0079	C 12.0107	N 14.0067	O 15.9994	F 18.9984
^{10}B 19.9%	^{28}Si 92.22%	^{31}P 100%	^{32}S 95.02%	^{35}Cl 75.76%
^{11}B 80.1%	^{29}Si 4.69%		^{33}S 0.75%	^{37}Cl 24.24%
	^{30}Si 3.09%		^{34}S 4.32%	
B 10.811	Si 28.086	P 30.974	S 32.065	Cl 35.453
				^{79}Br 50.69%
				^{81}Br 49.31%
				Br 79.904
				^{127}I 100%
				I 126.90

Isotope Atomic Mass used in "Exact Mass" calculations

Molar Mass Averages used in "Molecular Weight" calculations

Reference - http://physics.nist.gov/cgi-bin/Compositions/stand_alone.pl?ele=&all=all&ascii=html&isotype=some

Multi-Halogen Isotope Patterns for the Molecular Ion Region

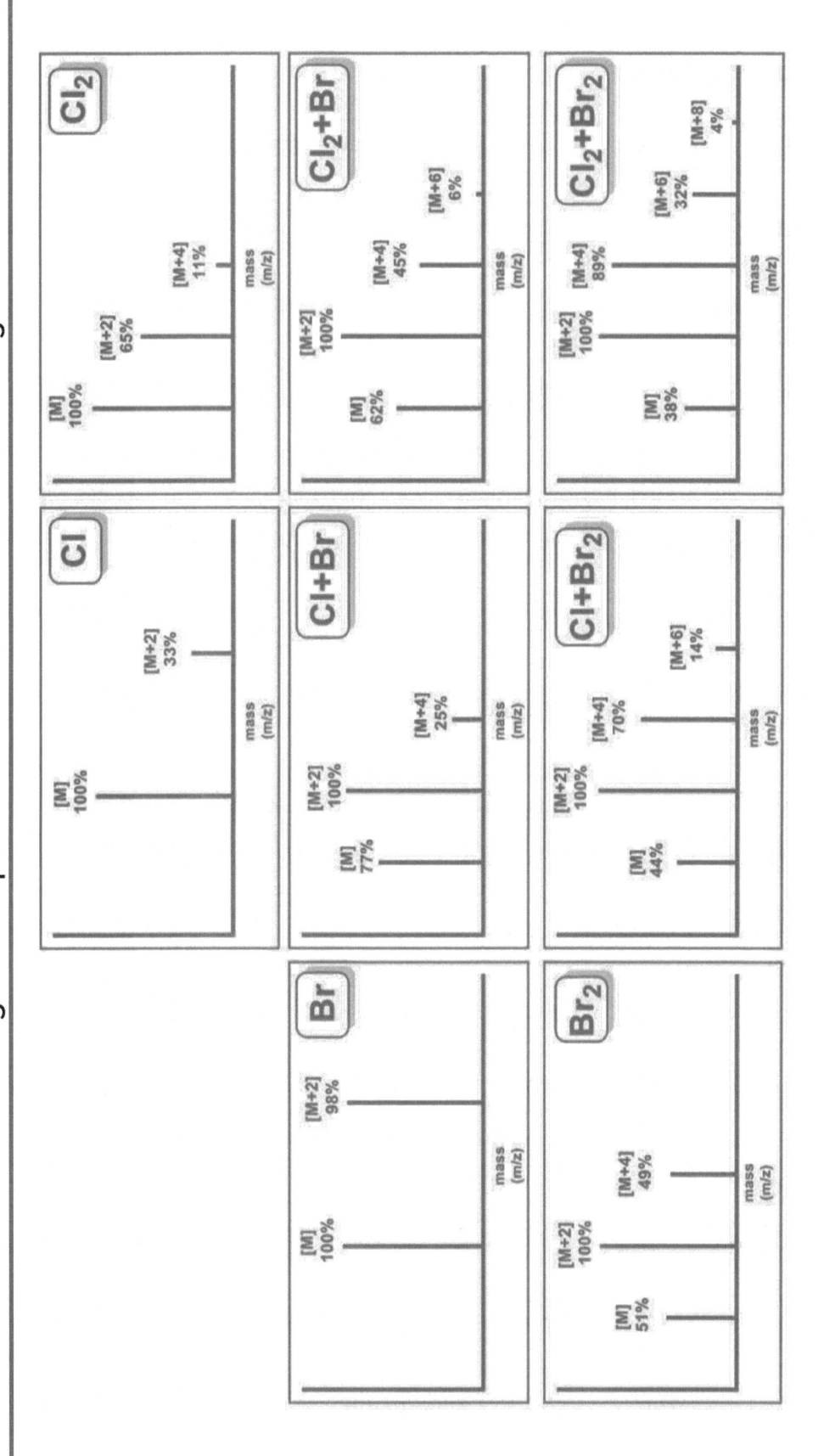

Cl
- [M] 100%
- [M+2] 33%

Cl₂
- [M] 100%
- [M+2] 65%
- [M+4] 11%

Br
- [M] 100%
- [M+2] 98%

Cl+Br
- [M] 77%
- [M+2] 100%
- [M+4] 25%

Cl₂+Br
- [M] 62%
- [M+2] 100%
- [M+4] 45%
- [M+6] 6%

Br₂
- [M] 51%
- [M+2] 100%
- [M+4] 49%

Cl+Br₂
- [M] 44%
- [M+2] 100%
- [M+4] 70%
- [M+6] 14%

Cl₂+Br₂
- [M] 38%
- [M+2] 100%
- [M+4] 89%
- [M+6] 32%
- [M+8] 4%

Rule of 13 Molecular Formula Equivalencies

mathematical equivalency

[M] 16 amu

$$\begin{array}{c} C_xH_y \\ -CH_4 \\ +O \\ \hline C_{x-1}H_{y-4}O \\ +1\ DOU \end{array}$$

[M] 28 amu

$$\begin{array}{c} C_xH_y \\ -C_2H_4 \\ +N_2 \\ \hline C_{x-2}H_{y-4}N_2 \\ +1\ DOU \end{array}$$

[M] 48 amu

$$\begin{array}{c} C_xH_y \\ -C_4 \\ +O_3 \\ \hline C_{x-4}H_yO_3 \\ -4\ DOU \end{array}$$

[M] 12 amu

$$\begin{array}{c} C_xH_y \\ -H_{12} \\ +C \\ \hline C_{x+1}H_{y-12} \\ +7\ DOU \end{array} \qquad \begin{array}{c} C_xH_y \\ -C \\ +H_{12} \\ \hline C_{x-1}H_{y+12} \\ -7\ DOU \end{array}$$

when to use

- #H's larger than indicated by NMR data (multiples of 4H)
- O indicated by IR or NMR data (H-O or C=O from IR, 3-4 ppm from 1H NMR)
- DOU increase supported by IR or NMR data

M is even and adding O inconclusive, or M is odd but
- (additional) N indicated by IR or NMR data (N-H, C≡N, O=C-N in IR, 2-3ppm 1H NMR)
- #H's larger than indicated by NMR data (multiples of 4H)
- DOU increase supported by IR or NMR data

#H's fit 1H NMR data but
- additional O's indicated by IR or NMR data (H-O or C=O from IR, 3-4 ppm from 1H NMR)
- calculated DOU is larger than indicated by NMR data
- #C's larger than indicated by NMR data ("leftover C's" in formula guess after IR and NMR analysis) (relatively few 13C-types, even with respect to symmetry)

- rule of 13 give integer number of C
- drastic DOU adjustment indicated by IR or NMR data
- drastic #H's adjustment indicated by IR or NMR data

structural equivalency

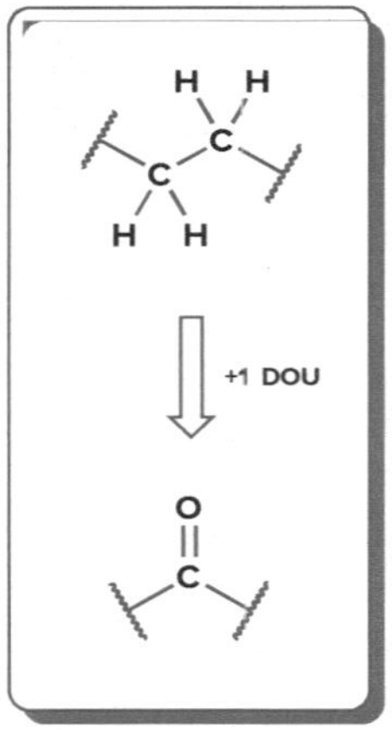

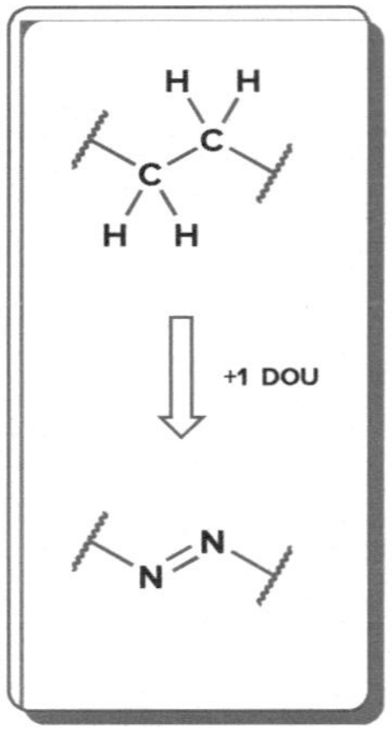

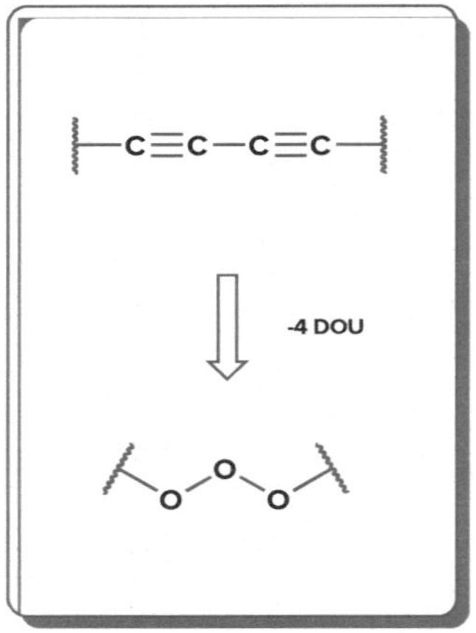

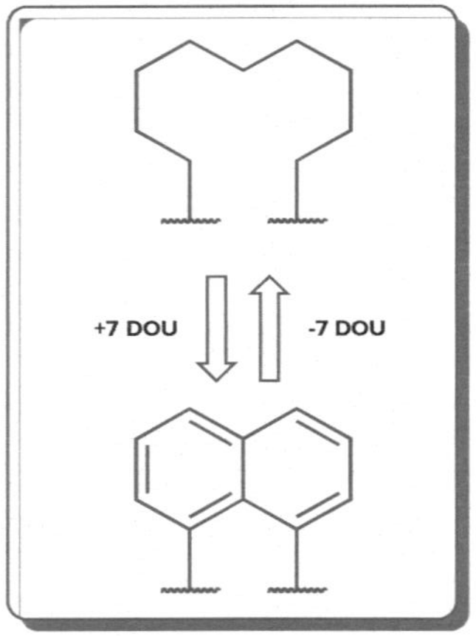

increasing effect on structure →

5.3 – Nuclear Magnetic Resonance Spectroscopy

Chemical Shift Zones

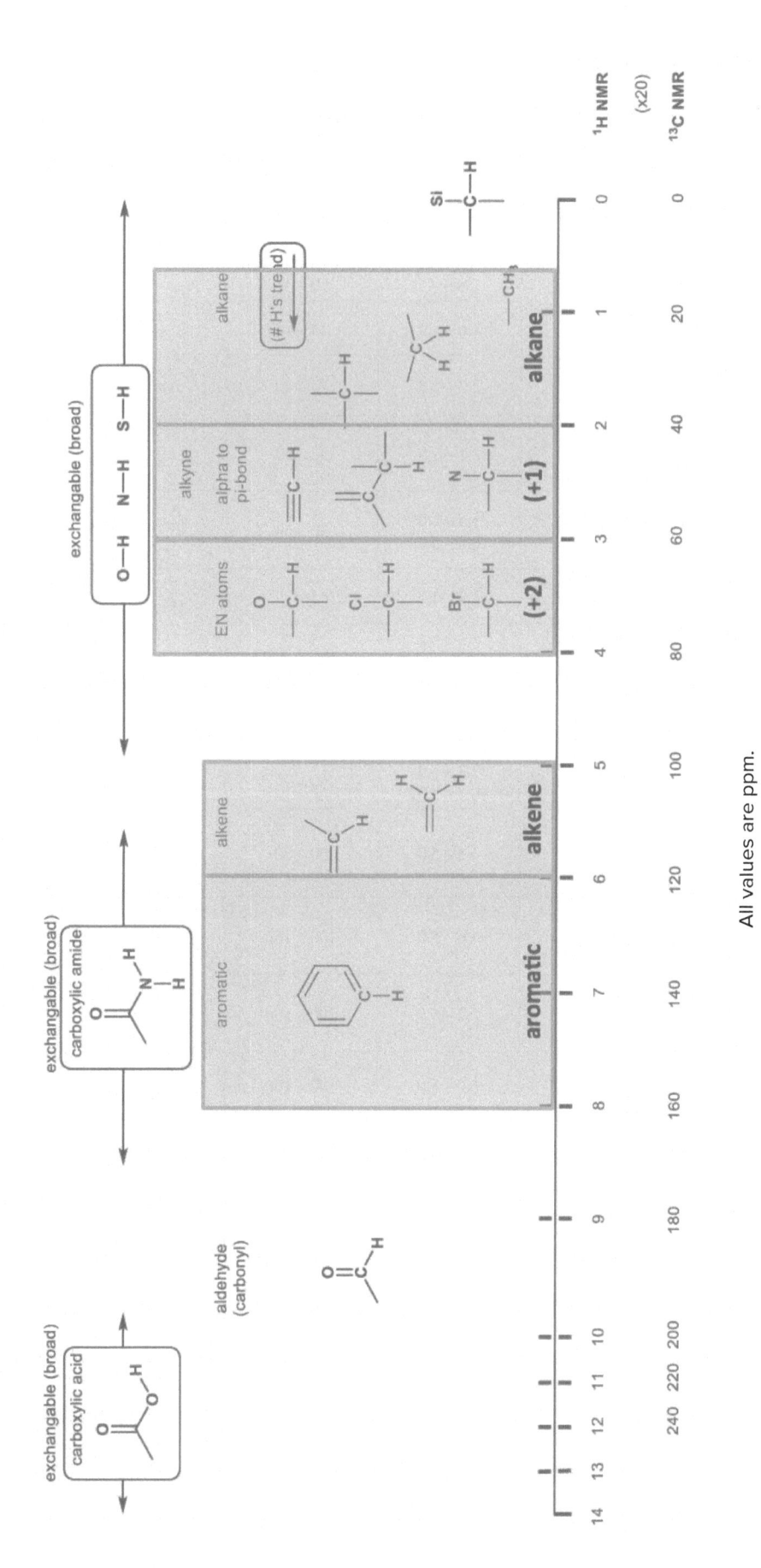

All values are ppm.

5.4 – IR and NMR Reference Values

name	structure	^{1}H NMR (δ)	^{13}C NMR (δ)	IR (cm^{-1})	
tetramethylsilane	Si(CH$_3$)$_4$	0.00	0.0	---	
1° alkyl (methyl) acid	R—CH$_3$	0.8 – 1.0	5 – 20	alkyl C–H stretch 3000 – 2850 (s)	
2° alkyl (methylene)	RCH$_2$R'	1.2 – 1.4	20 – 30		
3° alkyl (methine)	R$_3$C—H	1.4 – 1.7	30 – 50		
quaternary alkyl	R$_4$C	---	30 – 45		
allylic		1.6 – 1.9	20 – 40		
benzylic		2.2 – 2.6	20 – 40		
α to carbonyl		2.1 – 2.6	30 – 50		
amine	R$_2$CH—NH$_2$ (R—NH$_2$)	1.5 – 3.0 (0.5 – 5.0)	30 – 60	N–H stretch 3500 – 3250 (sh m-w) (2 peaks for RNH$_2$, 1 peak for R$_2$NH)	
alkyne	R—C≡C—H	1.7 – 3.1	65 – 95	C–H stretch 3330 – 3260 (s)	C≡C stretch 2260 – 2100 (m-w)
chloroalkane	R$_2$CH—Cl	3.6 – 3.8	25 – 50	800 – 700 (m-w)	
bromoalkane	R$_2$CH—Br	3.4 – 3.6	20 – 40	700 – 600 (m-w)	
iodoalkane	R$_2$CH—I	3.1 – 3.3	20 – 40	600 – 500 (m-w)	
ether	R$_2$CH—OR'	3.3 – 3.9	50 – 90	1300 – 1000 (s)	
alcohol	R$_2$CH—OH (R—OH)	3.3 – 4.0 (0.5 – 5.0)	50 – 90	O–H stretch 3650 – 3200 (br m-s)	
α to nitro		4.3 – 5.0	60 – 80	NO$_2$ stretch 1600 – 1500 (s) 1400 – 1300 (s)	
terminal alkene		4.6 – 5.0	100 – 160	C–H stretch 3100 – 3000 (s)	C=C stretch 1680 – 1600 (sh m-w)
internal alkene		5.2 – 5.7	100 – 160		
aryl		6.0 – 8.0	100 – 160	C–H stretch 3150 – 3050 (s)	C=C stretch 1600 – 1400 (m-w)
amide		5.0 – 8.0	165 – 175	N–H stretch 3400 – 3100 (br)	C=O stretch 1690 – 1650 (s)
aldehyde		9.0 – 10.0	190 – 210	C–H stretch 2900 – 2800 (m) 2800 – 2700 (m)	C=O stretch 1740 – 1720 (s)
ketone		---	190 – 210	C=O stretch 1725 – 1705 (s)	
carboxylic acid		10 – 14	170 – 180	O–H stretch 3300 – 2500 (br)	C=O stretch 1725 – 1700 (s)
carboxylic ester		---	170 – 180	C–O stretch 1300 – 1000 (s)	C=O stretch 1750 – 1735 (s)

name	structure	^{1}H NMR (δ)	^{13}C NMR (δ)	IR (cm^{-1})
anhydride	R−C(=O)−O−C(=O)−R	---	165 – 180	C=O stretch 1850 – 1800 (s) AND 1790 – 1740 (s)
acyl halide	R−C(=O)−X	---	160 – 170	C=O stretch 1815 – 1790 (s)
nitrile	R−C≡N	---	115 – 125	C≡N stretch 2260 – 2240 (m)
thiol	R−SH	0.5 – 5.0	---	S−H stretch 2550 – 2600 (br m-s)

NMR Coupling Constants

	name	Typical J (Hz)	J range (Hz)
	geminal (2-bond coupling, ^2J)	~0*	0–18
	vicinal (3-bond coupling, ^3J)	6–8*	0–18
	4-bond coupling (^4J)	~0*	---
	methylene or geminal (2-bond coupling, ^2J)	2	0–3
	vicinal, cis (3-bond coupling, ^3J)	10	6–14
	vicinal, trans (3-bond coupling, ^3J)	16	11–18
	vicinal (3-bond coupling, ^3J)	6	4–10
	allylic (4-bond coupling, ^4J)	2	0.5–3
	benzylic (4-bond coupling, ^4J)	~0*	0–0.5
	(1,2)- or ortho (vicinal or 3-bond coupling, ^3J)	8	6.0–9.5
	(1,3)- or meta ("W" or 4-bond coupling, ^4J)	2	1.2–3.1
	(1,4)- or para (5-bond coupling, ^5J)	0.5	0.2–1.5

*linear molecules with symmetry and free bond rotation

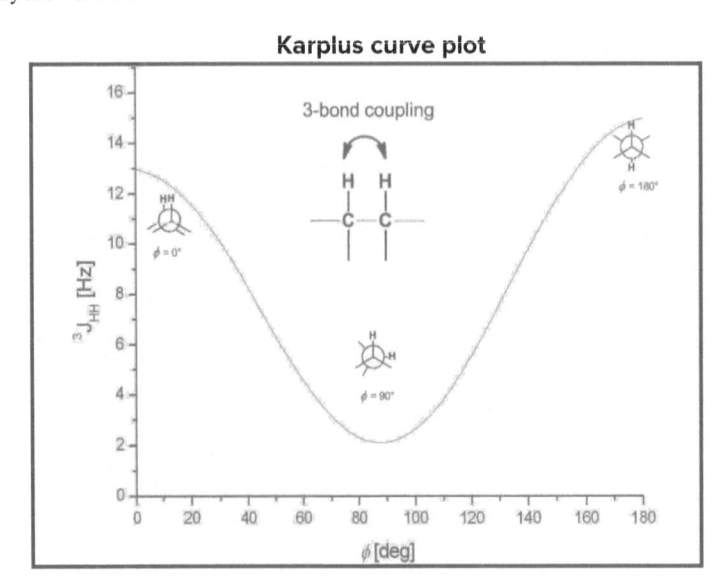

Karplus curve plot